ENGINES & ENTERPRISE

Sir Harry Ricardo FRS, photographed in 1955 at the age of sixty on the occasion of his visit to the USA to receive the Horning Memorial Award from the Society of Automotive Engineers.

ENGINES & ENTERPRISE

THE LIFE AND WORK OF
SIR HARRY RICARDO

JOHN REYNOLDS

Foreword by Sir Diarmuid Downs

SUTTON PUBLISHING

First published in the United Kingdom 1999 by
Sutton Publishing Limited · Phoenix Mill
Thrupp · Stroud · Gloucestershire · GL5 2BU

British Library Cataloguing in Publication Data
A catalogue record for this book is available from the British Library

ISBN 0 7509 1712 1

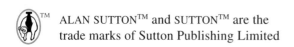

ALAN SUTTON™ and SUTTON™ are the
trade marks of Sutton Publishing Limited

Typeset in 10/12 pt Times
Typesetting and origination by
Sutton Publishing Limited.
Printed in Great Britain by
Butler & Tanner, Frome, Somerset.

Contents

Foreword by Sir Diarmuid Downs   vii
Preface and Acknowledgements   ix
Introduction   xi

1   An Idyllic Childhood   1
2   The Ricardo Heritage   8
3   The Rendel Connection   16
4   Father and Son   24
5   Rottingdean   33
6   Rugby   39
7   Memories and Machines   48
8   Cambridge   56
9   The Dolphin Affair   63
10   The Walton Years   76
11   The First World War   86
12   Formation of the Ricardo Firm   98
13   The Engines of War   109
14   Bridge Works   124
15   Sussex by the Sea   138
16   Ricardo's Comet   152
17   La Rosalie   166
18   War Clouds Threaten   178
19   The Oxford Years   196
20   Eventide at Graffham   214

     Appendix   233
     Bibliography   234
     Photographic Credits   235
     Index   237

The largest engine ever assembled and tested at Bridge Works – the experimental DA/1000 double-acting single-cylinder single-sleeve-valve two-stroke diesel engine of 1937. Its bore and stroke were 16½ × 18½ inches. Built for the Admiralty, it was intended as a prime mover for submarines.

Foreword

I had the great privilege of working for Sir Harry Ricardo for the last thirty years of his life, first as a young engineer and eventually as his chosen successor as head of the company. He was already famous for his pioneering work on the relationship between fuel quality and engine performance, central to our understanding of the operation of the spark-ignition engine. He had transformed the early side-valve engines by use of his turbulent head and had made significant contributions to both overhead-valve and sleeve-valve engine designs, the latter finding its major application in the aircraft engine field. Most importantly, his Comet combustion chamber had become the most widely used system for the high-speed diesel engines fitted to passenger cars and light commercial vehicles. It is these achievements that caused him to be described as the 'High Priest of the internal combustion engine' and to be consulted by engine and vehicle manufacturers throughout the world. His staff too, in continuing and building on these achievements benefited from the comments and guidance of Sir Harry himself, right up to his death in his ninetieth year.

While Sir Harry in his early days was a notable experimenter, I saw him essentially as a designer, a synthesiser of information gleaned from different sources, scientific and practical, to produce a marketable product. He thought with his pencil and was never happier, it seemed to me, than when discussing with one of his designers on the drawing board the finer points of his work – usually how to achieve some reduction in size or weight of the machine being designed.

A particular value of this book is the information it provides on the early history of the Ricardo and Rendel families, describing the way in which they and their friends together with the young Sir Harry's school and university acquaintances – also discussed in depth – influenced his subsequent career. In fact, because the author casts his net so wide, the book will be of interest to those who want to understand Britain's engineering achievements during the twentieth century as well as those of Ricardo himself. The information thus provided is very much more complete than that given by Ricardo himself in his own memoirs (*Memories and Machines*).

Reading those memoirs, one constantly comes across the adjective 'charming' to describe people he admired. It was, in fact, a characteristic which he himself epitomised with the result that he was held in affection, as well as esteem, by his staff and by his clients. In addition to 'charming' Sir Harry often used the phrase 'live wire' to describe someone of whom he approved; contrariwise, 'old ruffian' or 'charlatan' was applied to those of whom he disapproved – the former, however, with an element of grudging admiration. With Sir Harry there was no halfway house.

Sir Harry was a fine engineer and a delightful man. The story of his life, as described in this book, has lessons and fascination for us all.

Sir Diarmuid Downs CBE, FREng, FRS
Hove, 26 March 1999

Harry Ralph Ricardo in his prime – a formal portrait taken in the early 1930s, by which time he had already established an international reputation.

Preface and Acknowledgements

Many people have remarked on learning of its impending arrival that this book is long overdue. Indeed, most are agreed that it should have been written ages ago, and had Sir Harry Ricardo been an artist and writer of the conventional kind, doubtless it would have been.

But engineers, of the twentieth-century variety at least, do not attract the attention of biographers and publishers as do politicians, painters, musicians, film stars, entertainers and other personalities and celebrities, and so in the absence of interest from elsewhere, until today Sir Harry Ricardo has had to remain one of Great Britain's unknown heroes. Fortunately, however, the generosity of Ricardo Consulting Engineers Ltd has made it possible at last to bring the life story of the company's founder before a wider readership among both the international engineering community and the general public, who may be unaware of the profound contribution that Sir Harry made to the development of that mainspring of modern-day life, the internal combustion engine.

Had this biography been embarked upon five or ten years ago, it would certainly have been all the better for it; its writer would have had the opportunity to talk to many of Sir Harry's oldest friends, colleagues and associates who died only recently, including such key figures as J.H. Pitchford, Sir Ben Lockspeiser and Lord King's Norton, all of whom passed away before their recollections could be set down on paper. Indeed the death of Lord King's Norton was announced on the very same day that he was sent a letter requesting an interview. Sadly, Sir Harry's eldest daughter Kate also died while work was in progress, although earlier she had been able to contribute much vital information regarding Ricardo family matters.

In the event, however, *Engines & Enterprise* was compiled from a wide variety of sources, the most important being Sir Harry's own engineering and biographical writings including *Memories and Machines – The Pattern of My Life*, the remarkable autobiography which he produced in 1968 at the age of eighty-three, and which was dictated verbatim. No apologies need be made for quoting Sir Harry's own words so freely. As to his other writings, apart from his lectures or articles and his professional and business letters, little of his personal correspondence and none of his diaries have survived, as this material was destroyed during the war or shortly after it. 'We made a merry bonfire of it,' he wrote in the fifties. Nevertheless, his activities over seven decades can be closely traced through a study of the vast archive of documents, mostly technical and business correspondence, that has survived at Bridge Works, Shoreham, and from the unpublished 'History of the Bridge Works', a most scholarly work produced by his colleague and fellow director Ted Soar in 1975.

The story of Sir Harry's early life and family background has been compiled with assistance from his daughters and grandchildren, notably the late Dr Kate Bertram, Dr Camilla Bosanquet, Mark Bertram and William Bertram, together with his son-in-law Dr Colin Bertram, and also his close relations Peter Ricardo and Rosemary Rendel, all of whom were unfailingly generous and enthusiastic in their support and cooperation, most particularly in providing many of the fascinating photographs that illustrate this book.

Invaluable assistance was also provided by Sir William Hawthorne FRS of the Cambridge Engineering School, Professor Arnold Heertje of the University of Amsterdam, David Fletcher, Curator of the Tank Museum, and Andrew Nahum, Curator of the National Aeronautical Collection at the Science Museum, who kindly allowed the writer access to his important studies of the development of the Rolls-Royce Crecy engine, subsequently published elsewhere. Similarly, the motoring writers Jonathan Wood and Mike Worthington-Williams both volunteered information gleaned from their own investigations into Sir Harry's life and work, and also permitted the use of quotations from their books.

Many other individuals and organisations made important contributions towards establishing the details of Sir Harry's career, including David Ashton-Hill, Paul Berliet, Professor Gordon Blair, Malcolm Bobbitt, Stuart Broach, Neill Bruce, Angela Cherritt, Christopher Clarke, Viscount Combermere, Dick Foster-Pegg, Patrick Garland, Don Goodsell, Bill Gunston, Patrick Hassel, Peter Hull, Wouter Jansen, Michael Lane, Mrs Brian Lovell, Alec Lumsden, John Pitchford, Doug Taylor, Graham Skillen, Ken Smith, Major-General Sir John Swinton and John Walker, together with Peter Baines of the Rolls-Royce Enthusiasts Club, Mike Evans, Richard Haigh and Peter Pavey of the Rolls-Royce Heritage Trust, David Devons of Marks & Clerk, Patent Agents, Dr Ing Josep Merigo of the Sociedad de Tecnicos de Automacion and also the representatives of the Royal Society, the Institution of Mechanical Engineers, the Institution of Civil Engineers, the Royal Aeronautical Society, Rugby School, Trinity College, Cambridge, the Cambridge University School of Engineering, the Waukesha Engine Historical Society, Shell Information Services, High-Point Rendel, DERA Pystock and the National Motor Museum at Beaulieu.

At Bridge Works, Shoreham, unstinting help was received from the Ricardo personnel directly responsible for this project, most notably John Loveridge, Roland Christopher, Mike Monaghan and Dr Clive Hickman. My warmest thanks are also due to four former directors of the company, now retired, Sir Diarmuid Downs, Cliff Walder, Brian Millington and Dr Cecil French, all of whom gave generously of their time to talk about their association with, and memories of, Sir Harry.

Finally, a tribute of gratitude must be paid to Malcolm Wright (former Business Development Manager of Ricardo Consulting Engineers Ltd) whose idea it was to produce this book. Since retiring from the company shortly after it was commissioned in 1997, he has continued to support and encourage its progress throughout the two years of research and writing that it has taken to bring his far-sighted proposal to fruition.

John Reynolds
Lutterworth, Leicestershire
September 1999

Introduction

'Let us imagine ourselves inside the cylinder of a Diesel engine, seated comfortably on the top of the piston, at or about the end of the compression stroke. We are in complete darkness, the atmosphere is a trifle oppressive, for the shade temperature is well over 500C, and the atmosphere is very dense. Also it is very draughty, such that in reality we would be blown off our perch and hurled about like autumn leaves in a gale. Suddenly, above our heads a valve is opened and a rainstorm of fuel begins to descend. In fact, the velocity of the droplets approaches much more nearly that of rifle bullets than of raindrops. For a while nothing startling happens, the rain continues to fall, the darkness remains intense. Then suddenly, away to our right a brilliant gleam of light appears, moving swiftly and purposefully; in an instant, this is followed by a myriad others all around us, some large and some small, until on all sides of us the space is filled with a merry blaze of moving lights; from time to time the smaller lights wink and go out while the larger ones develop fiery tails like comets; occasionally these strike the walls of the cylinder but being surrounded with an envelope of burning vapour they merely bounce off like drops of water spilt on a red hot plate. Right overhead all is darkness still, the rainstorm continues and the heat is becoming intense; now we shall see that a change is taking place. Many of the smaller lights around us have gone out, but new ones are beginning to appear, more overhead, and to form themselves into definite streams shooting rapidly downwards or outwards from the direction of the injector nozzles. Looking round again, we see that the lights around are growing yellower; they no longer move in definite directions but appear to be drifting listlessly hither and thither; here and there they are crowding together in dense nebulae and these are burning now with a sickly smoky flame, half suffocated for want of oxygen. Now we are attracted by a dazzle overhead, and looking up, we see that what at first was a cold rain falling through utter darkness has given place to a cascade of fire as from a rocket. For a little while this continues, then ceases abruptly as the fuel valve closes. Above and all around us are still some lingering fireballs, now trailing long trails of sparks and smoke and wandering aimlessly in search of the last dregs of oxygen which will consume them finally and set their souls at rest. So ends the scene, or rather my conception of the scene, and I will ask you to realise that what has taken me nearly five minutes to describe may all be enacted in one five-hundredth of a second, or even less.'

With these words, delivered at a lecture before the Royal Society of Arts on 23 November 1931, Harry Ralph Ricardo revealed at a stroke all those qualities that made him so remarkable an engineer and experimentalist and placed him among the foremost pioneers of the internal combustion engine. His remarkable curiosity, ingenuity, originality and wit are all evident in this passage, as in so many other of his writings, together with his great imagination, vision and intellectual integrity.

Indeed, Ricardo was much more than just a mechanical engineer. During his sixty-year career – which effectively spanned the transition between the old world and the new, and saw great changes in the social and industrial fabric of Great Britain, brought about by the arrival of the motor cars and aeroplanes that he championed so enthusiastically – he also embraced the role of scientist, inventor, mechanical designer, practical craftsman, writer, educator, communicator and government adviser. Moreover, in founding his world-renowned independent laboratory and engineering consultancy at Bridge Works, Shoreham-by-Sea, West Sussex, and then directing its activities so successfully for more than forty years, he also deserves recognition as a businessman, organiser and administrator, although he was far too modest ever to have claimed any of these accomplishments for himself.

Nowadays, the reliability, durability and efficiency of the internal combustion engine are taken for granted. But that was certainly not the case in the early days of the motor car and aeroplane. Ricardo's pioneering work in unravelling the mysteries of the combustion process enabled engine manufacturers to master these difficulties and uncertainties. Indeed, when he delivered the Horning Memorial Lecture before the Society of Automotive Engineers at Atlantic City, New Jersey, in 1955, he was hailed as 'The High Priest of the Internal Combustion Engine' by the US automotive press.

As his fellow mechanical engineer Sir William Hawthorne FRS Emeritus Professor of Thermodynamics at Cambridge University wrote in his biographical memoir of Sir Harry, produced for the Royal Society in 1976:

Ricardo was born at a time when mechanical engineering was developing from a craft into a technology. The steam engine, the prime mover of the day, was only beginning to be threatened by the steam turbine, and the internal combustion engine was in its infancy. This engine was to become his lifelong interest. He brought to it not only the skill of an outstanding designer which was soundly based on personal craftsmanship, but also a long lasting curiosity and originality in engineering research.

His contributions to the understanding of the ignition, combustion and detonation processes in spark ignition and diesel engines was of the greatest importance; he gave the world the concept of the octane number as a means of rating the tendency of fuels to detonate. His application of this knowledge and his ability in design is seen not only in his early engines, for example in the two-stroke cycle Dolphin and the four-stroke cycle engines for the tanks in 1917, but in his light high speed diesel engines, the prime mover of the modern truck, and the sleeve valve aero-engines which were the last and best of the large British piston engines for aircraft.

Yet despite these manifold qualities, the life and work of Sir Harry Ricardo FRS remains one of Great Britain's best-kept technological secrets. His achievements were repeatedly honoured throughout the automobile and aircraft engine-building industries during his lifetime but, sadly, today his name is largely unknown to the general travelling public who benefit so greatly from the transport revolution that he helped to bring about. Because he preferred to work behind the scenes as an independent consultant, his name was never directly connected with any specific make of car or aeroplane, much less a product bearing his own name, and his gentle, retiring personality was all too often eclipsed by the more thrusting and domineering characters with whom he was associated.

None the less, his efforts on behalf of such well-known companies as Rolls-Royce, Vauxhall, Bentley, Bristol, Napier, Citroën and Fiat led to innumerable advances in the performance and reliability of military and civilian engines during the interwar years.

This book sets out to put the record straight. Beginning with an account of Sir Harry's family background and his education at Rugby and Cambridge, it traces his life's work through seven decades, showing that his public work began in 1917 when he designed the engine of the Mk V tank, and ended in 1951 when he was involved in a project to produce a revolutionary diesel-engined locomotive for British Railways. For sixty years, as a consultant engineer to the War Office, the Air Ministry, the Anglo-Dutch Shell Oil Company and the Rolls-Royce company among many others, he played a vital role in bringing about British victory in two world wars and made a major contribution towards the development of the internal combustion engine for both automobile and aircraft use, not least by improving the quality and uniformity of the petroleum fuels and lubricants on which it relies.

As *Engines & Enterprise* will relate, it was Sir Harry's genius that lay behind the success of the Bristol Perseus and Hercules series of sleeve-valve, air-cooled radial engines that powered the British military and civilian air-transport fleet for almost thirty years. It will also show how it came about that, when Sir Frank Whittle encountered difficulties in perfecting the gas-turbine engine during the early years of the Second World War, it was Ricardo's research laboratory that was primarily responsible for overcoming these technical problems.

This book will also discuss Sir Harry's role as a teacher and educator, and show how his work continues to influence the methods and thinking of the engineers of today. In 1922 he published *The High Speed Internal Combustion Engine*, which duly became the standard text book of automobile engine design, and his many subsequent scientific and engineering writings are still widely referred to and admired nowadays due, above all, to the precision and clarity with which their content was expressed. Not least of Ricardo's many gifts was the ability to explain complex and difficult engineering matters for those less technically minded than himself. For this aspect of his work, in 1929 he was elected Fellow of the Royal Society, and thereafter prestigious awards and distinctions were showered upon him throughout his life by learned societies and professional institutions in many countries. Ultimately, in 1948, he was awarded a knighthood by King George VI in recognition of his outstanding contribution to British engineering.

Finally, the character of the man himself will not be neglected. HRR, as he was universally known, was not a one-track-minded boffin concerned exclusively with his professional work, but a wholly formed and well-rounded human being with many enthusiasms, hobbies and pastimes, and it was this diversity of his interests, together with his unfailing charm and courtesy to others, that made him so deeply loved and respected within the close-knit circle of his devoted colleagues, employees and family.

Top: Harry Ralph Ricardo at the age of five, a drawing made by his relation E.D. Brinton in 1890.
Bottom: Sir Harry Ricardo's birthplace at 13 Bedford Square, Bloomsbury, London (second house from right) photographed in 1953. This famous Georgian square has remained virtually unaltered since it was built in 1775.

CHAPTER 1

An Idyllic Childhood

A lthough as yet there is no blue plaque on its handsome classical brick façade to commemorate the fact, it was at 13 Bedford Square in the parish of St Giles in the Fields, central London that, on 26 January 1885, Harry Ricardo was born. For an Englishman who was destined to become one of his country's most eminent mechanical engineers and scientists, a noted international pioneer of the internal combustion engine and a major contributor to the development of the automobile and the aeroplane, there could have been no more appropriate time at which to arrive in the world, for that year marked the birth of the motor car itself, though not in the United Kingdom.

Indeed, the closing years of the nineteenth century, when inventors and scientists such as Thomas Edison, J.J. Thomson, Marie Curie and Guglielmo Marconi made astonishing discoveries in the fields of physics and electronics, was a truly revolutionary era. Besides the motor car, the aeroplane, the telephone, the gramophone, the cinema and the radio, that short, intensely active, *fin de siècle* period brought with it more, and greater, scientific and technological changes than had so far occurred in the previous five millennia of recorded history, and thus it defined the character and future direction of the modern world.

Even so, the genteel environs of Bedford Square – his home until the age of twenty-five – provided a most unusual and unlikely background for a would-be automobile engineer, at least in the days before the ownership of motor cars became truly respectable and commonplace. As is well known, most early exponents of the car and the internal combustion engine were self-taught mechanics from humble provincial families who, like Henry Ford, Louis Renault, William Morris and Henry Royce, were generally the sons of blacksmiths, farmers, artisans or tradesmen. But as this fashionable West End address suggests, Sir Harry Ricardo had no such family tradition of handicraft and manual work to draw upon. He came instead from a prosperous upper-middle-class professional family which, although not entirely unconnected with engineering, had no previous business involvement with the design or manufacture of machinery.

As Sir Harry was the first to acknowledge, he started out at birth with every advantage that circumstances or money could provide, and with a more than usual share of good luck into the bargain, so that he really never had to struggle at any stage in his career in the material sense. But this is not to say that his life was all plain sailing or that he never encountered disappointment and disillusionment. On the contrary, as we shall see, there is much in the story of his career to suggest that his progress through life was made much more difficult and demanding by his unconventional interests than might have been the case had he chosen to ignore his true vocation and to follow the course mapped out for him by his family.

As the heir-apparent to a highly lucrative partnership in his grandfather's civil engineering firm, he could well have been content to plough a secure but undistinguished furrow from cradle to grave, plodding comfortably along in the footsteps of his forebears, the founders of the family firm. But instead he turned his back on the easy option and embarked instead on an unknown course, dedicating himself to a patient and persistent study of the internal combustion engine with no expectancy of great financial gain, but purely out of a fascination for this novel machine. And by stubbornly rejecting the safe and certain route through life, pursuing his enthusiasm to the exclusion of more mundane priorities, he became caught up in an all-absorbing quest for enlightenment, far more inspiring and satisfying than the search for personal advancement or professional prestige.

The first child of Halsey Ricardo, an artist and architect, and Catherine Rendel, the daughter of one of Great Britain's most successful and highly respected civil engineers, Sir Harry Ricardo was directly related to a number of the most influential and well-connected families in the country. A bona fide member of the High Victorian professional élite, by birth he owed an allegiance to the very people who, as it is all too often claimed today, were unanimously opposed to the arrival of the internal combustion engine at the turn of the century, and who did most to frustrate the adoption of the horseless carriage. If popular opinion is to be believed, men of Ricardo's position and background took no interest in the coming of the motor car and aeroplane and never soiled their hands by experimenting with such 'widgetry'.

But Harry Ricardo was an exception to this rather dubious proposition, and like many of his friends and contemporaries he welcomed the arrival of the automobile with enthusiasm. Moreover he was fortunate enough to have among his closest male relations two men who would provide the encouragement and support he needed to develop his talent for practical mechanics. Although they might both be labelled as members of the governing classes, these men – Halsey Ricardo, his father, and Sir Alexander Rendel, his grandfather – were in no way conservative or reactionary in their outlook, and they combined their resources to provide an environment in which Harry's interests and abilities as a mechanical engineer were allowed to flourish from an early age.

Certainly, to be the child of well-to-do upper-middle-class parents in the London of the mid-1880s was to be privileged indeed, and Harry enjoyed what can only be regarded as an idyllic childhood. As we shall see, his father, an orphan, had not been so fortunate in his upbringing, and he was determined that his own children should have the very best start in life that he could provide.

London was then the capital and epicentre of the greatest empire the world had ever seen, with its territories and dominions covering a fifth of the surface of the globe. Two years after Sir Harry's birth, in 1887, Queen Victoria celebrated her fiftieth year on the throne, and the festivities held to mark the Diamond Jubilee gave the nation an opportunity to offer thanks to the Almighty for the longest period of peace and prosperity that the British people had ever known. This period had not been one of calm and tranquillity, however, for the far-reaching technological developments that had taken place since the onset of the Industrial Revolution a century earlier had in turn produced enormous economic and social change. By 1851, the year of the Great Exhibition held to celebrate the achievements of the new manufacturing industries, Great Britain had arrived at a way of living previously unknown in the history of the world and as yet unique. Never before had the life and wealth of a nation been made to depend entirely on machines. And never before had the distribution of a nation's wealth been extended down from the aristocracy and plutocracy to empower the new middle classes, endowing them with political influence and enabling them to enjoy the luxury of conspicuous consumption.

A view of High Holborn (half a mile from Bedford Square) in 1890. The young Ricardo would
have been very familiar with this scene. It was not until 1911 that the number of automobiles on
the streets of London exceeded that of horse-drawn vehicles.

The 1880s were an exciting time of change and progress in practically every sphere of
social, commercial and industrial activity, and most especially in the realm of transportation
and power generation, as the old reciprocating piston type of steam engine gave way to new
technologies in what amounted to a second industrial revolution. Very soon, the expansion
of manufacturing and trade would be propelled by the rotating steam turbine or by the
internal combustion engine fuelled by petroleum oil or coal-gas, each employed
mechanically or harnessed to generate electricity. Sir Charles Parsons, the son of the 3rd
Earl of Rosse, introduced his steam-turbine-driven dynamo in 1884. Later he developed the
steam turbine principle to power ships; the speed of his experimental vessel the SS *Turbinia*
caused a sensation when it exceeded 34 knots at Queen Victoria's Diamond Jubilee Naval
Review at Spithead in 1897. But as yet, the horse and the piston-driven steam locomotive
still held sway as the only effective means of moving goods and people over land.

During Sir Harry Ricardo's childhood, therefore, London was still a town of horse-trams
and hansom cabs, clattering over granite setts; a London of silk top hats and frock coats, of
veils, bonnets, bustles and leg-of-mutton sleeves. It was also a London made grey and grim
by snow, slush and fog in winter and by soot and smoke in summer. Long before the
environmental pollution produced by the internal combustion engine began to cause concern,
the air of the United Kingdom's biggest city was far from being entirely pure and clean. At

all times of the year, the metropolis was smothered by a blanket of dust, constantly belched out by a million or more chimneys or kicked up by the incessant horse traffic in its streets.

It was also a London of stark social contrasts, of broad airy squares and wide ceremonial avenues suddenly giving way to narrow lanes and alleys leading in turn to dank culs-de-sac and slums. Despite the effects of the Industrial Revolution a hundred years earlier, about a quarter of all men in Britain still worked on the land, with one in six of the male population employed as farm labourers. But the flood of cheap food flowing into the country from the colonies and elsewhere was rapidly leading to a crisis in British agriculture and to the mass migration of labour from the country to the crowded towns and cities. Here, new manufacturing, clerical and retailing jobs were being created. This new pattern of employment produced for the very first time, a population that was essentially urban in its character and mentality.

As Sir Harry reflected in his autobiography, written eighty years later, all these developments could be seen in microcosm when he gazed out of the windows of his boyhood home. No. 13 Bedford Square was one of the group of fifty-three almost identical five-storeyed terraced houses built by the 4th Duke of Bedford between 1775 and 1783 to provide town houses for the minor gentry from the shires or for the rich merchants, lawyers and bankers of the City. Situated on the northern side of the square, the house was held on a lease from the Bedford Estate, an essentially private domain owned exclusively by the Trustees of the Dukes of Bedford and comprising a group of five residential squares – including Russell Square, Gordon Square, Tavistock Square and Bloomsbury Square. Access to the Bedford Estate was restricted to residents and the general public were barred by the series of lodges and gatehouses that ringed its perimeter until these gates were removed by the London County Council in 1893. Together with their connecting alleyways and carriage mews, the squares and streets of the estate made up the residential and business quarter known as Bloomsbury, which by the 1880s was occupied for the most part by other upper-middle-class professional families like the Ricardos, neither aristocratic nor plutocratic but essentially well-heeled and respectable.

At the time of Harry Ricardo's birth in the 1880s Bloomsbury was a locality favoured by doctors, lawyers, merchants and architects who, like Halsey Ricardo, carried out their work at home; indeed, the architect William Butterfield occupied a house on the southern side of Bedford Square. It was also the territory of writers, authors, artists, publishers and academics, since close at hand were the buildings of University College, the British Museum, the British Library and the Slade School of Art. Yet within a stone's throw of Bedford Square itself, along the Tottenham Court Road, young Harry could also see evidence of intensive commercial and industrial activity, including a sawmill, a brewery and a canning factory belonging to the Crosse & Blackwell firm.

At the centre of the square itself lay a beautiful private garden of lawns, flower beds, shrubberies and tall plane trees, intersected by gravel paths and completely enclosed by high iron railings. This garden was also reserved for the use of residents only; naturally, the Ricardo family held a key and it was here, on sunny summer days, that the young Harry was sent to play with children from the other surrounding houses. The garden was an oasis of greenery in the heart of the city, a safe and rather secret place where he could amuse himself with friends of his own age; there was even a wooden garden house where they could play hide-and-seek. 'My one dread was that I might get locked in all night, for the heavy iron garden gates were padlocked at dusk and the railings were much too high for me to climb out,' he recalled in his autobiography.

Clearly, there was never a shortage of interesting things for him to see and do without going far from home, and even when such distractions failed he was entirely capable of making his own entertainment, even from the earliest age. 'In those days the streets of London were full of fascination,' Sir Harry remembered. 'There was always the ubiquitous steam-roller to gaze at, and on rare occasions a fire-engine with its beautifully polished brass boiler at full blast belching showers of sparks high into the air as it dashed down the street with its horses at full gallop and with the helmeted firemen ringing its heavy brass bell.' So overwhelming was this spectacle in the eyes of an impressionable five-year-old boy that the scene was still vivid in his mind when he reached old age. Another typical sight of late Victorian London that never left his memory was of the itinerant entertainers and street vendors who regularly wandered through the neighbourhood of Bedford Square.

In common with most of the other children who lived in the square, Harry Ricardo was brought up by a succession of nursemaids and educated at home by his mother, until the time came for him to go away to boarding school at the age of ten. Although he was allowed to take lunch and tea with his parents, and was therefore far less segregated from adult society than the majority of his contemporaries, as a youngster his nursery was the centre of his universe. This large attic room, well stocked with toys including the inevitable rocking horse, was where he spent his free time until he was old enough to be allowed to set up a workshop of his own in the basement; his favourite amusement was building houses, forts and castles with a fine set of wooden blocks that his father had had made for him. All of these blocks were exactly 1 inch thick, but varied in length and width, thus providing him with an excellent training for his future work, in that they gave him the ability to judge dimensions by eye with great accuracy, a facility that he claimed was of great value to him all his life. Certainly, these blocks remained among his most treasured possessions and the set was still intact at the time of his death.

Halsey Ricardo was particularly fond of children and set aside time each day to read aloud to his son from Grimm's fairy tales, the stories of Hans Andersen or Edward Lear's *Book of Nonsense*, which was Harry's favourite book; later on he began to teach him Greek and Roman history. Halsey was steadfastly opposed to organised religion and instead of insisting his children make the normal Victorian attendance at church, every Sunday morning he took Harry and his sisters (Anna born in 1889 and Esther born in 1893) on an educational excursion by horse-drawn tram to London Zoo at nearby Regent's Park. Here the Ricardo children soon got to know some of the keepers who actually allowed them to feed and handle some of the smaller and tamer mammals. Regent's Park was also the normal destination of the daily morning walks along Tottenham Court Road and Euston Road that Harry made with his nursemaid, with his baby sisters riding in their perambulators.

Sometimes on these Sunday outings a short detour was made to the great terminus of the London, Midland & Scottish Railway at Euston, about a mile or so from Bedford Square. For a small boy with mechanical leanings, nothing could have been more exciting than to stand on the platforms of this temple of transport, to inspect the locomotives and talk to their drivers, who were men of considerable prestige. The engines, gleaming with polished brass, were like fire-breathing dragons, hissing out an angry torrent of steam and smoke at the bustling throng of porters and passengers. Not surprisingly, he was enthralled by the sight and sound of railway machinery at a very early age, and his fascination with steam propulsion endured throughout his life. Apparently, Halsey

Ricardo was also a steam-engine enthusiast. Although not mechanically minded, as an artist and designer he appreciated the elegance and beauty of the High-Victorian locomotive. According to Sir Harry, when in later years the steam engine was fitted with a bigger boiler, smaller driving wheels and a sawn-off funnel in the interests of greater performance, his father abhorred its aesthetic demise. 'The engine lost its figure and turned into a bloated overfed monster lacking in dignity and self-respect,' he observed.

The young Harry Ricardo (centre) seen playing with his eldest sister Anna (second left) and cousins at Rickettswood, his grandfather's country house in Surrey.

'The elegant ballet girl of the nineties grew into a corpulent and untidy frump.'

As Harry grew older, the walks and excursions through the heart of London grew correspondingly longer as other even more exciting parts of the city were explored. One well-trodden path that he regularly took with his mother followed a route down Shaftesbury Avenue or the Charing Cross Road to the Strand and onwards to the Victoria Embankment, where they watched the shipping passing by on the River Thames between Waterloo and Westminster Bridge. The Thames was then a major transport artery and teemed with shipping *en route* between the wharves that lined its banks and the great London Docks downstream. Endless streams of tugs and barges and dozens of ferry steamers, all crowded with passengers, plied up and down. The south bank of the river was given up almost entirely to warehouses, shipyards and factories owned

Harry's father, the architect and designer
Halsey Ricardo.

by engineering firms. Among these industrial buildings was one just visible across the water at Lambeth, standing on a site at the south end of Westminster Bridge in the place later occupied by London County Hall. Quite possibly, gazing out across the Thames he would have read the name Peter Brotherhood & Company sign-written in bold letters on the wall of these premises, but without realising that these words held any particular significance for him personally and that one day they would play an important part in his life.

The return walk took them back through Trafalgar Square and the Lowther Arcade, near the church of St Martin-in-the-Fields, where there were many small shops to delay their progress, all of them displaying a wonderful selection of toys and model steam engines. In Trafalgar Square they would sometimes stop to watch the departure of the Brighton stagecoach. This huge, brightly painted vehicle, drawn by four lively, high-stepping horses and steered by a coachman wearing a top hat and cloak, set off punctually at ten every morning, with much cheering and blowing of horns, exactly as in Regency days. As a serious means of transport, of course, it was already an anachronism and its journeys persisted mainly as an amusement for holiday-makers.

Nevertheless, the survival of the stagecoach served to illustrate the *status quo* in the London of the 1880s, which was a city balancing precariously on the dividing line between the old world and the new. Its busy streets and thoroughfares were thronged with a huge variety of horse-drawn vehicles – including trams, buses, coaches, cabs, carts and wagons – as they had been for centuries past. But although it would be at least another fifteen years before the first automobiles arrived in numbers to swell the traffic, behind the scenes the revolution in public and private transport in which young Harry Ricardo was destined to play so prominent a part was already gathering pace.

CHAPTER 2

The Ricardo Heritage

On many occasions during the closing stages of his career, Sir Harry Ricardo remarked, with characteristic diffidence and modesty, that his life's achievements were all the result of good fortune, and that his success had come about through nothing much more than a series of happy chances.

When delivering the Horning Memorial Lecture before the Society of Automotive Engineers at Atlantic City, USA, in June 1955, he prefaced his talk by saying that: 'If I give the impression of having leapt from one triumph to another, that would be most misleading, for I missed my foothold and floundered quite as often as anybody else, but all my life I have had rather more than the usual share of good luck, and of the generous help of many good friends.' There was of course, an element of truth in what he said; time and time again throughout his life he proved to be the right man in the right place at the right time. But in suggesting that his career was founded on little more than a string of fortuitous accidents, he did himself a grave injustice.

Even so, few engineers could ever have been better prepared by the circumstances of their birth and family background to rise to the challenges strewn in their path. On the one hand, he was related to one of the greatest engineering dynasties of the Victorian and Edwardian eras, a family of empire builders whose traditions of public service extended back over four generations. And on the other, he was descended from a family of bankers and financiers who had occupied a position at the centre of the nation's political and economic life for almost two centuries, and whose founder and patriarch had established the family name as a synonym for intellectual distinction and scholarly integrity.

The hereditary or genetic assets bequeathed to him by his long and distinguished Ricardo ancestry were impressive. The origins of the Ricardo family can be traced back over ten generations, to the sixteenth century and beyond. It is believed that by 1550 the Sephardic Jewish family from which they were descended had already been established in Lisbon, Portugal, for many centuries, trading as jewellers. Earlier, during the late fifteenth century, the Jewish communities in Spain and Portugal had been subjected to intense religious persecution and, in common with many of their faith, the Ricardos' ancestors had converted to Christianity in order to avoid expulsion. Ultimately, however, at the height of the Reformation in the mid-sixteenth century, this persecution became intolerable.

Consequently the forebears of the Ricardo family migrated to the free port of Leghorn in Italy, probably around 1593, when many Sephardic Jews from Portugal were invited to settle there by the Grand Duke of Tuscany who wished to develop the port as a centre of the then important jewellery industry based on Mediterranean red coral.

Medieval Christian doctrine forbade Christians from lending money or taking interest on loans, and so through their expertise in gold, diamonds and other precious or semi-precious stones, many of these Jewish jewelsmith families began to develop the business of banking and finance, which duly became an exclusively Jewish activity throughout

Europe. Forbidden to own land and excluded from the membership of the trade guilds, the Jews had no other legitimate occupation open to them in most places. As a result, by the eighteenth century they had developed their remarkable commercial and financial skills to such an extent that a small group of internationally based banking families, most notably the Rothschilds, dominated the finance of trade and government military expenditure throughout Great Britain, France, Germany, the Netherlands and the Austro-Hungarian Empire.

Perhaps to pursue these jewellery and goldsmithing interests at a higher level and become a banker or perhaps to seek the religious and ethnic tolerance that Holland was known for even then, in 1660 the head of the family, Samuel Moses Israel, moved to Amsterdam, then the commercial and financial capital of northern Europe. Indeed, the great Dutch port and trading centre was already home to a thriving Sephardic Jewish community.

Sir Harry Ricardo was descended from a brother of David Ricardo MP (1772–1823), the famous economic theorist, author of *Principles of Political Economy and Taxation*, first published in 1817.

Samuel Moses died in Amsterdam in 1692, having reverted to the Jewish faith by joining the famous synagogue that was built there in 1675. His eldest son, David Israel, who had been born in Leghorn in 1652, succeeded him as head of the family business, being described in the Amsterdam municipal records as a *koopman* or merchant. These records show that in August 1692 he married a Portuguese Jewess, Estrellia Amadios. At this time the family were known by the name Israel and it is not until 1720 that the surname Ricardo appears in the Amsterdam archives.

The first of the Dutch branch of the family to carry the Ricardo name, David Israel's son Joseph Israel, was born in Amsterdam in 1699 and died there in 1762. In January 1721, when living in the Kaizersgracht, he married Hannah Abaz, the daughter of another prominent Dutch-Jewish family. From the records of his estate, it is evident that Joseph Ricardo died a man of substance, having been able to establish himself as a leading figure on the Amsterdam Stock Exchange. He also operated as an international financier dealing in English securities, so beginning the family's first connections with Great Britain.

When, during the mid-eighteenth century, the importance of Amsterdam eventually diminished as a result of the growth of the port of London, Joseph's second son, Abraham Israel Ricardo (1733–1812) left Holland for England, having learned his business as a stockbroker in Amsterdam. He arrived in the City of London around 1760, at the height of the Seven Years War. Here, in 1770, he became a British citizen and was appointed as one of only six 'Jew-brokers' permitted to trade in securities within the

City's walls. By the time of his death at the age of eighty, he had amassed a fortune of some £45,000, gained by financing British government expenditure on the war and by shrewd speculation on the London Stock Exchange.

As the head of the British branch of the Ricardo family (the Dutch branch continued to flourish in Amsterdam) Abraham Ricardo married Abigail Delvalle, the daughter of an old-established British Sephardic-Jewish family in 1769; she bore him no fewer than eighteen children. The most eminent among these offspring was his third son, David Ricardo MP (1772–1823), the celebrated economic theorist and writer. In his book *Principles of Political Economy and Taxation*, first published in 1817, David Ricardo proposed his theory of rent and set out the law of diminishing returns. A friend and associate of James Stuart Mill, Jeremy Bentham and Thomas Malthus, his interest in economics was aroused by reading Adam Smith's *Wealth of Nations*, first published in 1776.

David Ricardo's independent and emancipated thinking was by no means confined to matters of economic theory. Against his father's wishes, in 1793 at the age of twenty-one, he married an English girl, Priscilla-Anne Wilkinson, the daughter of a Quaker family, and abandoned the faith of his ancestors to become a Christian. As a result of this breach he was excluded from the family business and cut off from his inheritance, and so was forced to make his own way in the world. Fortunately, he had inherited his father's great financial acumen and so was able to amass a vast personal fortune on the London Stock Exchange within a very short space of time. Indeed, by lending money to the British government during the Napoleonic Wars, by 1814 he had become so wealthy that he was able to give up stockbroking and banking and join the ranks of the landed gentry. As the Jews had earlier been prohibited from owning land, the acquisition of a country estate had become the greatest ambition of successful Israelite financiers.

The largest of David Ricardo's properties was Gatcombe Park, near Minchinhampton, Gloucestershire, an imposing Palladian mansion built in 1717 and set in 200 acres of parkland, plus 530 acres of farmland, 200 acres of woodland and 600 acres of Minchinhampton Common. Today the Gatcombe Park estate is the residence of Princess Anne, having been purchased by Queen Elizabeth II in 1976 as a wedding present for the Princess Royal. When he died in 1823, aged only fifty-one, David Ricardo's total assets were valued at no less than £700,000, a quite staggering sum. Not surprisingly in view of the shining example presented by his financial and scholarly achievements, his progressive views were followed by the majority of his brothers and sisters who also chose to marry gentiles and leave the Jewish faith.

After retiring from business and becoming High Sheriff of Gloucester, an appointment that required him to take the sacrament of the established Church, David Ricardo pursued his political ambitions by being elected Member of Parliament for Portarlington in Ireland. He had purchased this rotten borough, which had only twelve constituents, for a considerable sum. Although there is no record of him ever visiting Ireland, he held the seat from 1819 until he died in 1823, leaving a widow, four daughters and three sons, Osman, David and Mortimer, who on the strength of their father's enormous fortune were duly accepted into the Quality, as Members of Parliament and Masters of Foxhounds or, in the case of Mortimer, as a cavalry officer in the Lifeguards. Like parliamentary seats, commissions in the army could only be acquired by the wealthiest individuals.

By the time of Sir Harry Ralph Ricardo's birth, therefore, what little that remained of the Dutch-Jewish blood in the Ricardo veins had been entirely diluted by intermarriage with English stock, for his close male ancestors had all married out of Jewry to establish themselves as bona fide members of the British landed gentry. Throughout over a century of residence in Great Britain, four generations of his Ricardo forebears had been baptised in Anglican churches, educated at leading public schools such as Eton, Winchester, Charterhouse and Rugby and had gone on to achieve high military or professional rank. For example, Sir Harry's Gatcombe uncles, Arthur David, Ambrose St Quentin, William and Henry George Ricardo (David Ricardo's four grandsons) all served with distinction as senior officers during the First World War, as Rear Admiral, Brigadier-General, Captain and Lieutenant-Colonel respectively, although by then they were all aged over fifty. Lieutenant-Colonel Henry George Ricardo, of course, was the owner of Gatcombe Park throughout most of Sir Harry's lifetime, until it was sold to the Courtauld family shortly before the Second World War. However, there is no evidence to suggest that Sir Harry ever visited Gatcombe.

In fact, Sir Harry was descended directly from David Ricardo's younger brother Raphael or Ralph (1787–1875), the thirteenth of Abraham Ricardo's eighteen children. The very same paternal disapproval that befell David Ricardo was also meted out to Ralph (Sir Harry's great-grandfather), when in 1819 he followed his brother's example by marrying an English girl, Charlotte Lobb, and giving up the Jewish religion. Ralph was also a stockbroker and banker. A member of the London Stock Exchange for over fifty years, he began his career in the City employed as his elder brother David's clerk.

Charlotte and Ralph produced a daughter and three sons, the eldest being Percy Ricardo, who eventually acquired the Bramley Park estate near Guildford in Surrey thus founding another landowning, military branch of the family; his sons Horace and Francis Cecil both achieved the rank of colonel. The former commanded the Grenadier Guards from 1899 to 1904 while the latter became High Sheriff of Berkshire in 1913.

Ralph's second son, Harry Ricardo, followed in his father's footsteps by becoming a merchant banker in the family tradition. After marrying Anna Halsey, a member of a another well-known Stock Exchange family, he settled at Weston, near Bath, while carrying out his business in Bristol. But although Harry conformed to his family's time-honoured occupation and business interests, he did not share their traditional indifference to the arts. His true passion lay not in making money but in the study of classical buildings and sculpture. As architecture was not then considered a fitting profession for a gentleman of his social standing, his enthusiasm was confined to making exquisitely detailed drawings of the buildings of Bath and also those of Rome, Florence, Naples and the other cities that he was able to visit when touring Italy.

Harry and Anna Ricardo had five children, a daughter, Mary, and four sons, Halsey (Sir Harry's father), Percy, Arthur and Harry. Unfortunately, both parents died while their children were very young. Harry senior was killed in an accidental fall in 1860, while Anna died four years later in January 1864, her forty-fourth year, when Mary was ten, Halsey nine, and Harry junior three. Consequently, all five siblings were put into the care of their aunt and uncle-in-law, the Revd Robert Wedgwood, Vicar of Dumbleton in the Wye Valley. A Justice of the Peace for Gloucestershire, he was a descendant of the famous master-potter Josiah Wedgwood.

It seems that the Wedgwoods (who had only one child of their own) did not take kindly to having five orphans foisted upon them and made no more effort to make the Ricardo children welcome at the vicarage than was demanded by their duty as trustees and guardians. Apparently, they were religious fanatics who took more delight in anticipating the punishments of hell than the rewards of paradise, and the children were constantly chastised or threatened with torture in the fires of eternal damnation. On Sundays, when not actually attending church to hear their uncle preach his interminable sermons, the children were forbidden to play games or read any books except the Bible. Consequently, they all grew up with just one ambition in mind – to escape from the clutches of their surrogate parents at the earliest possible opportunity.

Mary was eventually able to get away from the vicarage by eloping with an elderly merchant whose business involved importing oriental works of art. Shortly afterwards, the couple went to live in Japan and Mary remained there until almost the end of her life, so that Sir Harry met her only once, on her return to England shortly before her death.

Percy Ralph Ricardo also ran away from the Wedgwoods as soon as he could find a route to freedom. After leaving his school, Cheltenham College, when he was only fifteen, he made his way to Australia in search of fame and fortune and, except for one brief visit, he never returned to his homeland again. The hardships of his childhood had prepared him well for the life of a colonial pioneer and he flourished in Australia, initially as a sheep farmer and horse breeder and later, like so many of his Ricardo relations, as a military man. It is known that by 1884 he had reached the rank of captain in the Queensland Mounted Rifles (QMR) but that by 1891 he was a lieutenant-colonel on the Permanent Staff of the Australian Army. After commanding the QMR in the Boer War in South Africa from 1899 to 1900, he returned to Australia to become, from 1902 to 1905, the Military Commandant of Western Australia and from then until his death in 1907, the Commandant of the Commonwealth Military Forces in the State of Victoria.

In 1879 Percy married Bella, the daughter of William Lyall of Harewood, Victoria, who bore him two children, a daughter, Amy, and a son, Ralph, who in 1897, at the age of twelve, was sent to England to continue his education at a preparatory school in Woking which catered for the sons of expatriates. During the holidays, Ralph was placed under the care of his uncle Halsey Ricardo at 13 Bedford Square, where, as we shall see, he became Harry's greatest boyhood friend and companion.

Of Halsey Ricardo's other brothers, Arthur Ralph Ricardo became a stockbroker in the customary family manner, while the youngest, Harry William Ralph Ricardo (1860–1939), went into the army, which

Harry's uncle Major Harry Ricardo, a favourite courtier of King Edward VII, wearing the uniform of the King's Bodyguard of the Honourable Corps of Gentleman at Arms.

by then had become as much of a family tradition as banking and stockbroking. As a major in the 17th Lancers he saw active service in India, Sudan and South Africa and later travelled widely on official business throughout Asia and South America. A great raconteur, his stories of far-away places fascinated his young nephew. According to Sir Harry he was 'tall, well-built and extremely handsome, and in full-dress uniform and mounted on a well-groomed horse, he cut a very magnificent figure'. Although Arthur had a fine sense of humour and the most polished manners, like his brother Harry, however, he was rigidly conventional in his habits and outlook and always observed the correct formalities in everything he did or wore.

In 1901, on his return from the Boer War where he had been second-in-command of the 17th Lancers, he became a member of King Edward VII's bodyguard, formed from the Honourable Corps of Gentlemen at Arms, and as a member of the royal household he attended the King at all ceremonial occasions. Indeed, he became a trusted courtier and confidant in the King's entourage and was often invited to join the famous private weekend shooting parties at Sandringham, or to play bridge at Windsor or Buckingham Palace. When he retired from the army in 1903, he was appointed Adjutant of the Royal Hospital, Chelsea, a position he held until 1917. However, shortly after the King's death in 1910, while hunting in Ireland he was thrown from his horse and suffered a fractured skull. The injury affected his entire personality. Although he was then aged only fifty, he turned suddenly from a ebullient and energetic bon viveur into a dour and melancholy old man who shunned society. Not a trace was left of his former vitality and good humour, and he remained for the rest of his life a lonely and reclusive bachelor.

The eldest of Harry and Anna's four sons was, of course, Sir Harry's father Halsey Ralph Ricardo (1854–1928). Halsey found his way out of the joyless confinement of the vicarage when he was sent to a preparatory boarding school at Twyford, Berkshire, at the age of twelve. From there he went on to Rugby School which he attended from 1869 to 1872. During his last years at Rugby, Halsey Ricardo witnessed the building of the school's famous chapel, designed by William Butterfield. Unusually for a British public school, this was Byzantine rather than Gothic in style. Undoubtedly this building came to exert a powerful influence not only on Halsey's choice of career but also on the decorative techniques that he used much later when he became an established architect. But a more profound influence still was surely the example set by his father, Harry Ricardo, from whom he had inherited his love of buildings and his gift of draughtsmanship. Although he was only six when his father died, Halsey always treasured his vivid memories of the man and had carefully preserved the sketchbooks, letters and diaries that recorded his father's travels in Italy. Undoubtedly, these mementos were to inspire and direct the course of Halsey's life.

Instead of going up to university, in the autumn of 1872 Halsey became articled to a Cheltenham architect, John Middleton, before moving on in December 1874 to spend two further years as a pupil and clerk with the better-known practitioner Basil Champneys of Chelmsford, the architect of Newnham College, Cambridge. By the summer of 1876, however, Halsey had reached the point at which he felt that he had learned enough (and saved enough) to realise his ambition of following in his father's footsteps on an architectural pilgrimage to Italy. Over the next eighteen months he toured the length and breadth of Italy by train, sketching the classical and medieval buildings of Rome, Florence, Venice, learning Italian and acquiring a profound love and understanding of that country and its culture. His wanderings were only cut short when he succumbed to a near-fatal attack of typhoid fever in March 1878, which obliged him to come home to England to recover his health.

On his return from Italy in 1878, Halsey Ricardo took up employment with an architect in Oxford for a while, attracted by the magnetic pull of the university city that was by then the acknowledged centre of the most avant-garde aesthetic movement of the day, the Pre-Raphaelite Brotherhood, whose ideas and principles inspired the Arts and Crafts Movement with which he was later to become so closely connected.

It was during Halsey's time at Oxford that he first came into contact not just with the ideas and personalities of the Arts and Crafts Movement, but also with many of the people who were subsequently to have the greatest influence on the course of his life, including his lifelong friends the artist Edward Burne-Jones, the ceramicist William de Morgan, and the man who, ultimately, was to become his most important client and benefactor, Ernest Debenham.

In 1879, at the age of twenty-five, Halsey gave up his employment in Oxford and moved to London to set up in practice on his own account, as an architect, decorator and designer, working from a rented home, Campden Cottage in Hampstead. This pleasant hilltop village was then a bohemian community standing quite apart from the metropolis in every sense and certainly rising above it in artistic endeavour; the haunt of numerous painters and writers, it was both socially and geographically the equivalent of Montmartre in Paris.

It is not known exactly how the connection came about, but Halsey's first commission was received that very year from his future father-in-law, the eminent civil engineer, Sir Alexander Rendel, who employed him to make alterations to the Rendel family's mansion at 16 Palace Gardens, Kensington. This work was soon followed by similar small but lucrative commissions from other members of the Rendel clan and their friends, and also from one of Halsey's own Ricardo uncles.

The Rendels were a wealthy and well-connected family of engineers and industrialists who, having established themselves in the higher strata of Victorian society, were then in the process of acquiring impressive town and country residences each requiring alterations and improvements. In 1879, Sir Alexander Rendel had purchased Rickettswood, a rambling old country house near Charlwood in Surrey and, being pleased with Halsey's earlier work in London, he called him in again to carry out the necessary improvements. It was while staying there to supervise this work in 1880 that Halsey met and fell in love with Sir Alexander's eldest daughter, Catherine Jane Rendel, known to all as Kate.

By the following year, with numerous satisfactorily completed jobs under his belt and more in hand from his Rendel and Ricardo connections, Halsey felt that he was well enough established to be able to approach Sir Alexander and formally ask for his daughter's hand in marriage. Clearly, the Rendels had already succumbed to his attractive personality and charm and had accepted him as one of the family; according to the comments of a member of a later generation of the Rendel family, Mary Stocks, they took him to their hearts as he was so different to the rest of them: 'He introduced into the lives of all the Rendels aesthetic interests which they might otherwise have lacked.'

Despite some initial doubts about Halsey's financial prospects and his lack of religious belief, Sir Alexander consented and the pair were married later that year. The first few months of their married life were spent at Halsey's Hampstead cottage but, thanks to Sir Alexander's generosity, before very long they were installed in the substantial six-storey London town house at 13 Bedford Square, along with a sizeable domestic retinue comprising a housekeeper, a cook and several housemaids. The imposing late Georgian terraced property rapidly became open house to Halsey's and Kate's wide circle of friends from the worlds of art, literature and music, most notable among them being Edward Burne-Jones, the wood engraver and book illustrator Walter Crane (appointed Principal of the Royal College of Art in 1898), the sculptor Hamo Thornycroft and, of course, the ceramicist William de Morgan.

Even then, Bloomsbury had already acquired its reputation as an artistic, cosmopolitan and even bohemian quarter. Some forty years later, during the 1920s and 1930s this area of London achieved a certain fame through its connection with the Bloomsbury Set, the intellectual and literary *coterie* which met at the homes of the society hostess Lady Ottoline Morrell and the publisher Leonard Woolf and his wife the novelist Virginia Woolf. However, Lady Ottoline Morell's residence at 10 Gower Street (only a few yards from 13 Bedford Square) did not begin until 1924, by which time Halsey Ricardo had long since left London, to spend most of his time in Sussex.

Although he was the very opposite of the popular stereotype of the impoverished, indolent and feckless bohemian, Halsey Ricardo was certainly no slave to convention. According to his son, he could never understand how his conventionally minded stockbroking relations could tolerate their humdrum and regimented existences in the service of Mammon. In short, he was a freethinker with a somewhat cavalier attitude to money and material success; both his lack of ambition and his reluctance to undertake uncongenial work (or to cultivate disagreeable clients) led many of his friends and colleagues to believe that he was a wealthy man of independent means who could well afford to be choosy in the commissions that he selected. The truth is that Halsey was cushioned from the necessity of accepting uninteresting, unsuitable or unpalatable work by the wealth and influence of his wife's family, the Rendels, whose patronage and generosity provided him with gainful employment during otherwise lean times throughout his career. The numerous members of this prosperous clan, whose wealth and influence was founded on the ever-increasing importance of the civil engineering profession in the late Victorian world, admired his abilities and did all they could to advance his career by employing him themselves or by recommending his services to their friends and clients.

It was the Rendels also who were to play so great a part in establishing Sir Harry Ricardo's career as an engineer, firstly by recognising and encouraging their grandson's talent and secondly by providing a secure and enlightened environment in which his latent ability and aptitude for mechanical design could germinate and grow.

CHAPTER 3

The Rendel Connection

The family that provided the other half of Sir Harry's genetic make-up represented an entirely different and contrasting face of the High Victorian professional élite. While the Ricardos owed their position to a long tradition of pre-eminence as bankers, financiers, landlords and *rentiers*, the Rendels were members of a dynasty of enlightened, liberal engineer-entrepreneurs in the mould of Brunel and Stephenson.

A typical product of the Industrial Revolution, they had emerged from an obscure agricultural background to play a vital role in the economic development of the United Kingdom during the nineteenth century, by surveying, designing and constructing the vital road, rail, canal and maritime transport and communications network, without which the remarkable expansion of British trade and industry could never have taken place. Like others of their new profession, they were in the forefront of progress and invention in all aspects of British life and were the leaders not just of technological advancement, but also of social and political reform.

The founder of the empire-building Rendel dynasty, James Meadows Rendel (Sir Harry's maternal great grandfather, 1799–1856) was the son of James Rendle, a yeoman farmer from Drewsteignton near Okehampton, Devon. Besides acting as an agricultural estate agent, valuer and auctioneer, James Meadows Rendel also had responsibilities for the upkeep of the county's roads under the turnpike trust system then in force. At an early age, he had formed the intention of becoming a civil engineer and he was fortunate enough to become apprenticed to Thomas Telford, the foremost road maker and bridge builder of that era. Initially he was engaged in surveying the roads of North Devon but, in 1816, he was sent to Telford's London headquarters and given his first major assignment – the preparation of detailed drawings for a suspension bridge across the Mersey at Runcorn. Although this bridge was never built, his work on the project doubtless contributed to the success of Telford's great suspension bridge across the Menai Straits, first proposed in 1818 but not completed and opened to the public until 1826.

However, in 1823, at the age of twenty-three, J.M. Rendel decided to quit Telford's employment and return to Devon, to set up in business as a consulting civil engineer on his own account at Plymouth. Enjoying Telford's full blessing (at least initially), the venture proved a great success; from small beginnings in the West Country, the practice grew rapidly during its founder's lifetime to become a major enterprise, concerned with the building of harbours, docks, bridges and railways throughout the United Kingdom and the empire, and in India in particular. James's principal achievements were the construction of the Victoria Docks in London, the Birkenhead Docks on Merseyside and Grimsby Docks, the building of the Royal Naval harbour at Portland Bill, the invention of the floating bridge, and the design and erection of the first-ever swing bridge, opened at Boscombe in 1826. Ultimately he became President of the Institution of Civil Engineers, and in February 1843 was honoured as one of the first civil engineers to be elected a Fellow of the Royal Society.

After sixteen years at Plymouth the business had expanded to such an extent that, in spring 1838, just a few weeks before Queen Victoria's coronation, James was obliged to transfer his headquarters to London. At first he occupied no. 34 Great George Street, Westminster, but later he moved a few doors along the street to no. 8; in both cases he lived and worked on the premises, so that his business affairs completely dominated family life.

By the 1840s Great George Street had become the recognised centre for the civil engineering profession; one of James's near neighbours, living at no. 24, was George Stephenson. By 1852, James's wealth and prestige had increased to such an extent that he was able to move his domestic accommodation once again, to a splendid new mansion at 10 Kensington Palace Gardens, one of the most expensive and fashionable addresses in Victorian London. Designed expressly for him by his friend the architect Thomas Henry Wyatt, this house survives today and until recently was occupied by the Russian Embassy.

In the course of designing the lock gates, cranes and other machinery installed in the numerous ports and harbours that he constructed, James Meadows Rendel had come to rely on the advice of a young lawyer and amateur engineer from Newcastle upon Tyne, who had a particular interest in hydraulic mechanisms. This man was William George Armstrong (1810–1900), who eventually became the munitions magnate Lord Armstrong of Cragside, perhaps the greatest of all the High Victorian industrialists and surely the richest. James persuaded William Armstrong to abandon the legal profession and devote all his energies to the design and manufacture of hydraulic machinery, with the result that in January 1847, Armstrong established his Elswick company on the north bank of the River Tyne at Newcastle. Moreover, it was James Rendel also who suggested to Armstrong the idea behind the invention of the breech-loading, rifle-barrelled, large calibre guns that the firm began to make in the 1850s, the accuracy of which very soon transformed both naval and military ordnance.

As a result of this collaboration a deep and enduring friendship was formed, which led, not unnaturally, to the establishment of an important and powerful allegiance between the Rendel and Armstrong engineering businesses, one civil, the other mechanical. When James Meadows Rendel died at Kensington Palace Gardens in November 1856, Armstrong was at his bedside and it was he who took charge of the situation and attended to the funeral arrangements.

Between 1829 and 1843 James and his wife Catherine Harris (who herself came from a family of 23 children) produced 10 offspring, 2 of whom had died in childhood. In turn the survivors of this brood produced 35 grandchildren, 56 great-grandchildren and 90 great-great-grandchildren, a score even better than that achieved by Sir Harry's paternal great-grandparents, Raphael and Charlotte Ricardo! Sir William Armstrong (as he had become by then) had no children, however, and so he looked on his friend's sons as his own. In due course, the three youngest boys – George, Stuart and Hamilton – all took up employment as junior partners in the Armstrong firm and duly rose to great wealth and prominence in the engineering profession.

The period immediately following James Rendel's untimely death was one of great anxiety for his family. Due to the relatively young age and inexperience of his sons and successors (the eldest, Alexander, was then only twenty-seven), the Admiralty appointed new consulting engineers to take over the uncompleted harbour works at Holyhead and Portland and also the projects then under way in South Africa. To repay his friend's early support and encouragement, which had led to the outstanding success of his own engineering enterprises, one of William Armstrong's first acts was to write to Robert Stephenson, seeking his assistance to secure the future of the Rendel firm. Within a few

Sir Harry's maternal grandfather was the distinguished Victorian civil engineer Sir Alexander Rendel (1829–1918) whose firm was chiefly responsible for the building of the Indian railway system.

months, the appointment of Alexander Meadows Rendel (1829–1918) as Consulting Engineer to the East Indian Railway Company was confirmed, a decision of incalculable benefit to the Rendel family. The association thus formed was to last for sixty years; right up to his death in 1918, Alexander Rendel was to be continuously involved in great civil and railway engineering works in India. His achievements for the British Raj eventually earned him the highest honours. In 1887, the year of Queen Victoria's Golden Jubilee, on the occasion of the opening of the magnificent bridge that he had designed to span the Hooghly River and link Howrah with Calcutta, he was invested Knight Commander of the Indian Empire by HRH Edward, Prince of Wales, the Viceroy of India.

It seems James had envisaged that it would be his second son, Lewis, who would join him in the business, and that his first-born child, Alexander (Sir Harry's grandfather) would take holy orders and be ordained as a cleric of the Church of England. Therefore, Alexander had been educated at King's School, Canterbury before going up to Trinity College, Cambridge, where he read both divinity and mathematics. But when Lewis died from consumption in 1851, aged only twenty-one, Alexander was forced to give up all thoughts of the priesthood and to turn to civil engineering. On his father's death five years later, he immediately assumed responsibility for the management of the entire Rendel practice. Over the following six decades he guided its affairs with distinction, so that its activities expanded to cover several continents. His ecclesiastical education had equipped him well for this task, for in addition to the soundness and probity he brought to bear on his engineering and business-management duties, he also possessed a keen sense of moral responsibility. He worked himself to an early death not merely for his own personal gain, but for the betterment of the peoples of Her Majesty's overseas territories and dominions. Such as it was, the reputation for progressive and enlightened administration enjoyed by the British Empire at the height of its powers was based entirely on the work of energetic, competent, high principled and wholly incorruptible men like Alexander Meadows Rendel. Sir Harry remarked that: 'through his wisdom and integrity, he had gained the complete confidence of Whitehall. The higher ranks of civil servants, more especially those of the Colonial Office and the India Office, relied on him absolutely.'

As Sir Harry recorded in his autobiography, all three of James Meadows Rendel's younger sons, George, Stuart and Hamilton, eventually achieved distinction in various ways, having been taken under William Armstrong's wing and sent to the Elswick Works for their engineering training before being made partners in the Newcastle firm. George

Rendel, to whom Armstrong was so devoted that he considered him to be his adopted son, was actually made a partner of the Elswick Ordnance Company at its foundation in 1859, when he was only twenty-six; he had entered the firm on leaving Harrow. George was regarded as the leading authority on the design of the steam machinery used for propelling very large warships such as battleships and cruisers and also on the design of their guns.

In 1882, however, he resigned from Armstrong's to take up the post of First Civil Lord of the Admiralty, a three-year appointment. When his Admiralty work was completed, George returned to Armstrong's, though not at Elswick. His doctor had advised that he should live abroad in a warmer climate and so he settled at Pozzuoli near Naples to manage the company's newly founded Italian shipbuilding subsidiary. Sir Harry recalled that he met him only once, when he was just a very small boy playing in his nursery. On that occasion his great-uncle won his heart by asking him to show him his first childish attempts at designing a steam engine. These drawings his uncle discussed 'in all solemnity, as though I was his designing draughtsman, which I found immensely flattering'.

Under Armstrong's tutelage, the fifth and youngest of the brothers, Hamilton Rendel, became an expert on hydraulics and was responsible for the design and development of the high-precision machinery that loaded and elevated naval guns and rotated the gun turrets on warships. He also designed the hydraulic equipment that raised and lowered Tower Bridge in London. Apparently, he suffered all his life from a stammer or similar speech impediment, which made him very shy; he never married but lived the life of a recluse at Elswick until his death. Sir Harry never met him.

The fourth brother, Sir Harry's great-uncle Stuart Rendel, was quite the opposite. A more suave and self-assured man would be hard to imagine. After completing his education at Eton and Oriel College, Oxford, where he read law before being called to the Bar, Stuart also joined Armstrong's, but in the role of an administrator and businessman rather than as an engineer. Based at the company's London offices, he was involved in negotiating contracts with the Admiralty and various foreign governments. In the course of this work he soon built up extensive military, political and diplomatic connections at home and abroad. Eventually, in 1880, he took up politics himself and entered Parliament as the Liberal Member for Montgomeryshire. By that time he had amassed a very large fortune, much of which he invested in property in London, Brighton and Cannes in the South of France. From the very moment that he first set foot in the House of Commons, Stuart Rendel enjoyed the friendliest of relationships with the leader of the Liberal Party, William Gladstone, and but for his very large shareholdings in the Armstrong concern, he would almost certainly have been given high ministerial office in Gladstone's administration. Instead he was sent to the House of Lords as a Liberal peer, being ennobled by Gladstone as the 1st Baron Rendel. Eventually his daughter Maude married Gladstone's son Harry, the future Lord Gladstone of Harwarden, an alliance that apparently brought both men enormous satisfaction. Stuart had no sons, however, and was therefore frustrated in his ambition to create a dynasty of Rendel peers.

Sir Harry remembered his great-uncle Stuart as being 'a very tall and dignified old gentleman', and recorded that they met on several occasions. As Stuart's political career progressed, there developed between Alexander and his brother feelings of rivalry and disenchantment. As Sir Harry put it in his autobiography: 'It was the habit of my branch of the Rendel family to laugh at Uncle Stuart, implying that while his brothers were all distinguished engineers, he was little more than a high-pressure salesman, and that he had bought his title by contributing largely to Liberal Party funds and by friendship with Mr Gladstone. This was probably quite unfair, and tainted possibly by a tinge of jealousy, for whatever my grandfather did, Uncle Stuart always contrived to go one better.' For example, when Alexander Rendel bought the Rickettswood estate, near Charlwood in Surrey, Stuart Rendel immediately capped this by purchasing Hatchlands, an even bigger estate not far away at East Clandon. Again, when, after the abolition of the Red Flag restrictions Alexander bought his first car, his brother reacted by acquiring a bigger, better and more expensive vehicle, and so on.

But to return to Sir Harry's immediate family: at the age of twenty-one, Alexander Rendel fell in love with Eliza Hobson, the fifteen-year-old eldest daughter of Captain William Hobson RN, the first Governor of New Zealand. Hobson had made his name by carrying out surveys of both Arctic and Antarctic waters for the Admiralty, and on one of these expeditions he became the first man to explore and chart in detail the coastline of New Zealand and to make friendly contact with the Maoris. On his return to England he was appointed by Queen Victoria to sail back and take possession of the country and to set up a constitutional government (established in the Treaty of Waitangi) giving the indigenous Maoris equal partnership with the British settlers and colonialists. There he remained until his untimely death in 1842, whereupon his widow and his two daughters, Eliza and Polly, returned to England. In fact, young Harry's great-aunt Polly never married, but lived out her days looking after her mother at the parental home, Penlee House at Devonport, a small but beautifully situated house standing high above Plymouth Hoe. Aunt Polly was a favourite among his Rendel relations and, doubtless, it was on the many happy childhood visits to her Plymouth house that he formed his enduring love of sailing ships and the sea.

Alexander and Eliza (or Leila as she was always known in the family) were married in 1852 and went to live at 44 Lancaster Gate, Bayswater. Eventually, however, they moved to 23 Russell Square in Holborn, at the same time acquiring their splendid country residence, Rickettswood, a rambling, half-timbered sixteenth-century house which stood in a 400-acre estate at Charlwood, near Dorking, Surrey. It became their custom to spend the summer months there, surrounded by their nineteen grandchildren and countless other nephews and nieces, whose needs were attended to by a large retinue of nursemaids and governesses in

Regularly every summer, Sir Alexander's extended family would meet at Rickettswood, his country house near Charlwood in Surrey.

Among the principal adult members of Harry Ricardo's family, seen here on the lawn at Rickettswood in the 1880s, were his father Halsey Ricardo and his mother Kate Rendel, seated to the left. His grandmother Leila Rendel is sitting second from the right of the photograph

accordance with the High Victorian precept that children should be seen but not heard. Many of Sir Harry's earliest memories were of playing with his Rendel cousins at these extended family gatherings at Rickettswood. It was there also that he was first introduced to many of the prominent Victorian engineers who were among his grandfather's business associates, including the physicist and artillery expert Sir Andrew Noble, a partner of Lord Armstrong, and the railway engineers and magnates Sir Percy Girouard and Sir Ralph Wedgwood, who was James Meadows Rendel's grandson and thus Sir Alexander's nephew.

During these late Victorian summers at Rickettswood, Sir Alexander became, in effect, one of the very first commuters. It was his habit to go up to London every morning by an early train, returning every evening at dinner time, a journey that involved a 5-mile drive by carriage and pair to Horley station and a half-hour ride in a first-class compartment of the Southern Railway to Victoria, from where he always walked to his office in Westminster. It is doubtful that the trip could be made any faster today.

Alexander and Leila had produced eight children: five sons, James, William, Arthur, Herbert and Henry, and three daughters, Catherine, Edith and Helen. The eldest son James never showed the slightest interest in engineering and spent his life in the City, as a director of various home or colonial companies. Of the younger sons, only two, William and Henry, had shown sufficient aptitude and interest in civil engineering to undergo professional training and join their father's firm. William Rendel became a partner in 1894 but sadly he died four years later leaving only Henry Wedgwood Rendel to succeed him at the Great George Street offices. Henry, who had been educated at the Royal Naval College, Greenwich, before training at Neilson's Locomotive Works at Glasgow and Armstrong's Elswick Works, had already proved himself to be a first-rate mechanical engineer. His first major responsibility was the erection of hydraulic machinery at the Indian government's dockyard at Bombay. He then joined his Uncle George at Armstrong's Pozzuoli Works in Italy for two years before entering his father's consulting firm in 1896, becoming a partner two years later.

The archetypal Victorian
patriarch, Sir Alexander
Rendel, pictured here
(foreground) with his
faithful bailiff Murphy
and his dog.

After a period spent in America, Henry was sent to Africa, to supervise the construction of the notorious Uganda Railway, a project that was then regarded as being of great strategic importance. A race to be the first to lay a track to Lake Victoria, connecting with the railway from Mombasa on the coast via Nairobi in Kenya, had developed between the British and German governments. The route had to pass through virgin territory infested by the deadly tsetse fly, which made the use of horses and bullocks virtually impossible, across forbidden areas haunted by 'evil spirits' which frightened the native labourers away. No fewer than twenty-two men engaged on the project were killed by lions. Henry survived this ordeal and completed the task, but sadly he died of pneumonia in 1903 at the age of thirty-seven. He never married.

The eldest of Sir Alexander Rendel's daughters, Sir Harry's mother Catherine Jane was also deeply involved in the family business and, having had some training as an accountant, she helped to keep the firm's accounts and look after other administrative matters. The second daughter, her sister Edith, never married and devoted herself to charitable works, while the third, christened Helen Constance but always known as

Connie, married a London doctor, Roland Brinton MD. Her eldest daughter Mary, Sir Harry's cousin, also devoted her life to politics and public service, as well as to writing and broadcasting. In 1966 she was made a life peer as Baroness Stocks.

In her autobiography published in 1970, Lady Stocks had much to say about her meetings with her Ricardo cousins at the turn of the century, at both Rickettswood and Bedford Square where on many occasions she saw young Harry constructing engines in his basement workshop. Evidently, Halsey Ricardo made a strong impression on her as a child. She described him as being 'a gifted if somewhat erratic architect . . . the arbiter of Rendel taste . . . a devoted family man'. She added that: 'He was a superb reader aloud and a stimulating talker' who encouraged her interest in drama, poetry and music. She also recalled the agreeable certainties of childhood at Rickettswood: 'One knew that . . . when the lamps were lit after high tea, Uncle Halsey would read to us while we drew and painted. What we didn't know was that our world was moving inexorably towards a break-up of much that made life gracious and secure for the privileged classes of the Edwardian Age.'

The death of his grandson Henry Rendel in 1903 came as a grievous blow to Sir Alexander, who was then on the point of retirement. He had always cherished the hope that Henry, as the only remaining qualified civil engineer in the family, might carry on business in the Rendel name for a further generation or by producing a son ensure its survival for another century at the very least. But Henry had spent his all-too-short working life abroad and never had the chance to find a suitable bride, much less to father an heir. From that point onwards, therefore, Sir Alexander came to look on his young Ricardo grandson, then aged eighteen, as his natural successor, taking steps to ensure that he was properly trained and groomed for such a role. After all, even as a small boy, Harry had shown signs of an interest in and a talent for engineering; now, the prospect of a partnership on his grandfather's retirement was assured.

These, then, were the family circumstances and traditions into which Sir Harry Ricardo was born. As we shall see, it was a milieu that he looked back on with admiration, respect and pride. For all his progressiveness and open-mindedness in engineering matters, he was no social revolutionary or iconoclast; he espoused the gentlemanly manners and morals of his Victorian and Edwardian forebears and shared their ideals and aspirations. Certainly, all who knew him recognised Sir Harry Ricardo as the quintessential upper-middle-class English professional gentleman.

CHAPTER 4

Father and Son

Sir Harry Ricardo's earliest recollection of his father, the architect and designer Halsey Ricardo (1854–1928), was of seeing him carried home to 13 Bedford Square on a stretcher, semi-paralysed by a dislocated back and suffering from a broken right arm and many other visible injuries. For a four-year-old boy, it must have been a terrifying experience. The accident occurred at some point in 1889, when Halsey was inspecting progress at the site of one of his architectural projects. While climbing high scaffolding, he had tumbled from an unsecured ladder in an identical fall to the one that had caused his father's death. Halsey was lucky not to have been killed outright. For a time his survival was in doubt, but fortunately his spinal cord had not been damaged and after lying encased in plaster for many months he eventually made a full recovery. The only lasting effect of the accident was that, by learning to use his left hand so as to overcome the temporary loss of his right arm and continue with his work, he became ambidextrous. Thereafter, for the rest of his life he was able to sign his name with his right and left hand simultaneously, or draw two exactly identical images of any symmetrical object at exactly the same time, by holding pencils in both hands. Halsey often repeated this party piece to amuse his children and their friends, much as other fathers might perform conjuring tricks with cards or coins.

Sir Harry admitted that this anxious period, during which his eldest sister Anna was born, had made a profound impression on him. Evidently, even by that tender age his father's kindly, generous nature and informal, easy-going manner had won his deep and lasting affection. Although protected from life's upsets and unpleasantnesses by the affluent and stable environment of Bedford Square, and by the well-ordered routine of his nursery upbringing, he must have sensed the threat that the accident posed to his family's continued well-being; his father's income was already somewhat precarious and insecure, at least by the standards of the prosperous Victorian upper middle classes.

All ended well, however, and throughout the following four decades, father and son grew ever closer together, their friendship flourishing not merely by virtue of their family ties and obligations but through an even stronger bond: the attachment that sprang from a mutual interest in, and a deep respect for, each other's professional activities and abilities. Halsey was no engineer, nor Harry an aesthete, but both were united by their common belief in the importance of practical handiwork. It was only through a thorough understanding of the nature and properties of materials that anything of lasting value could be created in either architecture or engineering, they believed.

All too often in well-to-do Victorian households, such as that which existed at 13 Bedford Square in the 1880s, the *paterfamilias* was a remote, stern and altogether authoritarian figure, quick to criticise and discourage the youthful interests and ambitions of his offspring, especially if they were in any way unconventional. But, fortunately, from a very early age, Harry was encouraged to develop his interest in practical craftsmanship by a father who took every opportunity to praise his youthful efforts and achievements, and to introduce him to the accomplishments of British engineering, science, technology and art, on visits to museums, galleries and other places of interest in London. Together, the pair made frequent expeditions and sightseeing trips around the capital, viewing its architectural assets and liabilities from the vantage point of the open-top deck of a London omnibus. Moreover, it was Halsey, of course, who set young Harry up with a well-equipped workshop in the basement at Bedford Square, where the true foundations of Harry's career as an engineer and scientist were laid.

As we have already seen, Bloomsbury was an island of prosperity and respectability in a sea of squalor, poverty and deprivation. Not far to the south of Bedford Square lay the notorious slums of Soho and the Seven Dials area, which were still a Dickensian haunt of prostitutes, vagrants and criminals, where drunkenness and debauchery were rife. An ordinary Victorian father would doubtless have been at pains to shield his son from these unpleasant facts of life, but Halsey had no such qualms. In his autobiography, Sir Harry described his wanderings with his father among the small workshops, factories and foundries that then lined the Tottenham Court Road and Grays Inn Road, so very near to Bedford Square. Now given over entirely to shops and offices, before the turn of the century these streets were centres of light industrial activity, where small woodworking or metalworking firms manufactured and repaired furniture, clocks, tools and other ironmongery, and generally supplied the household and domestic needs of London, 'We both took pleasure in watching really skilful craftsman do their work,' Sir Harry recorded.

When Harry was ten, on one of these rambles the pair encountered, sitting behind the window of a particular shop, an old man working on a very ancient metal lathe. 'Seeing my face glued to his window he invited me in and thereafter I visited him again and again during my first school holiday. He was the most highly skilled craftsman I have ever watched. There seemed almost nothing that the old man could not tackle, even with the simple tools and equipment at his disposal.' Very soon the old man had become young Harry's mentor, teaching him the tricks and techniques of his trade and introducing him to the periodical *The English Mechanic*, which duly became his favourite reading throughout his schooldays. 'Its publishers also produced a kind of encyclopedia of workshop practice which was for many years my bible,' Sir Harry added. 'From a scientific point of view it was perhaps not very profound, but it was compounded of nearly a century of hard-won practical experience.'

According to Sir Harry, his father was: 'Outstandingly good-looking and good-humoured . . . the happiest man I have ever known, for he never passed an idle or unproductive moment. He enjoyed every minute of his life, had no regrets, fears and forebodings.' Nor had Halsey allowed the miseries of his childhood at his uncle's vicarage to leave any visible mark on his character, although he was determined that his own children should never experience the religious bigotry and persecution that he had been forced to endure. 'An architect by profession but an artist by instinct and inclination', he was far more interested in the aesthetic than the constructional side of building, although he was in no way incompetent when it came to managing the mundane matters, such as costing materials, organising space and installing the wiring and pipework that make a building work. He was in essence a designer who took the greatest pains to beautify and perfect the smallest fixtures and fitments of the houses that he built, right down to the detail of the wrought ironwork of the staircase banisters or the patterns of the ceramic tiling lining the elaborate pictorial fireplaces which were his speciality.

Moreover, his artistic talents and interests were exceedingly diverse; apart from his exceptional gifts as a designer and draughtsman, he was a keen musician, a first-rate pianist and an avid concert-goer and opera-lover. Every morning, before work commenced, the rooms of 13 Bedford Square would ring to the sound of Halsey's singing and music-making. Although he was a nonconformist in almost everything he said or did, he was far too well brought up to defy the rigid social rules of his era. Instead, he preferred to express his unorthodoxy and individuality with small and inoffensive gestures, which gave the impression of mild eccentricity rather than outright radicalism. For example, he never wore stiff collars or formal morning or evening dress, preferring loose, comfortable yet stylish clothes, some of which he designed himself. The nearest that he ever came to upsetting the conventions of the day was to refuse to wear a hat, or to dress up in white tie and tailcoat at dinner time, as was then considered *de rigueur* in polite society.

From the very outset of his career, Halsey Ricardo adopted the unusual *modus operandi* of working alone without assistance and doing everything himself by hand, in the most meticulous way. He had no office as such and instead of employing a draughtsman and clerk to carry out his instructions, he made all the detailed plans and working drawings without assistance, also writing out the specifications, accounts and business correspondence in his superb italic handwriting, using a quill pen and coloured inks that he made himself – calligraphy and bookbinding were also among his talents. He never made freehand sketches to rough out his ideas; if mistakes were made or alterations and revisions became necessary, he simply tore up his first efforts and started afresh. Had he adopted a more ambitious and commercial approach and simplified his painstaking working methods, doubtless he could have taken on more commissions, produced more designs, acquired more clients, engaged staff and expanded his practice considerably, but he was never interested in making such compromises in order to pursue professional glory or prestige; his only concern was to retain complete control over the execution of his ideas. Above all, he avoided involvement with tedious or uninteresting 'bread and butter' projects and refused to deal with unsympathetic or disagreeable people. There can be little doubt that his son inherited his gentlemanly – disdainful, even – attitude to commercial matters.

By the time that young Harry was born, Halsey had been practising as an architect for about six years but the majority of his commissions during this early period had comprised alterations or additions to various Rendel and Ricardo family properties, or the refashioning of the interiors of a number of houses owned by aristocratic clients introduced by the Rendels. However, in 1888 Halsey Ricardo was given the chance to make his mark on the face of London with a major work that showed the full extent of his gifts. The assignment in question involved the complete refurbishment of Sir Alexander Rendel's offices at 8 Great George Street, Westminster, which had recently been damaged by a fire. Halsey proceeded to transform this Georgian terraced house beyond recognition, both inside and out, radically altering the arrangement of its windows to introduce more light into the offices within. Although great care was taken to maintain the scale and proportions of the new building in harmony with its neighbours, its classical frontage was entirely refaced with russet-coloured salt-glazed bricks, in the Arts and Crafts style. The result was a truly original and successful building that reflected Halsey's novel, if slightly idiosyncratic, approach and style. A striking combination of symmetry and irregularity, ornamentation and simplicity, the design was

Halsey Ricardo's
architectural drawing of
the premises of Sir
Alexander Rendel's civil
engineering firm at 8
Great George Street
Westminster, which he
rebuilt in 1888. The
building was demolished
in the late 1920s.

widely regarded as a work of artistic genius; indeed many of its avant garde features
were reproduced by Charles Rennie Mackintosh (1868–1928) in his own first great
achievement, the *Glasgow Herald* building built in 1893. Sadly 8 Great George Street
was demolished in the late 1920s, not long after Halsey Ricardo's death. This, of course,
was the building where Harry Ricardo worked at the outset of his career as an engineer,
when he was employed by the family firm from 1907 until 1917.

Halsey Ricardo's career demanded that he reside in London, but he was not a
townsman, for he considered that the poor quality of urban life in British cities, of which
indifferent architecture and inadequate town planning was a root cause, fell short of the
civic ideal that was established by the ancient Mediterranean civilisations and that was
still in evidence in Italy. Consequently, he always harboured an ambition to own a
country house situated in the fresh air of an open landscape, well away from the grey and
smoky influences of the metropolis, and he constantly made plans and preparations for
the construction of such a property. Unlike his Rendel relations who lived in the country
but remained Londoners at heart, playing no real part in rural life, Halsey Ricardo was a

true countryman, interested in every aspect of the natural world and extremely knowledgeable on all questions of flora and fauna. Sir Harry recalled that, in his youth, whenever his father joined the traditional Rendel family gatherings at Rickettswood, the pair of them would go for long country walks looking for signs of wildlife.

Regularly every year Halsey set aside two weeks of the summer for what he regarded as a proper family holiday, deep in the real countryside, far removed from the spuriously rural atmosphere of Surrey where the chimneys of London always seemed to cast a shadow, both physically and metaphorically. This holiday was usually taken at a small port or seaside resort – West Bay near Bridport in Dorset or Looe in Cornwall were the favourite destinations. On these holidays, from dawn till dusk the time was always fully taken up with intensely exciting adventures. Under Halsey's energetic and stimulating direction, lazing around in deckchairs or messing about with bucket and spade building sandcastles was simply not allowed. Instead, at low tide, father and son would busy themselves by trawling the rock pools for crabs and shrimps or digging in the sand for worms, which, at high tide, would be used as bait when fishing with rod and line, casting either from the shore or from an open sailing boat.

Halsey Ricardo's search for a rural retreat had begun long before the birth of his children. During the great bicycle boom that coincided with his marriage in 1881, he and his wife became keen cyclists and often made cycling and walking tours to explore the Home Counties, searching for a suitable place in which to settle and raise their family. On one of these expeditions to West Sussex, made in 1885, the year that Harry was born, Halsey and Kate Rendel came upon an attractive plot of land for sale near the tiny village of Graffham, between Petworth and Midhurst. Tucked away on a sheltered site in a belt of pine woods and lying on a sandy south-facing slope immediately under the lee of the South Downs, somehow the site reminded Halsey of the scenery of the Tuscan hills. With funds raised from undertaking a commercial commission for an acquaintance of the Rendels, he acquired the 12-acre plot and immediately began the work of clearing and terracing the site and planting an orchard. However, due to the almost continual lack of truly lucrative work that characterised Halsey's career, it was twenty years before the building of the house could begin. Throughout Sir Harry's childhood, therefore, Graffham was a place for occasional excursions and picnics whenever his father visited the place to survey the site and take measurements. Many men would have been discouraged by the delay in bringing their cherished plans to fruition, but not Halsey. 'For my father, these were happy years of anticipation during which he spent much of his spare time putting finishing touches to the design of his house-to-be,' his son recorded.

Partly through his interest in ceramics, and partly through the necessity of finding greater and more profitable employment, in the midsummer of 1888 Halsey Ricardo accepted the offer of a partnership with the potter William de Morgan, whom he had first met twelve years previously during his Oxford days. Some fifteen years Ricardo's senior, de Morgan had long been a leading disciple of William Morris and an established member of the Arts and Crafts movement. As much an engineer, mechanic, inventor and chemist as a craftsman potter, de Morgan's genius lay in making decorative tiles rather than in throwing pots. As a designer and decorator of ceramics, however, his artistry was unmatched, and his experiments with the firing of glazes and enamels had produced some exciting and colourful new effects that had taken the Victorian art pottery market by storm. Produced in large numbers and usually decorated with floral or botanical designs in the William Morris tradition, de Morgan's hand-painted tiles were extremely fashionable in late Victorian times, being employed to decorate the interior and exterior surfaces of private houses and public buildings alike.

Despite this ostensible commercial success, however, William de Morgan was bored by the managerial and administrative work involved in running a manufacturing business and in order to restore his failing health, on the advice of his doctors he had decided that henceforth he would spend most of the year abroad in the warmer climate of Florence, surrounded by the pre-Renaissance art and architecture that provided his inspiration. From here he intended to continue supplying his pottery company with designs, leaving the

Halsey Ricardo photographed at his desk at Bedford Square in the 1890s. He worked from home and undertook even the smallest details of his commissions himself.

responsibility of making and marketing the tiles and pots to Halsey Ricardo. The arrangement agreed by the two partners was that, in de Morgan's prolonged absences in Italy, Halsey would devote half of every weekday to managing the venture, each partner contributing an equal amount of capital – £8,000 – which actually came from their wives. The agreement provided Halsey with useful architectural work, for he was entrusted with the design and construction of a new factory for the firm at Sands End, near Wandsworth Bridge in Fulham, which replaced de Morgan's former premises at Merton Abbey. It also gave him the opportunity to develop his own considerable talents as a ceramic artist; a significant proportion of the tiles and pots produced by the de Morgan firm during this period were embellished by Halsey Ricardo's own designs. His partnership with de Morgan took Ricardo back to Italy on more than one occasion, and from here he sent letters home to his children, illustrated in the margins with amusing and informative sketches. These affectionate and evocative letters must surely have encouraged young Harry's interest in foreign travel. 'We have seen lots of lizards and villas and butterflies,' Halsey wrote to his son from Florence in May 1891 when touring Italy with his wife. 'Someday, perhaps, when you are grown up we may capture a villa outside the city walls and have a vineyard and an olive grove of our own.' On this occasion, as well as meeting up with William de Morgan in Florence, the pair also visited Rome, Venice and Naples where they stayed with George Rendel. Here the architect designed a new study for his wife's cousin.

One of the largest and most important projects undertaken by de Morgan's Fulham factory at this time was actually an order introduced by Ricardo, through a previous client of his architectural practice, Lord Sudeley, the Chairman of the P&O Steamship Company, who was a friend and business associate of the Rendel family. This was a contract signed in 1894 for the supply of a large quantity of tiles to decorate the corridors, cabins and public rooms of P&O's new fleet of six passenger liners. The inspiration for this novel idea was the work that the de Morgan firm had recently carried out on the Tsar of Russia's private yacht, the *Livadia*. This enormous project was fraught with technical problems from the start, mostly arising from the difficulty of fixing flat tiles to the complex curved surfaces of the vessels' hull and superstructure; in rough weather, tiles fell off the dining-room ceiling on to the tables beneath, so that the passengers had to be protected by netting.

This near disaster typified the failings of the enterprise, and pinpointed Halsey Ricardo's lack of technical expertise as a potter. Unlike de Morgan, he was first and foremost a designer, not a technologist and, try as he might, he was never able to master the production process satisfactorily, nor even to make a better job of managing the pottery's financial affairs. For example, there were constant costly failures in the delicate operation of firing the tiles, which only the skill and experience of the absent de Morgan could have solved. These problems increased rather than diminished with the passage of time: although at the height of its success the factory turned out tiles in enormous numbers, in the recession of the late 1890s a steep downturn in demand was experienced and so in 1898 the partnership was deemed unprofitable and wound up on an amicable basis; while remaining friends, each partner went his own separate way. In fact, the brilliant William de Morgan remained in Italy where he proceeded to develop a new and highly lucrative career as a novelist, and his pottery business was eventually closed entirely in 1903.

Sir Harry recorded that he remembered well how, when at Rickettswood, he overheard one of his Rendel uncles observe that the de Morgan pottery venture might well have been a great financial success had it concentrated on producing a few of the more popular designs of tiles and pots on a greater, more economic scale and on marketing these products with enterprising and dynamic sales methods. To this suggestion his father had replied that this might well have been the case, but doing so would have been no fun at all. Instead, he and his partner de Morgan and their small staff had bought, at a small price, the opportunity to enjoy ten years of pure creative pleasure, experimenting with new methods, designs and colour schemes, whereas the alternative of mass-producing a standardised line of products would have been sheer drudgery. This response typified Halsey's attitude to his work, which he undertook purely for creative satisfaction; he was neither ambitious, acquisitive nor materialistic, and his career was motivated only by the need to earn just enough to maintain a comfortable and agreeable standard of living. This, again, was a trait that he passed on to his son.

Given this uncommercial attitude, therefore, it is hardly surprising that Halsey Ricardo produced a comparatively small body of architectural work during his fifty-year-long career; and that of those few designs which were actually built, fewer still survive today. In fact, Halsey's sole major public building proposal to see the light of day was the railway station erected at Howrah, near Calcutta, in 1901 to serve as the joint terminus of the East Indian and Bengal railway companies. Naturally, Howrah station was another job that came about through the influence of his father-in-law Sir Alexander Rendel, whose firm of consulting engineers was responsible for the development of the Indian railway system, and thus for constructing the railway track to the stations together with the nearby Howrah Bridge over the Hooghly River. Although it was the largest and most prestigious project that Halsey was ever involved in, its construction was supervised entirely by post. Halsey saw nothing of his elaborate, eclectic composition of arches, towers, parapets and balustrades, built in brickwork and glazed tiles in the British Raj style; he simply could not afford the long journey to India to inspect it.

His last great commission, and the supreme achievement of his career, was the enormous, elaborate and extravagant mansion that he built between 1905 and 1908 at

8 Addison Road, Holland Park, West London, for his friend Ernest Debenham whom he had known since his Oxford days. For some years previously, Debenham had been living nearby in a house at 55/57 Melbury Road, Kensington, which Halsey had built in 1894 for Sir Alexander Rendel, and he had long been an enthusiastic supporter of the Arts and Craft movement. But now, much impressed with Halsey's latest ideas, and having made a vast fortune from the department store that bore his name, the millionaire decided to give his friend free rein (and an almost unlimited budget) to create a full expression of his theories on the use of colour in architecture. His hope was that the house would stand as a permanent testament to Halsey's inventiveness as an architect and designer, and to his own benevolence as a patron of the arts and in this aim he was entirely successful, for unlike the great majority of Ricardo's work, the house has survived to this day in its original unaltered state. Designed in the Italian style, this magnificent mansion was said by John Betjeman to be: 'the most beautiful Edwardian building in London, and certainly the most original'. Much neglected and misunderstood by the artistic world today, in its prime it attracted a great deal of interest and approval from both architectural critics and the general public alike, and

The mansion at 8 Addison Road, Holland Park, West London, that Halsey Ricardo designed for the department store millionaire Ernest Debenham in 1908. Sir John Betjeman thought it was 'the most beautiful Edwardian building in London.'

A fireplace at Addison Road decorated with hand-painted tiles produced at the Fulham pottery which Halsey Ricardo owned in partnership with William de Morgan

yet it remained a unique and isolated example of its kind, having failed completely to start a new trend as its creator had intended.

Described by de Morgan's sister Mrs Stirling as 'an Arabian Nights palace of delights', its astonishing exterior was clad with cream, blue and vivid jade-green vitreous tiles and topped by a roof of aquamarine Spanish pantiles, while its imaginative interiors were resplendent with exquisite materials and sublime craftsmanship. And, of course, every minute detail of this splendid composition was designed and drawn up by Ricardo personally. Perhaps the grandest and most luxurious Edwardian private house in London, the Addison Road palace cost Debenham over £50,000, a vast sum of money in those days.

Debenham's generosity had another important bearing on the Ricardo family's fortunes. With the fees that resulted from the commission (he was paid a percentage of the final cost) at last Halsey had the wherewithal to complete the building of his own house at Graffham, which was finished in 1905. As soon as Woodside had been completed, Halsey moved his affairs from London to Sussex.

The outbreak of the First World War, which spelled the end of the Edwardian *belle époque* and all that it represented, also brought about the premature end of Halsey Ricardo's career. He spent the war years as a cartographer at the Admiralty. As we shall see, his final major work and only significant postwar commission was to design the Bridge Works laboratories at Shoreham for his son's firm, Engine Patents Ltd, and on its completion in 1917 he virtually retired.

Halsey Ricardo died at Graffham in 1928 aged seventy-four, and was thus denied the realisation of the hope that had sustained him in his declining years: that one day his beloved son might be elected a Fellow of the Royal Society, an honour that was duly bestowed on Harry Ricardo the following year.

CHAPTER 5

Rottingdean

Halsey Ricardo had greatly enjoyed his time at Rugby School and had formed a profound admiration for the liberal education that he had received there. So almost from the moment that young Harry was born, he was resolved that he could do no better for his son than to provide him with the same advantage. In particular he had acquired a great respect for one of the Rugby masters who had taught him classics, Robert Whitelaw, whom he regarded as being not only an outstanding teacher but also a guide, philosopher and friend. Whitelaw had since been appointed a housemaster at the school and so it was that, within hours of his birth, Harry's name was put down on the list to go to Whitelaw's house at Rugby when he reached the age of thirteen. Providing that he passed the Common Entrance exam in due course, a place was reserved for him commencing in the autumn term of 1898.

In those days, of course, it was considered *de rigueur* for boys from upper-middle-class families to be sent away to boarding school; grammar day schools were for the less well off, and only girls and backward boys were educated privately at home by tutors or governesses. Moreover, it was also thought essential that before being exposed to the rigours of a public school every boy should first be weaned away from home comforts and hardened off by a spell at a preparatory school, where he could learn to fend for himself and fit in with other boys in a thoroughly masculine environment. So when Halsey Ricardo's family was enlarged by the arrival of his two daughters Anna and Esther, he decided that, of such capital that he possessed, his son's share would be applied to providing the best possible education that he could afford, while the rest would be left to be shared between the girls.

Normally, the headmasters of all large public schools had well-established links with a number of small, satellite preparatory schools, to provide them with a constant supply of young and eager new recruits and Rugby was no exception to this rule. But Harry Ricardo did not follow the normal, well-trodden path to Rugby via one of these traditional supply routes. Instead, in 1894 at the age of ten he was sent to a newly opened establishment, located at Rottingdean near Brighton. This school had been recommended to Halsey Ricardo by his friend the artist Edward Burne-Jones, who happened to have a weekend cottage nearby.

Sir Edward Burne-Jones, perhaps the most celebrated of all the late Victorian painters, was then at the height of his fame and prestige, having been made a baronet that very same year. So it seems that, simply out of deference to the opinion of the great old man and on the basis of reading the school's prospectus and making a cursory visit of inspection, Halsey and Kate Ricardo chose to send their first-born to this unproven establishment, perhaps in the hope that its newness and lack of tradition would prove to be an educational advantage in encouraging originality of mind. The headmaster, an old Rugbeian, claimed to have rejected corporal punishment and his

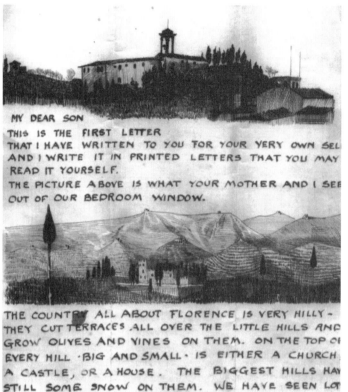

MY DEAR SON
THIS IS THE FIRST LETTER
THAT I HAVE WRITTEN TO YOU FOR YOUR VERY OWN SEL
AND I WRITE IT IN PRINTED LETTERS THAT YOU MAY
READ IT YOURSELF.
THE PICTURE ABOVE IS WHAT YOUR MOTHER AND I SEE
OUT OF OUR BEDROOM WINDOW.

THE COUNTRY ALL ABOUT FLORENCE IS VERY HILLY -
THEY CUT TERRACES ALL OVER THE LITTLE HILLS AND
GROW OLIVES AND VINES ON THEM. ON THE TOP OF
EVERY HILL ·BIG AND SMALL· IS EITHER A CHURCH
A CASTLE, OR A HOUSE. THE BIGGEST HILLS HAV
STILL SOME SNOW ON THEM. WE HAVE SEEN LOT
OF LIZARDS, BUT NOT ONE MONITOR AS YET.
GIVE ANNA A KISS FROM ME.
                  YOUR LOVING. FATHER
                  HALSEY RICARDO.

An illustrated letter written by Halsey to his son in 1891 (when young Harry was six) while staying in Florence with his partner, William de Morgan.

professedly progressive views on discipline may also have appealed to young Harry's liberal-minded Bloomsbury parents.

Their experiment was a disaster, however. For though the school was exceedingly well equipped in the material sense, it was singularly ill-prepared to cater for its pupils' true requirements. In his memoirs, Sir Harry said that, looking back on his unhappy stay there, he had come to realise that not one single member of its staff had any real interest in, or understanding of, a child's mental processes or demands. 'It was far too new. Our bodily needs were well looked after; we were well fed and kept warm.' But otherwise there was an utter lack of inspiration, stimulation and encouragement on the part of the adults in charge. Whatever the boys did to occupy themselves and stave off boredom in their spare time was considered wrong, but no one in authority had any alternative occupation to suggest when bad weather made games and other organised outdoor activities impossible. During his first years at the school, an atmosphere of quarrelsome boredom and resentment brooded over the whole place, he recalled. 'The only way to avoid doing wrong was to do nothing at all, while to read a book or indulge in a hobby was to be dubbed a freak or a swot, by boys and masters alike.' For a lively-minded, imaginative, self-motivated boy (who had already taught himself the basic techniques of metalworking and had become an accomplished model-maker) this negative and unenlightened regime must have been intolerable. 'My father had done all he could to stimulate any initiative on my part and build up my self-confidence. Rottingdean School did its best to destroy both,' he claimed.

To make matters worse, under the headmaster's supposedly benevolent regime, delinquent boys had to undergo a form of punishment far more painful and humiliating than any normally handed out at Victorian prep schools. The school matron, popularly known as 'The Sneak', was an elderly spinster who spent her time peering out of the windows of her top-floor room, from where she had a commanding view of the courtyard and playground beneath. From this vantage point she spied on the boys continually and reported their misdoings to the headmaster, who then summoned the miscreants to his study. Here they were forced to endure not a thrashing but the far more insidious agonies of a 'pi-jaw', the Rottingdean School slang for a severe talking to or ticking off. During these endless interrogations, the headmaster would cross-examine his errant pupils about the hidden motives behind their misbehaviour before finally haranguing them with a pious sermon, forewarning them of the disasters that would surely come in later life if they continued in their wicked ways. Sir Harry always maintained that he had derived no comfort or moral instruction whatsoever from these religious pi-jaws, which were clearly intended to instil the concept of original sin and establish in the minds of the Rottingdean pupils the intrinsic state of guilt applying to all humanity in general and small boys in particular. All they did was to reduce him to a state of bewilderment and tears. 'I would far rather have endured a few strokes of the cane and have done with it,' he claimed in his autobiography.

Not surprisingly given this discouraging environment, Harry Ricardo achieved no distinction whatsoever in his schoolwork while at Rottingdean, either in the classroom or on the playing field. But, as is usually the case with imaginative boys, boredom and frustration led to surreptitious invention. In recalling his schooldays he described how, during class when the master's back was turned, he and his classmates used to shoot paper darts at each other across the room using a simple elastic band or, sometimes, a more elaborate catapult. The snag with these conventional weapons, of course, was that they required two hands to operate them, and that they could not be pre-loaded, ready to aim and fire at a moment's notice. He therefore set out to produce a miniature crossbow made from a clock spring, incorporating a proper pistol grip and trigger and with a bamboo tube acting as a barrel. This device could be kept ready for action hidden inside his desk, its spring action cocked and loaded with a projectile, to be rapidly withdrawn and fired whenever a target of opportunity presented itself. Ricardo recorded that, at the time, he was inordinately proud of this achievement for it was the first piece of design, manufacture and development that he had completed entirely on his own!

Each day began and ended with prayers conducted by the headmaster, but on Sunday mornings the entire school trooped off to the local village church where the boys were forced to sit through an interminable sermon delivered by a dreary parson. To while away time during the sermon, Harry and his fellow pupils devised the sport of woodlice racing. With hymnbooks removed, the shelves running along the backs of the pews provided an ideal racetrack along which the competing woodlice would be made to run, each boy encouraging the performance of his respective insect which was distinguished by a spot of coloured paint, by tickling it with a feather. It was an art that called for considerable skill and experience; too much stimulation and the competitors would suddenly roll themselves into tight balls and withdraw from the race.

Harry Ricardo and his class-mates at Rottingdean School in 1895 when he was ten. He is in the middle of the second row, standing at the centre of the group.

Many English ex-public schoolboys, indoctrinated by long and regular church attendance in their formative years, continue to be regular churchgoers by habit long after leaving school when there is no longer any compulsory requirement to do so. Their motivation, perhaps, is the comfortable and reassuring re-enactment of a deeply inculcated ritual rather than the expression of any profound religious beliefs. Harry Ricardo proved to be an exception to this rule. Despite the Christian teaching heaped upon him at Rottingdean, and later ladled out in even greater measure in the High Anglican chapel at Rugby, he remained a sceptic on questions of religion and rarely if ever went to church in his adulthood. Yet he always described himself as being an agnostic rather than an atheist.

However, as Harry Ricardo and his school together grew older, conditions improved and his homesickness at the start of each new term diminished; eventually it was no longer quite so tearful an experience for him to say goodbye to his mother at Victoria station when returning to Rottingdean by the school train at the end of the holidays. Even so, it would seem that he learned a great deal more of benefit to his ultimate career as an engineer while at home, rather than at school. In London he was free to wander at will and explore the city during daylight hours, frequently going by bus to the Science Museum and other such places of interest. He also had his workshop in the basement at 13 Bedford Square where he could keep himself amused with various projects, using the tools and equipment that he had collected as Christmas presents or that he had bought for himself from his pocket money. During his first Christmas holiday from Rottingdean School, when he was only ten, his father had presented him with a fine 5-inch screw-cutting lathe (obtained second-hand from Uncle Arthur Ricardo) and learning how to use this sophisticated machine occupied him fully for several holidays to come. The present was 'a wonderful surprise'. No time was lost in employing it on a major project; the construction of a one-twelfth scale model vertical double-acting steam engine, using plans and castings obtained through an advertisement he had spotted in *The Model Engineer*.

Not far from the village of Rottingdean lived Sir Edward Burne-Jones, the man who, perhaps, was most responsible for young Harry's current plight. By way of consolation, Burne-Jones would often invite him to Sunday tea. At one of these tea parties the conversation turned to the subject of books and writers. On learning that the boy's favourite author was Rudyard Kipling, Burne-Jones announced that the great man was, in fact, his nephew. Having spent most of his life so far in India, Kipling and his family were at that very moment *en route* by ship to England. Moreover, they were coming to live in a house near by. Burne-Jones promised that as soon as Kipling arrived, he would introduce the famous author to his appreciative young reader, adding that Kipling (unlike Burne-Jones himself) would doubtless be more than willing to talk to the young would-be engineer about engines and machinery. Kipling was indeed extremely interested in mechanical engineering matters; in due course he became one of Britain's earliest motorists, buying his first petrol-engined car, a Lanchester, in 1902. The news that Kipling could talk about engineering came as a thrilling prospect to young Harry, who had found that making stilted conversation with the sixty-year-old Burne-Jones about matters of art and literature was something of an ordeal. 'He expected no doubt that I had inherited my father's love and appreciation of art, but I am afraid that he found me an utter Philistine. I'm sure he found those Sunday tea-parties as embarrassing as I did,' he recollected in his memoirs.

Kipling arrived at Rottingdean with his wife and children during the summer of 1897. Exactly as Harry Ricardo had hoped, he was quite charming in an informal, avuncular way, and he soon put the young schoolboy at his ease. They talked enthusiastically about the local Downland flora and fauna – and butterflies in particular – and it was soon arranged that Ricardo would take Kipling for a walk on the Downs, to show him where certain species were to be seen. For the young schoolboy, this request was flattering indeed.

On the appointed day, Kipling and his daughter arrived at the school armed with butterfly nets and the expedition set off across the Downs to an area where the rare and beautiful dark green fritillary was generally to be found. On this occasion the butterfly hunters were not disappointed, and the great storyteller rewarded his young guide in a most kind and generous way. As Sir Harry was fond of recalling, during the walk Kipling talked to him as though he was his equal in age and experience. At that time, he was still very shy about expressing any opinions of his own to any but intimate friends or relations, but Kipling was a good listener with the gift, vital for any writer, of drawing people out. To Harry Ricardo's surprise he found himself chatting freely about his hopes and ambitions, and airing his views on all manner of important subjects. Before the walk was over he had told him all about life at Rottingdean School, his invention of the crossbow pistol and the technique of woodlice racing, and most of all about his hatred of the matron and the headmaster's sanctimonious pi-jaws. Many more similar country walks and butterfly expeditions occurred during the year that followed, the period when Kipling was writing his *Just So Stories*. Perhaps it was during these rambles with Kipling that Ricardo acquired his deep and lasting affection for the Downland landscape and scenery; indeed, he was destined to live his entire life under the shadow of the South Downs.

Undoubtedly, Kipling's presence made life much more tolerable during Harry Ricardo's final months at the school. None the less, he left Rottingdean in July 1898 without any regrets, except parting from his new grown-up friend, the famous author. Twenty years later, after setting up his laboratories at Shoreham, Ricardo made this part of Sussex his home. But according to his daughter, Camilla, throughout his long stay in the Brighton area, which lasted for another twenty years until he moved to Graffham near Petworth, he always avoided revisiting the scene of those dreaded boyhood pi-jaw punishments by making lengthy and circuitous detours in his car in order to avoid the need to pass through Rottingdean and relive memories best forgotten.

CHAPTER 6

Rugby

In September 1898, Harry Ricardo arrived at Rugby School to take up the place in Whitelaw's house that had been reserved for him at his birth. Rugby was then counted among the top five public schools in the country. It was also justly celebrated, of course, for being both the birthplace of Rugby football and the location of *Tom Brown's Schooldays*, the notorious chronicle of public school life and customs published in 1857. Thirty years later the school was still trying to live down the scandal created by this book, which painted a horrifying picture of sadistic floggings and initiation rites routinely inflicted upon its junior pupils, not by the masters but by the senior boys. Halsey Ricardo had assured his son that conditions had changed completely and that these bullying practices had been abolished long ago, like public executions, but having recently read the book himself, young Harry (he was now aged twelve) had set off to start his first term at Rugby with some trepidation.

In fact, during the five exceedingly happy and constructive years that he spent there, Ricardo found that the school was far from being the austere and cruel penal institution portrayed in Thomas Hughes's grim tale. Thanks to the reforming zeal of Dr Arnold, Rugby had succeeded in attracting boys from a far wider range of backgrounds than was the case with rival schools like Eton, Harrow, Winchester and Westminster. Dr Arnold's reforms had not only led to a far more liberal and progressive educational outlook on the part of the school's staff, but had also encouraged a more broad-minded and egalitarian attitude among the boys themselves. Being located in what had already become an important industrial and manufacturing centre, in Ricardo's day Rugby was essentially a provincial upper-middle-class school, attended by the sons of industrialists, business-owners and professional men rather than aristocrats, and thus it was rather less hide-bound and snobbish than many of its rivals.

Although Rugby offered what was still essentially a classical education, with a strong emphasis on Latin, Greek, French and history, it was unusual in that it was one of the first public schools to allow the study of natural science, which included elements of physics, chemistry and biology. For this work, proper laboratories had been provided, so that the boys could investigate the mysteries of the material world for themselves on a practical level. Besides the obligatory Officers' Training Corps, numerous extra curricular activities were also permitted, so that in their spare time pupils could join a wide variety of societies catering for every kind of hobby and interest. For example, there was a debating society, an arts society, a musical society (which supported a school orchestra) an entomological society and even a bird-watching society. But most importantly, from Harry Ricardo's point of view, there was also an engineering society, of which he later became Secretary. The school also boasted well-equipped workshops where both metal and woodworking skills could be practised. Throughout his days at Rugby, it was here that Ricardo spent every available moment of the limited free time allowed for individual pursuits.

Robert Whitelaw's house was a self-contained community centred on a quadrangle, around which were arranged the studies in which the boys worked when not in the classrooms, laboratories or library of the main school. Also leading off the quad were the large dormitories, in which they slept in rows of iron cots, and the great hall where they took their meals, surrounded by wooden plaques and panels bearing the names of all their precursors who had distinguished themselves in the school. Downstairs, there was a changing room lined with lockers and rows of cubicles each containing a galvanised iron bath tub known as a tosh, where the boys took their daily early morning cold baths. Upstairs, lay the realm of the senior and sixth-form boys, including the room where the Head of House meted out rough justice with a swish of the cane.

At that time, Rugby still employed the traditional public school system of hierarchical self-government and law enforcement, in which rules were imposed and discipline maintained by the boys themselves; petty crimes were detected and the appropriate punishment summarily dispensed by the élite of the sixth form rather than by the masters. Through a kind of spiritual osmosis fostered by the school's High Anglican ethos, the moral code of obedience, loyalty, honesty, self-reliance, responsibility and fair play was inculcated and transmitted from one generation of pupils to the next. For the rest of his life, Ricardo was quite content to follow the public schoolboy's test of soundness and character

The Old House and Chapel of Rugby School, a view unchanged since Ricardo's time there a century ago.

when assessing the reliability and trustworthiness of would-be employees or business associates. Irrespective of class or creed, wealth or poverty, the world's population could be divided into two simple categories of individual: there were either good eggs or bad eggs, fine fellows and nice chaps or rogues, ruffians and charlatans. Schoolboy slang and sports-field expressions salted his conversation and writings. When reporting to his clients on the progress of an engine under test, it was not unusual for him to state that he was just about to make improvements that would 'whack up the performance a bit'.

During Ricardo's stay at Rugby, and indeed for many years after, the old public school system of fagging still held sway. Boys in the lower forms were all required to act as the servants of their superiors in the upper school and to do their bidding without question. When summoned by the call of duty, the fags were expected to perform a wide range of menial tasks for their seniors: to make their tea, light their fires, shine their shoes, and even to warm up their lavatory seats by sitting on them. At any moment, any one of these senior boys could put his head out of his study window and yell 'Faaag', whereupon all the underlings in the studies beneath had to leave whatever they were doing and dash out into the quadrangle. The last boy to arrive was expected to run whatever errand his elder and better chose to send him on. It is not known for whom Ricardo fagged, but it is interesting to note that in his first years at Rugby, the head of Whitelaw's house was R.H. Tawney, who afterwards became a noted left-wing economist, author of *The Acquisitive Society* and one of the leading theoreticians of the Labour Party.

For part of his time in Whitelaw's house (which in 1902 provided accommodation for 56 of the 583 boys attending the school) Harry shared a study with Arthur Ransome, who some thirty years later became the author of *Swallows and Amazons*, *Peter Duck*, *Coot Club* and many other highly popular stories for children, all with nautical themes. In his autobiography, Ransome described how he and the 'ingenious' young Ricardo would usually spend their spare time building a variety of miniature prototype steam engines and electric motors in the school workshops. Although Ransome probably had already experienced the fun of messing about in small boats while on holiday at Windermere, it is doubtful that, at that point, he had yet had the chance to put to sea in a full-scale sailing vessel. But Ricardo most certainly had, while on holiday with his father, Halsey. Is it possible that, in the course of describing his own profound love of sailing and the sea, Ricardo inspired his fellow pupil to seek out similar adventures, and eventually to write about them?

Earlier, at some point in 1897 while he was still at Rottingdean, another of Ricardo's greatest boyhood friends and companions had entered his life. This was his cousin Ralph Ricardo who arrived from Melbourne, Australia where his father, Halsey Ricardo's younger brother Percy, was the Military Governor of Victoria. It had been arranged that, for the next six or seven years, Halsey would be responsible for his nephew, supervising his schooling in England and looking after him during the holidays. Instead of going to Rugby, however, Ralph was sent to a school at Woking that specialised in educating boys from a colonial background.

Ralph was exactly the same age as Harry and the pair soon became virtual brothers, as their interest in, and aptitude for, machinery and model-making coincided to a remarkable degree. Ricardo described his cousin as being 'unfailingly cheerful and happy, and ready to turn his hand to anything,' adding that: 'he had a highly developed commercial instinct and was full of schemes for making a fortune. His colonial upbringing had taught him how to make bricks without straw; in many ways he was very ingenious and a past-master at improvisation.' He recalled that almost as soon as Ralph turned up on the doorstep at Bedford Square, he joined him in his basement workshop and was fascinated to see the latest steam engine that he, Harry, was currently constructing: 'Straight away he urged that we should go into partnership and produce vast numbers that we would sell at a high price and so make our fortunes.' With Ralph doing the fitting and soldering and Harry the machining and lathe work, the pair made a good team, and soon they had produced about seven or eight copies of the prototype, which the proprietor of a nearby model shop agreed to offer to his customers on their behalf. But on this occasion, commercial success eluded them; bored with the repetitious work involved, the pair soon abandoned the project and began to look for other short cuts to fame and fortune. At an early age, Ricardo had learned more about the problems of engine design and manufacture, first-hand from his own mistakes, than could ever be gleaned from textbooks or teaching.

It was to take another few years for his collaboration with Ralph to bear fruit. Impressed by the possibilities of the workshops at Rugby, Harry was fired with the ambition to design and construct yet another steam engine, far larger and more sophisticated than any of his earlier attempts, and he immediately embarked on a scheme to build a single-acting Uniflow engine incorporating a conventional vertical fire-tube boiler. By the time that he was fourteen, he had largely accomplished this project, working either on his own at Rugby during term-time or at home in London during the holidays, in partnership with Ralph.

After two years of further refinement, the cousins judged the engine ready to be shown to the adult world, so during the Easter holidays of 1902 they were bold enough to demonstrate it at the annual exhibition of model engines and locomotives held at the Horticultural Hall in Islington, London. Here it attracted the attention of the Managing Director of the Liverpool Casting Company, which specialised in supplying the unmachined metal components used by amateur model-makers. Over lunch the following day, this gentleman proposed that his company make the various castings needed to build Ricardo's design and that together with the necessary plans and instructions, these should be marketed as a kit, at the price of 20 shillings. Moreover, the engine was to be called by its designer's name and, by way of remuneration, Ricardo was to receive a royalty of 2½ per cent or sixpence a set. In due course, during his last term at Rugby, Harry received a postal order for 12 shillings from the Liverpool Casting Company, being the royalties on the first twenty-four sets sold, and for several years thereafter he continued to receive a steady trickle of money from this source. Needless to say, this postal order, the first of countless royalty payments that the young engineer was destined to earn, was proudly shown to Mr Whitelaw and many of the other masters at Rugby!

During his last year at the school, Harry Ricardo amused himself and his friends by mounting his steam engine and boiler on his bicycle, just as a joke. The engine itself was fixed rather crazily behind the pedal bracket with the drive to the rear wheel being carried not by the chain wheel but by a roller bearing against the tyre. The boiler and water tank were lashed to the handlebars and extended way above the frame because of a 3-ft high funnel that was attached to the boiler to provide a forced draught while the contraption was in motion. In its stationary form, the steam engine had been fired by a paraffin primus burner, but when this proved ineffective in the motionary state, Ricardo resorted to coal firing, making sure always to carry a good supply of fuel in his jacket pocket. He reported that once he had succeeded in getting up a good head of steam using a bellows, it was possible to travel between 100 and 200 yards with a good burst of speed, but then it was necessary to dismount, refuel and get to work again with the bellows. His demonstrations of this absurd machine provided vast amusement for all at Rugby but it seems that his exploits caused great anxiety for his housemaster. The headmaster called a masters' conference to decide whether or not Ricardo should be allowed to continue to use the machine at school. Opinion was divided; some masters argued that it was downright dangerous and set an awkward precedent, while others suggested that to forbid its use would be to discourage enterprise and initiative. The latter camp won the debate but it was agreed that henceforth, after Ricardo had left the school, the use of self-propelled vehicles of any kind by pupils would be banned.

In his autobiography, Sir Harry maintained that constructing this 'crude, dangerous but most exciting machine' was his sole claim to fame at Rugby School and that he achieved no distinction whatsoever either in academic work or in sport. In fact, he was a good rugby football player and long-distance runner. During his last year at Rugby, in March 1902, he earned a place in the school cross-country running team, having won third place in the Harborough Magna Run, a hare-and-hounds event run between Rugby and the nearby village of Newbold-on-Avon and back, a distance of 6 miles which he completed in 42 minutes 5 seconds. Although he enjoyed cricket, he was rather less successful at the game, due, as he explained, to his mental and physical reactions being far too slow for sports involving a fast-moving ball. Similarly, although his obligatory service in the Officers' Training Corps showed that he was a good shot at a fixed target in the rifle-shooting butts, he was far less successful at hitting a moving target with a shotgun. Even so, as a young man he often went rough shooting on the Rickettswood estate with his Rendel cousins.

During his final year at Rugby also, Ricardo read his first ever paper or lecture; devoted to the subject of small power machinery, it was delivered to the Physical Section of the Natural History Society. In this talk, later published in the Society's Report with engineering drawings and other illustrations made by the author, he reviewed the wide range of steam and internal combustion engines or electric motors currently available to power automobiles and small boats, and to drive pumping and power-generation equipment. Considering that he was dealing with a subject few contemporary engineers were familiar with, his talk was a most accomplished performance for a seventeen-year-old, clearly showing the promise of the great achievements as a writer and lecturer that lay ahead. One particular type of automobile engine mentioned was a novel unit manufactured by the French company, Chenard & Walcker. The young Ricardo could have had no inkling of the fact that, some thirty years hence, he would himself become a Consultant Engineer to this famous motor car firm.

Doubtless, this talk was motivated by an event that took place in London during the Christmas holidays of 1901, when Harry and Ralph attended a series of lectures given at the Royal Institution by the distinguished scientist and engineer who was then regarded as the highest British authority on the internal combustion engine, Sir Dugald Clerk FRS (1854–1932). Little-remembered today, Clerk was one of the true pioneers of internal combustion engine research in Great Britain and his talks and writings had a profoundly inspiring effect on the two boys. In Sir Harry's own words he was 'one of those rare individuals who combined scientific theory with direct practical experience and that in equal measure. As a lecturer he was almost ideal, alike for the clarity of his teaching . . . and the charm of his personality. In Clerk's hands, the most abstruse problems connected with the internal combustion engine melted away, leaving only conclusions that were simple and almost obvious.' According to Ricardo, Clerk's lectures were a pattern of lucidity. He had a gift for explaining complex matters in simple terms that his schoolboy audiences could understand, and the tyro engineer made up his mind that if ever he came to lecture on such subjects, he would do his best to follow Clerk's example.

Indeed, in this and many other ways, Sir Dugald's formative influence provided the goal or ideal towards which Ricardo's own career in the field of internal combustion engine research was directed. Some thirty years later, when writing an obituary notice on Sir Dugald for the Royal Society, he stated that: 'The vast modern development of road and air transport made possible by the internal combustion engine, we owe directly or indirectly to Sir Dugald Clerk. He, beyond anyone else, is responsible for its development; directly by the work of his own hands and indirectly by his teaching to his innumerable disciples all the world over, all of whom derive the greater part of their knowledge and inspiration from his work.' As we shall see, by then, of course, Clerk was not only Ricardo's guiding light, but also his mentor and friend, having helped and encouraged him directly in the formation of his own research company.

Born in Glasgow a little before the invention of the internal combustion engine, Clerk started his engineering career as a practical mechanic at the early age of fourteen and built his first gas engine in 1876 when only twenty-two years old. He then went on to study chemistry and physics, first in Glasgow and then in Leeds, before devoting his energies to a thorough investigation of the nature of the internal combustion engine through systematic scientific research. It was Clerk who devised the RAC horsepower formula, used by the government until 1948 to calculate the variable amount of excise duty due on individual cars and commercial vehicles.

Sir Dugald Clerk was one of the first to realise the great significance of flame propagation and induction turbulence in the process of combustion. During his long career he was responsible for many inventions, the best known of which was the Clerk Two-Stroke engine which he patented in 1877, and which was the first practical manifestation of the two-stroke cycle, as opposed to Dr Nicholas Otto's four-stroke cycle which had been demonstrated in Germany the previous year. Ultimately, however, Clerk abandoned practical engineering and became a highly respected patent agent in partnership with George Marks, founding in 1894 the firm of Marks & Clerk which still exists today. In this capacity, Clerk was frequently called upon to act as an expert witness in patent law litigation involving technical and scientific matters, including the famous Selden Trust action in America in 1906, in which he acted for the plaintiffs in their claim against Henry Ford.

Clerk was also noted as a scientific writer. In 1886, he published his book *The Gas Engine*, revised and reissued in 1909 as *The Gas, Petrol and Oil Engine*. Indeed, Ricardo considered that: 'the abiding value of his work lay in its educational side – in his brilliant analyses of the engine's working processes, and his admirably clear exposition of them'. As he was soon to discover for himself: 'In engineering problems a ceaseless conflict rages between the theorist and the practical man; the former is often bigoted and categorical, the latter merely scornful . . . Clerk showed that theory was not always infallible and seldom so inflexible as to be irreconcilable with the findings of the practical man.' Throughout his life as a research and development engineer, Harry Ricardo followed Clerk's example by striving to reconcile abstruse scientific theory with empirical observation and practical common sense.

The leading British pioneer of the internal combustion engine, Sir Dugald Clerk FRS (1854–1932), who was Harry Ricardo's mentor, friend and guiding light.

One of the most interesting ideas discussed by Sir Dugald Clerk in his lectures was, to Ricardo's mind at least, the concept of stratified charge, which proposed that the speed of an engine could be varied and controlled not by the inefficient and thermodynamically wasteful method of throttling, but by varying the strength of the charge in such a way that instead of an even, homogeneous mixture being present throughout the combustion chamber at all times, its composition could, in effect, be layered in strength according to the load at which the engine was running. This way, during idling or at times of low demand when the engine speed was reduced, the fuel/air mixture immediately adjacent to the spark plug would be just rich enough to support combustion but would grow progressively weaker further away from the spark. This stratified charge technique (which, as Ricardo was later to discover, proved extremely difficult to master) is still regarded as highly advanced today and, indeed, remains the subject of much research by automobile engine manufacturers seeking to improve fuel economy.

These difficulties notwithstanding, Harry and Ralph immediately resolved that they would attempt to put Clerk's theories into practice by employing the stratified charge principle in a petrol engine that would eventually be used to drive a water pump at the house that Halsey Ricardo was planning to build for himself at Graffham. A well had

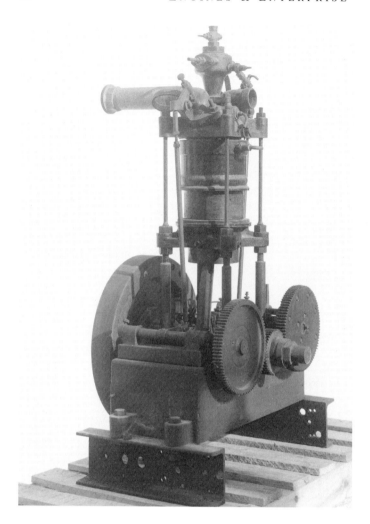

The first full-scale working internal combustion engine designed and built by Harry Ricardo in 1903. It was used for many years to pump water from a well at his parents' country home at Graffham, West Sussex.

already been dug at the site, but as it had been driven to a depth of nearly 100 ft before reaching the water table it was realised that, there being no mains gas or electricity supply available in the area at that time, some form of reliable independent engine – steam, hot air or petrol – would be required to ensure an adequate water supply.

The result, built in stages by the boys during their school holidays between 1901 and 1903, was to be Harry Ricardo's first attempt at designing and constructing an internal combustion engine. Its piston, connecting rod and crankshaft were salvaged from a disused gas engine, scrounged by Ralph, but its cylinder and other castings were new, specially made to Harry's drawings by a helpful London foundry. The job of machining these castings and other components was too big to be undertaken in their basement workshop at Bedford Square, or even at Rugby, but the ever-resourceful Ralph found that, for a small fee, they could have use of the very large and well-equipped machine shop at the Regent Street Polytechnic, not far from their home. According to the designer himself, after certain teething troubles had been overcome, his 2-litre engine ran beautifully, being smooth, quiet and economical in operation.

When the building of Woodside, Graffham, was eventually completed in 1905, the engine was erected in a small engine house at the well-head, where it served to supply all the Ricardo family's domestic water needs for the next seven or eight years. In the light of this promising achievement, Harry Ricardo became an enthusiastic advocate of the stratified charge principle. It was not until much later that he discovered its limitations. Over the next sixty years he made repeated attempts to perfect Clerk's concept (and witnessed many more similar efforts by other engineers) but outright success always eluded him. By the time of his death, a completely satisfactory stratified charge system had still not been achieved in a road-going petrol engine.

Another of the leading lights of the Rugby School Engineering Society was Kyrle Willans, son of the inventor of the Willans central-valve, high-speed steam engine. This and other large items of stationary electrical power-generating machinery were actually manufactured in the town at the new factory of the Willans & Robinson firm, which subsequently became the English Electric Company. Kyrle Willans arranged for members of the society to tour his father's works and on the visit Ricardo made friends with a certain Mr Templar who was responsible for the erection and testing of the firm's steam engines. On hearing about Ricardo's attempts to build a Uniflow steam engine in the school workshops, Templar invited him to bring the finished machine for trials on the Willans & Robinson test-beds; before very long, Harry found that he was *persona grata* at the factory, welcome to wander round the place whenever he wished. Many instructive half-holidays were spent on the company's premises, observing its products under every stage of manufacture, assembly and testing, so that Ricardo soon acquired a thorough grasp of the very latest manufacturing techniques such as grinding, honing and broaching that were being introduced there. For example, whereas most manufacturers of that era still relied on steam or coal-gas engines to provide motive power, which was normally distributed mechanically throughout their factories, working their machinery by a complex arrangement of pulley-belts and line-shafts, the machine tools in the Willans works were all electrically driven, with the current being generated in a powerhouse on the premises by a battery of Willans steam engines directly coupled to dynamos. The factory itself was of the most modern design, a long single-storey building with the foundry and forge located at one end and the erecting and test shop at the other, with machining operations taking place in the middle section. To make the movement of heavy materials from one end to the other a simple and effortless task, the building was equipped with travelling overhead cranes, supplied by the Manchester firm, F.H. Royce & Co; long before Henry Royce met the Hon. C.S. Rolls and entered the motor car business, he had started his engineering activities as a crane-maker.

The upshot was that, after leaving Rugby in midsummer 1903, at Mr Robinson's invitation Ricardo spent several months at the Willans & Robinson works as an honorary apprentice or assistant to Mr Templar, who taught him a great deal about the practicalities of testing engines and diagnosing their faults. Clearly, the young Ricardo was already able to impress experienced professional mechanical engineers; he was a pupil of the very highest potential and was considered a worthy recruit to their numbers. Certainly, the knowledge and experience that he gained at Willans & Robinson was to serve him in good stead in October 1903, when he went up to Cambridge and he embarked on the next stage of his formal education as an engineer.

CHAPTER 7

Memories and Machines

A s well as his extraordinary steam-powered bicycle, young Harry Ricardo notched up another claim to fame while at Rugby, an achievement that became an even greater source of prestige among his fellow pupils than the invention of this hazardous, impractical and bizarre means of personal transport. He was the very first boy in the school to learn to drive a motor car, a feat he accomplished in the summer of 1898 at the age of thirteen, while staying at Rickettswood with his grandfather Sir Alexander Rendel, who was a motoring pioneer.

Although Sir Alexander was in his seventies, earlier that year he had astounded his family by buying his first car, a single-cylinder 3½hp Benz four-seater dog-cart. Driven about by the chauffeur-mechanic whom he had engaged to look after his expensive yet fragile new toy, he made many outings through the Surrey countryside, although always followed at a distance by his horse and carriage in case of breakdowns, which were both inevitable and numerous. Like most other types of early automobile, the Benz was a crude, primitive and unreliable contraption, cobbled together from mismatched components borrowed from the bicycle and the horse-drawn carriage. It was steered by a tiller rather than a wheel and lacked proper brakes. When ascending a hill, a metal rod shaped like a chisel (called a sprag) had to be let down behind it to stop it from rolling backwards. Its rudimentary engine was open to the elements and entirely unprotected from dust and damp, while its transmission consisted of a complicated system of leather pulley-belts acting in lieu of a gearbox, with the final drive to the rear wheels being taken by an arrangement of metal chains and sprockets.

In spite of the machine's unreliability on several occasions in 1898, Sir Alexander attempted to drive the whole way from Rickettswood to his London house in Lancaster Gate, a distance of 26 miles, but always without success. His grandson Harry was a member of the four-man team that accompanied him on these trips, and Harry described their adventures graphically in his autobiography, *Memories and Machines*:

Our route ran through Reigate and over Reigate Hill, a long climb of about three-quarters of a mile, with an average gradient of about one in twelve, but with several much steeper stretches. This obstacle proved our undoing on every attempt. Having prepared and tuned up the car overnight, we made an early morning start, loaded up with two large watercans, a bag of tools, oil-cans and a tin of grease and several spare sparking-plugs, plenty of sandwiches and several bottles of ginger beer. Thus equipped we set out and reached Reigate, a distance of six miles, without any untoward incident. There we called upon an enterprising ironmonger who, with much foresight, had laid in a supply of petroleum spirit in one-gallon tins. We then set out on our attempt to ascend Reigate Hill. At the foot of the hill we stopped at a farmhouse where we drained our cooling system which consisted of a coil of gilled tubing mounted at the front of the car, but without any fan. We then filled up both the cooling system and the two watercans with fresh cold water. After going round all the numerous exposed bearings including the camshaft and valve mechanism with an oil can, replenishing and screwing down the grease cups and dressing the leather driving-belts with resin we then started on the climb.

From past experience we knew that if once we had to engage low gear there would be little or no hope of getting back into a higher gear until we reached level ground. We made a good start in second gear, and by careful nursing of the engine surmounted the first length of steep gradient, but the next proved too much for us, and we had perforce to engage bottom gear. With this absurdly low ratio we could have climbed the side of a house, but our radiator was already boiling furiously and we had lost a lot of water. We therefore had to stop and replenish the cooling system.

It seems that with this very low gear in operation, at any speed above 2 mph vibration became quite intolerable. So in an attempt to increase the speed, all on board the Benz with the exception of old Sir Alexander had to alight and walk on ahead. In these situations, young Harry followed behind, ready to thrust a brick under the back wheel whenever a further stop to replenish the radiator was required. Thus, slowly and noisily the *automobilistes* ground their way uphill, jeered at by the occasional passers-by. But long before they reached the crest, the radiator had swallowed up the last drop of water, and they reluctantly gave up the attempt for that day. 'We made two or three more attempts that September to conquer Reigate Hill, but without success,' Sir Harry recalled.

As a reward for his services on these expeditions, Harry was given the honorary, unofficial position in Sir Alexander's household of the chauffeur's assistant, and in this capacity he was allowed to drive the Benz about the estate, though not on the public highway, and to help in its care and maintenance. He recalled that throughout the summer of 1898 he and his grandfather never once met another self-propelled vehicle as they toured around the country lanes of Surrey, carrying out test runs and practising gear changes. At that time the motor car was viewed as nothing but a rich man's folly; affluent avant garde motorists and their playthings were most unpopular with other road-users, especially in rural districts, where their activities were regarded as degenerate and anti-social. 'My grandfather was one of the first landed proprietors in the country to commit such an act, which was frowned upon by most of his neighbours', he admitted. 'All the local gentry were great horse-lovers and viewed with horror the prospect of the roads being infested with noisy and smelly mechanical vehicles which frightened their horses with their strange appearance and alarming sounds.' Nor was it merely the gentry who opposed the coming of the automobile. The older generation of farmers and countrymen also viewed it with hatred and contempt. Most drivers of the farm carts they encountered on their travels flicked their whips at them and showered them with abuse.

Unlike the Ricardos who were enthusiastic members of the country gentry and took a leading part in country sports (one of their number was a master of the Pychley Hunt) Sir Alexander made no effort to join in rural activities or to make himself agreeable to his landowning neighbours; in fact, he left the running of the farms on his estate entirely to his faithful Irish bailiff Murphy. His interests did not extend beyond the welfare of his extended family and the success of his business affairs, and he played no part in the local community; he was, indeed, a prototype commuter whose roots remained in London

No photograph of any of Sir Alexander Rendel's cars has survived, but this is the Panhard & Levassor owned by Harry Ricardo's father-in-law, Dr Charles Bowdish Hale.

despite his annual summer transplantation to Surrey. Apart from a limited integration with its surroundings on a purely domestic level, Rickettswood was a closed Rendel community. The accounts of visitors relate that the household had almost no social contact with the surrounding countryside. No vicar called, much less any other, grander, secular visitors. Nor did the Rendels visit neighbouring houses or throw parties for the notables of the county. Their home was entirely self-sufficient and relied for its entertainments and amusements on the talents of the family members themselves. Sir Alexander was, above all, a devoted family man who gained all the human social contact that he desired from the companionship of his wife and the company of his children and grandchildren, nephews and nieces. And this, undoubtedly, was a trait that he passed on to his grandson.

Despite his early motoring difficulties and disasters, however, Sir Alexander persisted in his enthusiasm for the automobile, and by 1902 his garage held a whole collection of vehicles including a 10hp, two-cylinder Wolseley, an 8hp, single-cylinder Argyle and a 6hp, single-cylinder de Dion Bouton. Ultimately, in 1899, the Benz dog-cart was exchanged for a new and much improved model from the same maker, with a more powerful 5hp engine. This was an altogether far better and more manageable machine. On it, Sir Alexander and his grandson were at last able to conquer Reigate Hill and make the journey from Rickettswood to London in one day, with only a few minor breakdowns on the way. In this way young Harry Ricardo gained his experience of the contrasting technical advantages and disadvantages of various different makes of early automobile, knowledge that he was more than glad to pass on to fellow members of the Rugby School Engineering Society at their meetings. At these gatherings, just as happened at meetings of his uncles and cousins at Rickettswood, arguments raged on the question of the relative merits of steam or petrol engines, or on the various forms of transmission such as belt versus gear drive, and so forth.

Harry Ralph Ricardo was actually born in the year that saw the conception and creation of the automobile and in a very real sense the two infants, man and machine, grew to maturity together. In 1885, Carl Benz of Mannheim and Gottlieb Daimler of Stuttgart both produced horseless carriages powered by internal combustion engines, working quite independently of each other. By the time that Harry was four, the commercialisation of this invention was well under way on the Continent, its development having been given great impetus by the important international exhibition of industry and commerce that was held in Paris in 1889.

In Great Britain, however, unlike France, Germany or America, the infant automobile had yet to break through a barrier of prejudice and conservatism. Here, as is well known, its early development was frustrated and retarded by the effect of the notorious Locomotive Acts, first enacted by Parliament in 1861. Until this legislation was abolished in November 1896, the only non-horse-drawn vehicles to be seen on the roads of the United Kingdom were traction engines and steam rollers, for not only was the speed of self-propelled vehicles limited to 2 mph in towns and 4 mph in the country, but all had by law to be proceeded by a person carrying a red flag or lantern. In effect, this Red Flag Act meant that all motorists travelling on the public roads had to confine their progress to the pace of pedestrians or face prosecution, which rather defeated the whole object of the exercise. The earliest British car owners were thus obliged to limit their motoring activities to their private estates.

Long after the abolition of the Red Flag Act, however, the automobile continued to be the object of public hostility and derision in Great Britain. Until the Motor Car Act was passed by Parliament in August 1904, cars were classed as light locomotives and their speed restricted to 12 mph. The new Act required motor vehicles to carry number plates and their drivers to have licences, but it permitted the speed limit to be raised to 20 mph. Even so, public hostility, bad road conditions and the difficulty of procuring petrol (for which there then existed no organised distribution system) all combined to put a brake on progress, with the result that there was little or no incentive for entrepreneurs to establish manufacturing concerns to undertake the design, development and production of motor cars in this country. According to Ricardo, even in London at the turn of the century the appearance of a motor car was infrequent enough to draw a crowd: 'The distant sound of an approaching automobile brought everyone rushing to the window to see it pass, while if it stopped it immediately became the centre of an inquisitive group of spectators.' Not surprisingly, the great majority of these curiosities had been imported from the Continent or America.

But then, in high society at least, attitudes began to change. Following the coronation of King Edward VII in 1901, the austere respectability that had characterised the last years of Queen Victoria's reign gave way to an exciting new era of optimism, progress and prosperity. 'I remember the Edwardian era so well as a period of relaxation, bringing a more liberal outlook on life in general and on the automobile in particular,' wrote Sir Harry some sixty years later. 'The new King was immensely popular; he was fond of sport and all the good things in life. He had a great sense of humour and a capacity for enjoyment which made a great appeal to all ranks of his subjects. When it was realised that he was a keen motorist and often to be seen driving his own car in Hyde Park, the whole attitude of society changed from one of abhorrence to one of tolerance, and even of encouragement towards the new-fangled form of locomotion.' The King had taken delivery of his first car, a British-built Daimler, in March 1900 when he was Prince of Wales, having driven an automobile, also a Daimler, for the first time at Buckingham Palace in November 1897.

Thanks in no small measure to the blessing conferred by this royal patronage, by 1905 the motor car had become a practical and reliable way of making a long journey in Great Britain and a viable alternative to the railways. Improvements in its design and construction gave the motorist a reasonable certainty of arriving at his or her destination on time. Ten years earlier, no one, not even Sir Alexander Rendel, would have seriously considered setting out in an automobile to catch a train or to keep an appointment. But soon it would be the horse and carriage that was regarded as the rich man's plaything.

If British-made examples of the internal combustion engine were thin on the ground before the outbreak of the First World War, they were even scarcer in the air. As is well known, the petrol engine took to the skies for the very first time in December 1903, two months after Harry Ricardo went up to Cambridge University, when the Wright brothers made the world's first genuine fully controlled and sustained powered flight, at Kitty Hawk, North Carolina, in the USA. Within another two years, they had developed the world's first truly practical aircraft. News of these momentous events in the USA was slow to reach Europe, but there can be no doubt that, by the summer of 1904 when the facts of this feat were known in Cambridge, Ricardo's youthful interest in internal combustion engine design had received another powerful boost. In future, the use of this prime mover would not be confined to the automobile alone!

This realisation would surely have been strengthened in January 1908, when Henry Farman, an Englishman resident in France, made the world's first round trip in an aircraft, following a measured 1-kilometre circular course under observed conditions to land at the point from which he had taken off, thus establishing air travel as a concrete reality. Eighteen months later, in July 1909, Louis Blériot demonstrated the point more forcibly still by flying across the English Channel. He landed near Dover and was hailed as a hero and fêted by the general public. As was noted in the press, Great Britain was no longer an island, easily defended from invasion by the might of the Royal Navy, as it had been for the past five centuries. Strategic realities had been changed forever by the opening up of this new dimension in transport, communications and warfare, but the War Office remained unimpressed. For a further three years, the military authorities steadfastly refused to acknowledge the arrival of this new weapon. Both the army and navy ignored the potential of the aeroplane and were interested only in balloons and airships, either captive or dirigible and for observation purposes only.

Even so, many of the very first British aviators were military and naval officers, who had to learn to fly at their own expense. In 1910, several Royal Artillery officers began to practise target observation and spotting from aircraft while on manoeuvres at the Larkhill ranges on Salisbury Plain. To undertake these trials, they were obliged to use their own primitive private aircraft, with no support forthcoming from the government, which, at

All the excitement and romance of early motoring is crystalised in this photograph of Mrs Ralph Ricardo at the wheel of her husband's 30hp four-cylinder Dolphin car, taken during their honeymoon in Scotland in June 1909. It is doubtful that she could actually drive, however!

first, accepted the recommendation of the Committee for Imperial Defence that all such experiments with aeroplanes should be discontinued. Thus it was not until 1912 that the need for military aviation was admitted and the Royal Flying Corps was formed, equipped, initially at least, with French-built machines. That year, an official competition was staged at Larkhill to decide on an aircraft to be built in quantity for the army. Although the winner was an aircraft entered by the American expatriate Samuel F. Cody (Chief Instructor of Kiting at the Army's Balloon School at Farnborough), this machine was passed over in favour of another, not actually a formal entrant in the trials, designed by Geoffrey de Havilland and powered by a French-made 70hp Renault engine. A suitable source of aero-engines was urgently needed in Britain, but at that time few major engineering companies had the foresight to develop products to meet this important potential military and civilian demand, mainly because they were given no encouragement or assistance by the government. In his autobiography, Sir Harry Ricardo referred to this regrettable situation, pointing out that before 1912 'the military authorities took no interest whatever in flight by heavier-than-air machines, nor was there any incentive to encourage industry to develop a British designed aero-engine.'

Sir Harry played no part in these earliest developments in British aviation, nor did he become involved in the design of aero-engines until the closing stages of the First World War, but even so he took a keen interest in aeronautical matters from the start. He remembered in his autobiography that Blériot's feat caused a thrill of horror among his family and friends when it was realised that 'our island fortress might not be so impregnable as we fondly believed. Hitherto the British public had regarded aviation as dangerous sport at which a few well-to-do dare-devil young men were prepared to spend their money and risk their lives, but Bleriot's flight changed the whole picture.' Numbered among these daredevils were the Hon. C.S. Rolls, Geoffrey de Havilland, A.V. Roe and J.T.C. Moore-Brabazon (later Lord Brabazon of Tara), all of whom (with the exception of Rolls who was killed flying in 1910) Sir Harry came to know well. These pioneers had already built, or were currently building, aircraft of their own, but all had to rely on French engines for propulsion.

Following Blériot's exploit, public demonstrations of flying were organised both in England and in France, and competitions were staged at which huge financial prizes were offered to successful aviators by commercial interests such as the *Daily Mail* and other newspapers. For example, at the Grande Semaine d'Aviation held at Rheims in August 1910 before a crowd of over a million spectators, Henry Farman flew round and round a circular course for more than three hours at an average speed of 45 mph to cover 111 miles non-stop and won the Grand Prix for endurance – worth 60,000 francs – put up by the champagne industry. Present at the Rheims event was David Lloyd George, Chancellor of the Exchequer. On returning to England he was reported to have said, 'Flying machines are no longer toys or dreams; they are now an established fact. The possibilities of this new system of locomotion are infinite. As an Englishman I feel rather ashamed that we are so completely out of it.'

In 1911, Colonel Mervyn O'Gorman (who subsequently became one of Ricardo's closest friends) was appointed the first Director of the Royal Aircraft Factory at Farnborough, (known from 1918 onwards as the Royal Aircraft Establishment). The name of this factory was perhaps misleading, for it had been established by the government in 1909 solely to produce balloons and kites, not aeroplanes. 'O'Gorman's terms of reference were to carry out research and development work on captive balloons, non-rigid airships and man-carrying kites on behalf of both services, but no funds were available to him for the development of heavier-than-air machines,' Sir Harry noted.

Indeed, O'Gorman was one of the key figures in the foundation of British military aviation and is credited with establishing a proper scientific methodology in aeronautical research and development, and with recruiting the various talents who formed the nucleus of aircraft and aero-engine design in this country. Described as a witty, flamboyant and thoroughly unconventional Irishman of great imagination and courage, he was also a somewhat eccentric character who dressed in immaculately tailored suits and affected a gold-rimmed monocle, a long cigarette holder and a bushy brushed-up moustache, which gave him the appearance of an Edwardian boulevardier. After meeting in the First World War, they had struck up a friendship which lasted for three decades, for although O'Gorman's outspokenness had caused him to be relieved of his Farnborough post in 1916, he continued to serve alongside Ricardo on the Engine Subcommittee of the Aeronautical Research Committee throughout the interwar years. He died in 1958, recognised more by his fellow engineers and scientists than by the officialdom that was so often the target of his caustic Irish wit.

Writing in *Memories and Machines*, Sir Harry said: 'Looking back over those years it seems shameful that we in England should have allowed ourselves to lag so far behind in the development of aeroplanes and engines, but it was lack of incentive, not ability, that brought this about. Both in France and in Germany, the military authorities were quick to see the huge part that aviation would play in future warfare, and lavished huge sums on development, but the authorities in this country were blind to the possibilities, while industry as a whole was not prepared to gamble on the chances of its commercial use. In after years O'Gorman told me that he got severely ticked-off by the War Office for having "squandered" over £2,000 of his grant for airship development on aeroplanes and engines that would never be of any military value.'

However, at the time, as a Cambridge undergraduate heading, as he thought, for a career in civil, not mechanical, engineering, the young Harry Ricardo would have been quite unaware of the future course of the British automobile and aircraft industries, much less that he would ever play a major role in their development himself. But, clearly, he was among the first Englishmen to appreciate and understand the problems that had to be overcome in order to bring about the commercialisation of the internal combustion engine in Great Britain, so that, when the time came, he was well placed to help provide these solutions.

CHAPTER 8

Cambridge

By the time that he went up to Trinity College, Cambridge, in October 1903, Harry Ricardo had already become a committed supporter of the new cult of 'automobilism', and was actually one of the leaders of this increasingly fashionable cause, rather than merely an enthusiastic follower or acolyte. Having begun to build engines and drive motor cars as a schoolboy, he had already acquired a fund of practical knowledge of the internal combustion engine far greater than that of the majority of his university contemporaries, few of whom had had any hands-on contact with this new form of transport.

At Cambridge, as at Rugby, there existed a great number of societies to cater for the spare-time interests of undergraduates, some political, some religious, some artistic or dramatic and others scientific, but there was no engineering society as such. However, just nine months prior to Ricardo's arrival at Trinity, a new society, the Cambridge University Automobile Club had been formed, in January 1903 and this he joined with alacrity. Eventually, in April 1906, he was elected its Secretary. The moving spirits of the club were three lecturers in mechanical sciences, Messrs Inglis, Dykes and Rothenberg, who were fortunate enough to have cars of their own, unlike the majority of undergraduate members, Ricardo included, who relied on motorcycles.

It was through his membership of this club that Ricardo made contact with the two men who, above all others, were to become his closest lifelong friends and associates – Harry Hetherington and Oliver Thornycroft. Together, this trio of gifted automobile enthusiasts was destined to collaborate for over thirty years, initially as undergraduates but later as professional engineers with the commencement of Ricardo's research activities and the establishment of his laboratories at Shoreham in 1918. Here, the friends became colleagues, working closely together for almost two decades until, eventually, ill health and the outbreak of the Second World War combined to cause a parting of their ways.

Among the aims and objectives of the club was the organisation of competitions and trials, for motorcycles as well as cars. As soon as Ricardo saw the excellent facilities available to him in the workshops of the university's engineering department, then located in Free School Lane, he decided to make a motorcycle of his own design with which to 'satisfy the lust for speed' and compete in these events. He had already ridden many different makes and models and, knowing the comparative advantages and disadvantages of these various designs, he had plenty of ideas for making improvements. So using materials and ready-made components purchased from the same London suppliers that he had patronised as a schoolboy mechanic, over the next two terms he put together a 900cc, single-cylinder, four-stroke machine which, although primitive by modern standards, included several novel and sophisticated features. According to its designer, although its top speed was disappointing, its acceleration was most impressive.

Ultimately, the success of this home-made, hand-built motorcycle was responsible for changing the whole future course of Ricardo's career, for it brought about a meeting with a man whose influence led him away from a training in civil engineering, as envisaged by his grandfather, and pointed him instead towards mechanical engineering. The man in question was Professor Bertram Hopkinson, who at the remarkably young age of twenty-nine had recently assumed the Chair of Mechanism and Applied Mechanics at Cambridge.

In Ricardo's own words, Hopkinson was 'the most brilliant, versatile and imaginative research leader' that he ever met. He considered him to be 'an inspiring experimentalist who took nothing for granted, had no preconceived ideas and was always ready to scrap any theory, however cherished, if the evidence warranted it. He had the most acute perception, coupled with sound and balanced judgement.' And like Ricardo himself, his approach was essentially practical. Indeed it was Hopkinson's example as a research scientist that inspired and guided Ricardo for the rest of his life. Until this point in time, Harry's interests had lain in the direction of mechanical engineering generally and manufacturing processes in particular, and he had taken no special interest in an intensive study of the internal combustion engine as such. 'But under Hopkinson's inspiring tutelage I soon became thrilled with the scope and possibilities of the internal combustion engine, which at that time was coming into wide use with the advent of the motor car.' In truth, it was purely as a result of Hopkinson's intervention that Harry Ricardo decided to dedicate his life to a systematic investigation of the internal combustion engine and its fuels and lubricants.

Hopkinson was the eldest child of Dr John Hopkinson FRS, a noted consulting engineer, scientist and inventor whose specialist field was the development of optical glass. Educated at St Paul's School, London, and Trinity College, Cambridge, Bertram Hopkinson had read for the mathematics tripos, being placed in the first division of the first-class degree before going on to study law. After being called to the Bar in 1897, he had begun his career as a counsel by joining chambers that specialised in patent actions and that often employed his father as a technical expert. The following year, however, when sailing to Australia to carry out a legal inquiry, at Aden he received a telegram recalling him to London. While on a mountaineering holiday in Switzerland his father and three of his brothers had been killed in an attempt to climb the Matterhorn. As

A contemporary photo showing the gateway of Trinity College, Cambridge, as Sir Harry Ricardo would have known it when he was an undergraduate there between 1903 and 1906.

a result of this personal catastrophe, Hopkinson decided to relinquish the law and study engineering, so as to be able to maintain his father's practice in partnership with his uncle, Charles Hopkinson.

In this capacity, he soon became involved in the design and construction of electric tramway systems in a number of British cities, work for which he was subsequently awarded the Watt Gold Medal by the Institution of Civil Engineers. When, in 1903, the Chair of Mechanism and Applied Mechanics became vacant, however, Hopkinson tendered his application and was elected unanimously despite having no teaching experience, such was his professional reputation. The appointment required him to take charge of the Cambridge Engineering School that under his predecessor, Professor Ewing, had already undergone a period of rapid expansion to become an active and important department of the university.

Sir Harry recalled that his first meeting with Hopkinson took place at the end of his first year at Cambridge, when the Professor invited him to his office for an informal discussion about the progress of his studies. On his grandfather's insistence he had enrolled on a course of studies leading to an honours degree, but had already begun to find the lectures rather tedious. 'Hopkinson told me that both Dykes and Inglis had been talking about me as a skilled mechanic, and had reported on my activities as the constructor of a motor-cycle,' he remembered in his autobiography. 'He asked me to tell him about my background of experience and commented that I had been fortunate indeed to have come in at the infancy of the petrol engine and at the birth of aviation, for both of which he predicted a tremendous future.' Moreover, it was apparent to Ricardo that; 'above all else, Hopkinson was keenly interested in the problem of flight by heavier-than-air machines, and that his interest had been greatly stimulated by the remarkable achievement of the Wright brothers in America a few months earlier'.

Hopkinson then went on to ask about his student's plans for the future. 'I told him that I was destined to join my grandfather's firm of consulting civil engineers, but that my real interest lay in moving machinery rather than in stationary structures such as harbours, tunnels and bridges.' Ricardo admitted that he could raise only tepid interest in attending lectures on surveying, geology and the theory of structures as required by the course, and that he found the formal, academic study of both pure and applied mathematics, on which his tutor laid so much stress, both incomprehensible and irrelevant. 'I told him that I felt I would never be able to take an honours degree or to become a good civil engineer, and that I merely cherished the hope that one day I might have the opportunity to extend the range of the firm's activities to embrace mechanical engineering.'

Hopkinson listened sympathetically to this plea, saying that he would consult with his colleagues on the matter and that they would wait to see how Ricardo fared in the end-of-term examinations before making a decision. He then turned to the subject of the forthcoming competition for motorcycles, organised by the University Automobile Club. This event must surely have been one of the first fuel economy trials ever held in the United Kingdom. Hearing that Ricardo was proposing to compete on his home-made machine, but that he did not think he had much chance of success because the engine of his bike was much larger than that of any of the other competitors, Hopkinson expressed a keen interest in the outcome. He encouraged Ricardo greatly by saying that this disadvantage gave him all the more scope to exercise his ingenuity by modifying the engine and carburettor and by experimenting with other ways to maximise economy. Ricardo's confidence was immediately restored. 'At this my first interview with

Hopkinson, I fell a victim to his charm and personality. I sensed that he would attach more importance to my showing in the competition than to my end of term examinations. I determined, therefore, to go all out to make the best show I could.' Right away, he began to tune up his motorcycle and make a number of alterations and adjustments, ready for the trial that was due to take place in the summer term of 1904.

The route chosen was a circular tour heading south from Cambridge to Royston, north to Newmarket and then south again back to Cambridge, a distance of about fifty miles. The rules were that all competitors should assemble on the Trumpington Road, where their petrol tanks and carburettor would be drained and their pedal chains removed. Each bike would then be refilled with exactly 1 quart of petrol and sent on its way. Thereafter, it was up to each rider to eke out this supply as best he could and to go as far as possible round the circuit before running out. When all their fuel was consumed they were to wait by the roadside until either Inglis or Rothenburg arrived to record the distance travelled, and to refuel their bikes for the return to Cambridge. Speed was to play no part in the trial; the competitors could go as fast or as slowly as they thought fit, the only criterion being the actual distance covered on 1 quart of petrol.

The betting was that, as the engine of Ricardo's bike had by far the largest cylinder capacity, he would be the first to fall by the wayside. But spurred on by Hopkinson's challenge, Harry had devoted three or four weeks to careful preparations for the event, carefully familiarising himself with the course, so that he knew exactly how to get the most out of his limited supply of fuel. As the course was flat and even, with no severe gradients to climb, or bends and corners calling for sudden slowing down or acceleration, he calculated that by fitting a high gear ratio in the drive from engine to wheels, he could maintain a steady uniform cruising speed of about 25 mph for almost the whole circuit.

While preparing for the event, Ricardo read an article about lubrication and friction in a technical journal which gave him an intriguing idea. The article pointed out how it had been discovered in cotton mills that a large saving in power consumption could be achieved by lubricating the high-speed spindles of the machinery with sperm oil, which had a low viscosity. At that time, the popular belief was that to be effective a lubricant must have plenty of 'body' and the favoured lubricating oil for petrol engines was a thick but viscous product called Price's Heavy Gas Engine Oil. Finding that sperm oil was sold by ironmongers as sewing machine oil, he decided to experiment by changing the heavy engine oil for the thin and limpid sewing machine lubricant. On a short test run he found that it increased his mileage by at least 10 per cent and decided right away to use it in the competition.

On the day of the event, the conditions were ideal; the weather was calm and sunny with little wind and the roads were dry. At the start about fifteen competitors were gathered, riding an odd assortment of machines with engines that varied from 150cc to 600cc; Ricardo's bike, which displaced 900cc, was much larger in capacity. All were waved off at intervals and most immediately disappeared at high speed down the road in a cloud of dust, the consensus of opinion being that the faster you went, the further you got. But Ricardo had other ideas. After spending the first mile in setting up his controls to give a steady constant speed of about 25 mph, he settled down to enjoy the journey in the hope that he would meet with no obstructions *en route* that would force him to disturb his finely balanced adjustments.

On his way to Royston he was overtaken by numerous late starters who waved to him as they passed. Yet hardly had he reached this town when he found an unlucky contestant sitting by the roadside with his machine, having already run out of petrol after completing a mere 16 or 17 miles. At intervals thereafter Ricardo passed most of the rest of the field standing by their abandoned bikes. By the thirtieth mile he had passed all but two or three of the competitors, and was still going strong. These riders he overtook during the next three or four miles, until he also came to a standstill only a little short of his fortieth mile, and several miles ahead of his nearest rival, who was riding one of the smallest engines in the trial.

'That win, although in a very minor competition, stands out in my memory as being my greatest triumph, for I had put my whole heart and all my thoughts into its achievement,' he claimed with justifiable pride, although acknowledging that he had had every advantage in his favour. Road and weather conditions had been ideal throughout, and during the run he had encountered virtually no traffic. 'It had also been my good fortune to have been on intimate terms with the petrol engine since its first appearance in England, while in the hands of most of my competitors the motor-cycle was but a newly acquired toy,' he added.

Hopkinson had been watching the competition closely and on the return to Cambridge, he congratulated the winner, asking him to explain exactly what he had done to improve

Bertram Hopkinson FRS (1874–1918), Professor of Mechanism and Applied Mechanics at Cambridge, the man who steered Ricardo towards his career as a mechanical engineer, and whose example inspired and directed him throughout his life.

the fuel efficiency of his machine and his reasons for doing so. Ricardo recounted all the modifications he had made and mentioned also his choice of engine lubricant, saying that he thought that the low friction imparted by the thin but slippery sperm oil might have played an important part. This was a new line of thought for the Professor.

A few days later Hopkinson invited Ricardo to lunch and revealed an exciting proposition: it was his intention to carry out a systematic programme of research into all the factors controlling the performance of internal combustion engines and to do that he needed the help of an assistant with a high level of engineering aptitude and experience. Of all his students, no one was better qualified to undertake this important work than Ricardo, Hopkinson confided. He went on to say that he had discussed the matter with his colleagues Dykes and Inglis who agreed that their pupil had the makings of good mechanical engineer, but took a dim view of his prospects as a civil engineer. This invitation put Ricardo in a quandary; if he accepted it would mean abandoning all hope of taking an honours degree as his grandfather had desired, but that hope he fully acknowledged was faint in any case. On the other hand, if he took up the offer he would be able to pursue his interest in engines to his heart's content and he would have no difficulty whatsoever in getting a pass degree.

Hopkinson settled the matter by pointing out that a good mechanical engineer would be of far greater value to the Rendel firm than a second-rate civil engineer. He suggested that in the future, as the work of building bridges and harbours became more and more mechanised, civil engineers would become increasingly dependent on the skills of mechanical engineers; the tools of the trade were changing as the pick and shovel was replaced by the mechanical excavator and the sledgehammer gave way to the pneumatic drill and hydraulic riveter. In the years to come, this mechanisation would increase by leaps and bounds and the internal combustion engine would surely sweep the board in all forms of transport and power production, providing it could be manufactured in a sufficiently light and mobile form, he predicted.

'I was immensely flattered by this invitation, for I could imagine nothing better than to carry out research under his direction,' Ricardo recounted. Straightaway, he wrote to his father informing him of all that had passed, saying how much he would like to take up Hopkinson's proposal. A few days later, Halsey Ricardo visited the Professor at Cambridge and came away from the meeting as much impressed with Hopkinson as his son had been. Clearly, Halsey fully understood the strength of his son's interest in practical mechanics and, as a craftsman himself, was completely in sympathy with Harry's desire to avoid the arid and sterile study of higher mathematics. Moreover he considered Hopkinson's project to be a most opportune and promising area of research, and was completely in favour of acceptance. Soon, the young Ricardo's future course was settled. 'I was in seventh heaven,' he recalled, sixty years later.

For the next three years (two as an undergraduate and one as a postgraduate research student) Ricardo worked closely with Hopkinson in his investigations, being treated more as a partner than as an assistant. During the latter part of their collaboration at least, the primary objective of their research was to analyse and define all the manifold obstacles and difficulties preventing the design and development of a really light and efficient petrol aircraft engine.

Chief among these problems was the phenomenon of knock, which at that time was universally attributed to premature ignition brought about by the fuel–air mixture coming into contact with some overheated surface within the cylinder and igniting well before the firing of the spark-plug. This detonation, indicated by a characteristic and quite unmistakable high-pitched ringing sound emanating from within the cylinder head, led to a marked loss of power and, eventually, to considerable damage to the valves and pistons, and even to the crankshaft.

In those days it was generally believed that the power of a two- or four-stroke cycle internal combustion engine was produced by a continuous series of explosions – timed and triggered by the spark-plug – which consumed the fuel–air mixture instantaneously. Hopkinson and Ricardo's observations showed that, on the contrary, the combustion process, though rapid, was actually a much slower and gradual burning of the fuel, initiated by a wave or pulse of flame that spread progressively outwards from the plug across the combustion chamber, releasing the latent energy of the charge through the resultant expansion of gases, which forced the piston downwards on its power stroke. In fact, this process was so slow that a certain amount of artificially induced turbulence was required in order to stir up the incoming charge and spread the flame more rapidly to increase the rate of burning and thus improve the engine's power output. Hopkinson and Ricardo established that the phenomenon of knock was indeed an abnormality, caused by the pressure wave of an explosion impinging on the cylinder walls, as had earlier been suggested by Sir Dugald Clerk.

These experiments culminated in 1906, Ricardo's last year at Cambridge, when a four-cylinder, high-speed Daimler petrol engine was obtained by the Engineering Laboratory. The workings of this engine, which represented the very last word in contemporary engine-building technology, were observed by means of an ingenious piece of apparatus that Hopkinson had devised – an optical indicator which allowed them to see exactly what was happening inside the combustion chamber under the full range of operating conditions. When Ricardo left the university that autumn, having previously obtained an ordinary degree in Engineering (he got a second class in the first part of the examinations and a first in the second, more important, part), Hopkinson presented him with this indicator, which he was to find an invaluable tool in the years that followed.

Two years later, Hopkinson referred to these experiments in the reference that he wrote for Ricardo when he took up his employment as a civil engineer with Rendel & Robertson, as the family firm had by then become known. In view of Ricardo's subsequent career, it is worth quoting the Professor's words at length:

> My personal knowledge of Mr Ricardo is chiefly based on the work which he did as my assistant in the year 1906 . . . assisting me with some experiments on a Daimler motor-car engine. Mr Ricardo's work was more than that of a mere assistant; in addition to carrying out practically the whole of the experiments, he made many valuable suggestions as to the methods of experiment, and I found his practical knowledge of the working of engines . . . of the greatest possible value in getting results and putting them into a form in which they might be of use to engineers.
>
> I found Mr Ricardo to be an uncommonly acute and trustworthy observer. His knowledge, though not of the mathematical kind which is necessary to obtain Honours in engineering examinations, is both extensive and accurate, and he is able to appreciate the significance of matters that meet his observation better than many men who are more highly trained in engineering theory.

CHAPTER 9

The Dolphin Affair

Sometime during the summer term of 1905, Harry Ricardo received an unexpected visitor at his rooms at Trinity College, Cambridge – his Australian cousin and boyhood friend Ralph Ricardo. The sudden arrival of this forceful character presaged a renewed collaboration between the pair and heralded exciting new events.

As we have seen, as schoolboys some ten years earlier the two had formed a remarkable partnership, designing and producing a number of interesting and ingenious machines in their holidays, working either in the basement workshop of the Ricardo family home in Bedford Square or in the engineering laboratories of the Regent Street Polytechnic just a few streets away in central London.

The boys represented opposing poles of engineering creativity. Ralph had the vigour, flair and enterprise to suggest new directions and approaches for their projects but it was Harry who possessed the ingenuity to solve the resulting design problems with meticulous logic and painstaking attention to detail, and thus to make the ideas succeed in practice. For Ralph, the incentive for their numerous innovations was always the far-off prospect of commercial profit; for Harry it was purely the satisfaction gained from systematic practical investigation and problem solving.

Neither Harry nor his father had heard much of Ralph throughout the past three years for, since leaving school in 1902 at the age of sixteen, Ralph had been engaged in learning his profession with two well-known northern engineering firms. In June that year he had joined the North Eastern Railway at Gateshead-on-Tyne as a premium apprentice. Under this arrangement, which involved a substantial payment to the company by his father, Ralph embarked on the technical training essential for a career as a manager in the railway engineering industry. Before the advent of technical colleges and universities, this system was the recognised way for middle-class boys to gain a thorough, practical grounding in engineering; many distinguished engineers began their careers in a similar way, including W.O. Bentley, another ex-public school boy who started out by building railway locomotives with the Great Northern Railway works at Doncaster.

It seems that by April 1906 Ralph had developed a far keener interest in the career opportunities offered by the new-fangled automobile, for that month he left his job at Gateshead and moved to Scotland to gain experience with the motor manufacturers Arrol-Johnston of Paisley. Along with Napier, Lanchester and Daimler, this firm was counted among the leading British quality car builders of the Edwardian era.

At Arrol-Johnston his entrepreneurial and organisational talents were very soon recognised and he was put in charge of the vehicle testing department, a job that also included demonstrating cars to customers. From this position he was rapidly promoted to Assistant Works Manager, and then to Manager of the company's Glasgow sales office. As a result of taking part in many important English and Scottish motor trials, he had become both an expert driver (at that time there were very few such men in the whole of Great Britain), a persuasive automobile salesman and an enthusiastic promoter of the virtues of the motor car.

Since going up to Cambridge, Harry Ricardo had continued to experiment with the highly unorthodox and original two-stroke petrol engine that he and his cousin had first produced in 1902, inspired by the ideas of Sir Dugald Clerk. Encouraged by his tutor, Professor Bertram Hopkinson, and assisted by his two undergraduate friends, Harry Hetherington and Michael Sassoon, he had developed it into a size and form suitable for powering a light car. Seeing the engine on test, the enterprising Ralph Ricardo lost no time in proposing that the four of them should form a company to manufacture a range of two- and four-cylinder versions of the two-stroke engine in large numbers. And not only that; they would also construct the chassis and bodies into which the engines could be fitted for sale as complete ready-made cars. The design and construction of this two-stroke engine was unorthodox and ingenious in that it comprised two separate cylinders, both of 4-inch bore and stroke, arranged in a 75°V. Both shared the same crankshaft and were mounted on a common crankcase, but the connecting rod of the first was attached to the connecting rod of the second, rather than to the crankshaft. The second cylinder served as the working cylinder and operated in the normal two-stroke cycle, but the first was purely a pumping cylinder; the petrol–air mixture was compressed in this first cylinder instead of in the crankcase through the downstroke of the working piston as in a conventional two-stroke engine. This arrangement led to a far more efficient scavenging of the exhaust gases than is normally the case. The compressed fuel–air mixture was fed from the pumping cylinder to the working cylinder through a communicating crosspipe, which led through an automatic, spring-loaded inlet valve to the bulb that constituted the combustion chamber. This bulb was carefully designed to take advantage of the theories propounded by Sir Dugald Clerk and enabled the strength of the charge to be varied without throttling. This stratified charge technique allowed the Dolphin engine to idle much more smoothly than other small two-stroke engines of that era.

In Harry Ricardo's view, his cousin was 'an incurable optimist' and 'a go-getter who was always on the lookout for interesting new employment and who never let the grass grow under his feet'. Not surprisingly, Ralph's plans for the business were exceedingly ambitious. His idea was that he would give up his job with Arrol-Johnston as soon as possible and return to the south of England, bringing with him a Scottish friend, an apprentice draughtsman named Fielding Thornton, whom he also wished to introduce into the partnership. Acting as Managing Director and Sales Director it would be Ralph's responsibility to get the project under way, but as soon as the business was properly established and actively trading, Michael Sassoon and Fielding Thornton would also undertake full-time responsibilities; Sassoon would be put in charge of production matters while Thornton would look after the drawing office and be general secretary. Even at the outset, however, it was never intended that Harry Ricardo would become involved in the day-to-day management of the Two Stroke Engine Company, not even as a director; instead, he was to be appointed honorary consulting engineer and designer.

There remained only the small problem of raising capital, locating suitable premises and finding sufficient advance orders – a process of negotiations that took a full two years to complete, such was the pace of commercial and legal affairs in those days. Thus although Harry patented his engine design in 1906, it was not until 1908 that Ralph Ricardo felt sufficiently confident to leave Arrol-Johnston and take up full-time work for the new venture. In fact, the Two Stroke Engine Company, a private limited company with a nominal share capital of £10,000, was actually registered in March 1908. The directors were Ralph Ricardo, Fielding Thornton and his father Norman Thornton, Michael Sassoon and Harry Ricardo's uncle Herbert Rendel, who acted as Chairman.

The bulk of the capital was provided by Michael Sassoon with additional contributions from Herbert Rendel and Fielding Thornton. Neither of the Ricardo cousins had money to put into the venture, nor was Halsey Ricardo prepared to invest. According to Sir Harry's account, he smiled benevolently on the project and remarked characteristically that 'you young people will gain experience and have a lot of fun, but don't expect to grow rich on it', a shrewd prophecy as things turned out. Nevertheless it was he who contributed one of the Two Stroke Engine Company's most valuable intangible assets by suggesting that its products be marketed as the Dolphin marque, and by modelling a beautiful little bronze dolphin mascot in the Art Nouveau style, to be mounted on the radiators of the cars.

Michael Sassoon was a wealthy gentleman of leisure whose interests lay in engineering matters. Just like Ricardo, the smell of hot oil and the feel of finely machined steel were meat and drink to him, and he was skilled in the use of high-precision metalworking tools, having set up a well-equipped workshop at his country house at Weirleigh in Kent where, in the holidays, he single-mindedly pursued his hobby of engine design and construction. When at Cambridge during the academic terms, he would spend nearly all of his time in the university workshops.

His father, the banker Alfred Ezra Sassoon, had recently died, leaving him an income of £600 a year, even though, as the first of the Sassoon family to marry outside Jewry, Alfred had been cut off from the greater part of the vast Sassoon fortune. His mother, Theresa Georgina Thornycroft, was the sister of Sir John Thornycroft, the distinguished naval architect and founder of the famous Tyneside shipyards, and from this side of the family he had inherited a strong technical bent, quite untraceable in the Sassoon blood which tended towards literary and artistic achievements. His younger brother, of course, was Siegfried Sassoon, the writer and poet, while his first cousin was another of Harry Ricardo's greatest Cambridge friends, Oliver Thornycroft.

Harry Ricardo's closest Cambridge friend, Harry Hetherington, also sprang from the landed gentry; his parents owned a large country estate known as Berechurch Hall, near Colchester in Essex, which he was due to inherit some day. Although he was reading for a degree in law, he was a talented, self-taught mechanical draughtsman who was glad to assist Ricardo in preparing such drawings as were necessary for the Two Stroke Engine venture, but although he was also an investor in the company he played no active part in advising its directors or managing its business affairs. Though he had had no formal engineering training, his hobby, too, was engine design and he was a mine of information on the state of the art in those early days. According to Sir Harry, the pair of early automobile enthusiasts spent many happy hours in his rooms at Trinity Great Court, scheming out their designs and discussing future trends, sometimes joined by Oliver Thornycroft and Michael Sassoon's youngest brother, Hamo.

Indeed, in those halcyon years before the outbreak of the First World War, Cambridge was the birthplace of modern-day British mechanical and electrical engineering expertise. In this fertile breeding ground was sparked off the technological talent that energised research laboratories and powered the expansion of the nation's aeronautical and automotive industries throughout the first half of the twentieth century. And by being

Shoreham harbour , *c.* 1906. The premises of the Two Stroke Engine Company at the Old Shipyard were located in the sheds to the far left.

present during this fecund period, and by being a key part of it, Ricardo was provided with a network of influential friends and contacts among the highest strata of industry, government and the armed forces that endured throughout his life.

The choice of location for the Dolphin venture was odd indeed, but it marked the beginning of the long association between the Ricardo name and the Sussex town of Shoreham-by-Sea that has endured to this day, although the site presently occupied by Ricardo Consulting Engineers Ltd (its home since 1919) is in no way connected with the premises chosen for the Two Stroke Engine Company in 1907.

Both Ralph and Harry knew the Shoreham area well, their connection with the region having begun when Harry was at his Rottingdean prep school some thirteen years earlier. It is possible that, together, they already had spent many happy hours messing about in sailing boats in Shoreham harbour, or in the estuary where the River Adur runs through a gap in the South Downs and out into the sea. In those days, Shoreham was still an active fishing village, no more than a group of old houses and boat sheds clustered around the port, and it had yet to become the resort and working town that it is today. Even if the cousins had never actually spent a holiday at Shoreham itself, by then they had certainly enjoyed numerous holidays at similar fishing ports, such as Bridport in Dorset, and Looe in Cornwall. For no other apparent reason than the good opportunities for boating and fishing offered at Shoreham, therefore, it was decided that this Sussex port would make a most congenial location for the fledgling engine company's operations. Rather than establishing their firm in one of the more obvious industrial centres of London or the Midlands, where the great majority of Edwardian motor manufacturing concerns were then being set up, the directors put their recreational needs ahead of banal commercial priorities such as good road and rail communications and proximity to customers and suppliers.

A small, derelict shipyard located next to the Dolphin Ferry slipway in Shoreham High Street was selected and this group of ramshackle buildings comprising a large wood and corrugated-iron shed, an office, a jetty and a slipway leading to the harbour duly provided the Two Stroke Engine Company with both its accommodation and, at Halsey Ricardo's suggestion, its brand name of Dolphin. Negotiations to purchase the Shoreham site and float the company took longer than expected and it was not until March 1908 that it was registered and truly open for business. As we shall see in the next chapter, by this time Harry Ricardo had left Cambridge and, after cramming for his professional exams, had joined the Rendel & Robertson firm in London in the summer of 1907, fully qualified as an associate member of the Institution of Civil Engineers.

Meanwhile, some important developments had been going on in London connected with a small engineering company that Harry had discovered some six or seven years previously. Ever since boyhood he had been fascinated by the profusion of small, specialist manufacturers in districts such as Clerkenwell, Islington and Tottenham. In his teens he had continued to prowl about such places delving into the affairs of these small firms so as to familiarise himself with every aspect of metalworking technology. On one of these rambles in the High Holborn area he had come across the workshops of Hurst & Lloyd, a firm of mechanical engineers that specialised in tackling difficult or unusual jobs and in making prototype or experimental machinery. Eventually, he became good friends with Lloyd, the senior partner of the firm. In his autobiography, Sir Harry described Lloyd as being a man after his own heart who ran his establishment more as a hobby than as a commercial enterprise. By leaving the financial and administrative side of the business to

The interior of the Two Stroke Engine Company's workshops at Shoreham by Sea, with several examples of the 30hp four-cylinder Dolphin motorcar under construction.

his partner, Lloyd was free to follow his own personal interests and inclinations, and to concentrate on developing his skills as an expert mechanic and experimenter. For Ricardo, the whole set-up represented the perfect working environment, and a model of all that he could wish for in his own future professional life!

When, in 1905, Harry Ricardo mentioned to Lloyd that his two-stroke engine was to be produced at Shoreham, Lloyd immediately offered help and advice that proved most valuable. Since the Two Stroke Engine Company Ltd was not yet in a position to manufacture engines itself, it was agreed that Lloyd should build two examples of the improved design, one to supply power to the machine shop at Shoreham and the other for testing and demonstration purposes. Compared with the original experimental engine, these gave a considerably improved performance, producing maximum power of between 15hp and 16hp over the normal speed range of 1,000rpm to 1,500rpm.

By this point in time, the London firm had already entered the automobile market in a minor way, by manufacturing gearboxes and clutches and even by building two or three complete cars to order for local clients. Before the coming of specialist automobile manufacturers, producing vehicles in numbers and concentrating on this activity, cars were generally constructed on a bespoke basis by garages or engineering firms that put together components produced by a variety of other small manufacturers.

In fact, well before Ralph Ricardo's arrival on the scene in 1905, on Harry's recommendation his uncle Herbert Rendel had commissioned Lloyd to build a large and imposing touring car to his own personal specification, powered by a 30hp, four-cylinder, four-stroke engine. This was to be fitted with a luxurious five-seater body built by a firm of coach builders in Croydon. But, of course, as soon as the Two Stroke Engine Company was established, Ralph succeeded in persuading Herbert Rendel to order a Dolphin engine for the car, fully expecting that this could be supplied by the end of the year, well in time to be fitted to the completed chassis.

When this proved impossible, the two cousins reluctantly agreed that this engine should be built by Lloyd's firm also, and in four-cylinder form, to provide sufficient power to propel the heavy vehicle. This work was completed in very quick time and Uncle Herbert's car was ready for its road test in July 1906. Sir Harry recorded that, after the usual teething troubles, the car performed very well indeed – so much so that the following year his grandfather Alexander Rendel, his uncle Arthur Rendel and his cousin Felix Wedgwood all placed orders for vehicles powered by the Dolphin four-cylinder engine. But these vehicles were to be built at the newly established Shoreham Works, rather than by Lloyd.

However, under the original plan set out at its foundation, the intention was that the Two Stroke Engine Company's principal product should be a smaller, less expensive car, powered by the Dolphin engine in its two-cylinder form, and that, at the same time, the company should manufacture proprietary Dolphin engines for use in the products produced by other manufacturing firms. Consequently, throughout 1905 and 1906, Harry Ricardo had spent many hours during the term-time evenings at Cambridge, scheming out designs for a light 16hp, two-seater car to weigh not more than 12cwt. The constructional features of its chassis and running gear were kept as simple as possible, so that a high proportion of these components could be produced at Shoreham on the limited range of machine tools that the company had so far been able to acquire. The construction of this prototype Dolphin model was the first job undertaken at Shoreham and it appears that the work took far longer than expected, due to difficulties in obtaining those parts that the company could not make for itself and to the general problem of

The sole surviving example of Ricardo's novel Dolphin single-cylinder two-stroke marine engine, owned by Ricardo Consulting Engineers Ltd. The engine employed the stratified charge principle, developed by Sir Dugald Clerk.

under-capitalisation. Ralph Ricardo was therefore frustrated in his work as a salesman in building up the order book because he had no demonstration car.

So it was that the Two Stroke Engine Company found itself being side-tracked into a rather different market from that which it had first set out to satisfy. According to Sir Harry's account, the directors had all been so obsessed by the glamour of the motor car that it came as a great surprise to find that there was another, even more hungry, market for the Dolphin engine right on their doorstep at the Old Shipyard. Instead of building automobiles, therefore, for the first twelve or eighteen months of its existence, the company worked flat out to motorise the local fishing fleet, which hitherto had depended on sails alone.

The idea for this diversification had come from an enterprising Scots mechanic who Ralph Ricardo had brought with him to Shoreham from the Arrol-Johnston works.

Angus, as he was universally known, was a fishing enthusiast whose hobby it had been to go to sea with the Clyde herring fishery fleet at every opportunity. Thus not only was he singularly well informed about the technique of handling drift-nets and trawls, but he was also thoroughly at home in the company of fishermen and talked their language. Angus had observed that the local fleet was engaged in a continual struggle to overcome a natural handicap – the difficulty of entering or leaving Shoreham harbour at certain stages of the tide, when the powerful stream of water passing through the narrow channel between the Adur estuary and the open sea through the breakwaters at the harbour entrance regularly reached a velocity of 5 knots. With the wind masked by the piers, no sailing boat could make headway through the channel against so strong a current, as rapid as a mill-race, and so the fishermen were forced to wait until the tide ebbed before returning with their catch. Steam power, of course, was quite unsuitable for use in such craft and had never been employed, but with a small, compact petrol engine installed, these large Shoreham fishing boats would easily be able to negotiate the harbour entrance at any time, whatever the tide or weather.

Already the two-stroke Dolphin engine had shown signs that it would be very suitable for marine use by virtue of its ability to idle at low revs. So to prove the point to the satisfaction of the local Shoreham fishermen, Angus managed to procure the loan of one of these fishing craft as a demonstration vessel. This was hauled up the slipway at the Dolphin premises and the engine, gearbox and propeller were soon installed; at the next spring tide, he gave a convincing display of seamanship, entering and leaving the harbour at all points of the tide. With the economical little 10hp Dolphin engine running at full power, the speed of the boat through the water was about 6 knots, giving just enough momentum to overcome the current of the water through the harbour's entrance channel at full flood. Moreover, as Angus demonstrated, there was yet another great advantage in favour of the Dolphin engine so far as fishing boats were concerned. By virtue of the unique design of its combustion chamber, the little two-stroke was capable of turning over steadily for hours on end at only 120rpm, which made it ideal for drift-net work. With the engine turning barely at tick-over speed, the fishing boats could make just enough headway through the water for the helmsman to maintain control of the rudder, and for the nets to keep to their correct position spread out in a long line behind the boat.

Before very long, the Two Stroke Engine Company had converted virtually the entire Shoreham fishing fleet to Dolphin petrol-engine power, at an all-in price of £100. But having saturated this local market, their profitable work ran out and despite maintaining a steady stream of advertisements in the marine press throughout the country during 1908, the firm was quite unsuccessful in attracting customers from further afield, so great had the competition become. According to Sir Harry, all efforts to sell marine engines in other areas came to nothing, for by that time other, larger firms had entered the market. These manufacturers could offer better prices and service, most notably by providing spare parts off the shelf that would actually fit. The Two Stroke Engine Company could not do so, for each of its engines was hand built, and although equally as well made as those of its competitors, the individual component parts were not interchangeable. Any renewal of parts had to be carried out at the Shoreham premises and this limitation formed a fatal barrier to the use of Dolphin engines elsewhere. A vital lesson – and one that many other infant automotive manufacturers found painful to absorb – was learned the hard way!

Having neglected the automobile market for too long, the company was now obliged to revert to its original business objectives, by turning its attention to the development of the projected range of Dolphin two- and four-cylinder motor cars once again. Accordingly, an example of the 30hp four-cylinder chassis priced at £500 was exhibited at the October 1908 Olympia Motor Show and again the following year, while a series of advertisements began to appear in the national motoring press. Although he had been out of touch with events at Shoreham during the fishing fleet episode, Harry Ricardo was now able to assist his friends in their endeavours by playing a much more active role. His contribution was to redesign the operation of the two-stroke engine, replacing its original spring-loaded poppet inlet valves with reed valves made from special copper sheet, which served to increase power while reducing noise. These improvements made the Dolphin units much more attractive for automobile use, but not, it seems, to the extent of creating a rush of would-be owners to the Shoreham workshops. For despite its inherent economy, reliability and simplicity, the two-stroke engine had already acquired its image among British motorists as a crude and plebeian device, suitable only for stationary power-generation duties and quite unworthy of the task of propelling a gentleman's carriage.

Great advances had recently been made in the development and refinement of the automobile internal combustion engine, and the new-found smoothness and silence of the four- and six-cylinder, four-stroke petrol engine had now established its supremacy over more exotic concepts, making it the standard, universally accepted prime mover for larger cars and commercial vehicles. In fact, such engines were now considered *de rigueur* by the wealthy (and, perhaps, snobbish) clientele who dictated the direction of technical advancement in the Edwardian era.

The smaller of the two Dolphin cars, the 16hp two-cylinder Dolphin two-seater designed by Harry Ricardo and built by the Two Stroke Engine Company at Shoreham.

So it was that on 18 November 1909, the following announcement appeared in the columns of *The Motor Boat*: 'Marine motor business for sale as a going concern, on river frontage. Grand opportunity for a gentleman or company with capital. Good connections and prospects. Present working staff would remain with purchasers. Apply to Box 263.' There were four employees including Angus in addition to the two active working partners, Fielding Thornton and Ralph Ricardo.

Clearly, throughout the previous year, the Dolphin business had begun to flounder. The long-expected demand for its cars had failed to materialise and, far from diminishing with time and experience, the difficulties of producing those very few vehicles that had actually been ordered was increasing daily, due to constant problems with suppliers. Yet the company lacked sufficient capital and accommodation to expand and take on this work itself. Not surprisingly, therefore, disillusionment had set in among the young directors and even the energetic and ebullient Ralph Ricardo had begun to lose interest. Without the wealth and financial security enjoyed by the other partners, he was not in a position to take a detached or dilettante attitude to these problems. Moreover, he had recently married the daughter of a Brighton merchant, in June 1909, and having returned from a honeymoon spent touring Scotland in a Dolphin, he was now acutely conscious that his bachelor days were over. Now, his first priority was to seek better, more secure prospects on which to build a home and raise a family.

Thus, despite a favourable consulting engineer's report commissioned by Michael Sassoon and delivered in October 1909, which concluded that both business and products were sound and that with a further injection of capital to tide things over this lean period, the long-term prospects were encouraging, it was decided that rather than face the uphill battles that lay ahead, the time had come to call it a day before the business got deeper into debt. As the elders of the Ricardo family had pessimistically foretold at the outset, the Dolphin venture was not likely to make a fortune for anyone, so in November 1909 the Shoreham Works were closed, although the formal dissolution of the Two Stroke Engine Company Ltd did not take place until August 1911. The assets realised from the voluntary liquidation were just sufficient to clear existing debts and repay the shareholders' original investments.

In fact, the venture's record had been far better than most. Of the 270 firms that entered the motor car manufacturing business between 1901 and 1909, no fewer than 125 failed within two years. According to Sir Harry, during its three years of trading the company had assembled or constructed just nine finished cars, in addition to its fishing fleet work; eight of these were four-cylinder vehicles, of which seven were sold to private customers with one remaining for use as a works or demonstrator car, while the other was a single example of the two-cylinder version, the original prototype, which he acquired for his own use. Apparently it served him well for over ten years. However, other estimates suggest that no fewer than twelve cars were built in total; either way none has survived. The only remaining example of the Shoreham Work's products is the Dolphin marine engine presently owned by Ricardo Consulting Engineers Ltd.

The end of the Dolphin company did not spell the end of Harry Ricardo's two-stroke engine, however. In 1895, the Hurst & Lloyd firm had been reconstituted as Lloyd & Plaister Ltd, moving in 1898 to more spacious premises at Station Road, Wood Green. Here its activities had expanded greatly so that, as we have already seen, by 1909 it had become deeply involved in the manufacture of all types of petrol engines for road, rail and marine use, and also in the construction of bespoke cars for private customers.

SIR A.M. RENDEL, K.C.I.E.
F. E. ROBERTSON, C.I.E.
CIVIL ENGINEERS.

13 Dartmouth Street
Westminster s.w.

Oct 24th 1912

My dear Kilburn

Many thanks for your letter.
I have asked Lloyd & Plaister to
send you particulars of the little
car, but in the meantime here
are its leading features. The carburettor
it is, at present, fitted with, is
an automatic one of my design, but
I have no doubt that the
addition of a Polyrhoe carburettor
would be a very great improvement.
With regard to price £140 is to

include body and tyres, the body
being a two-seater with a rattle
dash —

Engine   2 cylinders 72 %₁ x 90 %₁ too
£2.2.0   actual B.H.P about 12.
Ignition - high tension magneto (Bosch)
Cooling   water-cooling - thermo-syphon
Clutch . Leather faced cone
Gears - 2 speeds and reverse ordinary
sliding type giving 15 & 35 m.p.h at
1500 R.P.M of engine
Wheels   rear wheels 710 x 90 front wheels
710 x 75 (These apply to the first
car only - I believe L & P intend to
fit equal sized tyres in future but
am not sure what size)
Wheelbase   about 7'. 6"

L and P promise to have the first
one of these on the road next
week; it has been bought by a
friend of mine - a Mr Morrice and
he will I am sure be only too
glad to bring it round to show it
you.
            Yours sincerely
            Harry R Ricardo

Please do not take the price £140
as hard and fast, that is the price
named, and the price for which the
first one or two will be sold, but it
may subsequently be increased or
reduced,

In fact, the automobile side of its business had flourished to such an extent that Lloyd was now intent on building cars on a far larger scale by offering a very lightweight, two-seater vehicle that could be produced and operated very cheaply. A wide demand had already grown up for such 'cycle-cars', which were invariably powered by tiny single-cylinder engines of the de Dion type. Produced by numerous manufacturers, these vehicles offered the joys of motoring to the ordinary middle-class man of modest means, albeit that the general standard of their engineering and construction was usually exceedingly frail and often merely makeshift.

A handwritten letter from Harry Ricardo to his patent agents, Messrs Kilburn & Strode outlining his design for the light car which was eventually manufactured and marketed by Lloyd & Plaister in large numbers, as the Vox. None has survived.

Lloyd realised that the small and inexpensive two-cylinder, two-stroke Dolphin engine was ideal power plant for such a vehicle and immediately following the winding up of the Two Stroke Engine Company he commissioned Ricardo and Harry Hetherington to

THESE
DOLPHINS
on the
RADIATOR
of a car are the
SIGN of ITS

SIMPLICITY

in that, being fitted with a perfectly balanced Two-Stroke Engine (which does <u>not</u> compress in the 'crank chamber), there are NO CAMS or TAPPETS or the attendant timing wheels, the new 30 H.P.

DOLPHIN CAR

excels all in RELIABILITY, ECONOMY, and SIMPLICITY, so before buying one of another make get our catalogue and a trial run.

**THE TWO-STROKE ENGINE CO., LTD.
SHOREHAM - - - - - SUSSEX.**
A.C.

'Reliability, Economy and Simplicity' promised these advertisements for the Two Stroke Engine Company's Dolphin cars. Ricardo's own example certainly gave good service for well over ten years! The Dolphin radiator mascot was designed by Halsey Ricardo.

design a scaled-down 700cc version, producing about 12hp. This he proposed to fit into a a car weighing not more than 8cwt, the component parts of which could be made within the firm, including the engine itself. His proposition was that the pair should be paid a royalty of 30 shillings on every car sold, an offer which the designers readily accepted. Indeed, they collaborated very closely in the project, and may even have contributed to the design of its chassis as well as its engine.

Lloyd's first prototype cycle-car was completed for road testing early in 1911 and proved to be a complete success. Within a year, a batch of twenty cars had been built for sale under the name of Vox to test the market. Priced at only £140 complete with body and tyres, these were quickly sold, and from then on until the outbreak of war in 1914, Lloyd & Plaister continued to turn out Vox cars, producing well over 100 before the Kaiser put a stop to their activities. This success brought Ricardo a welcome additional income, which was put to good use. As we shall see in the following chapter, he ploughed these funds into the spare-time research work that he was then conducting at the weekends and in the evenings after returning home from his job with Rendel &

Robertson, in the sheds that he had built in the garden at his house at Walton on Thames. Indeed, Hetherington generously waived his share of the Lloyd & Plaister royalties to contribute to this work.

Nor was the Vox cycle-car the only use that was found for the Dolphin engine in the years immediately prior to the First World War. In 1909, Hetherington had made contact with the Britannia Engineering Co. of Colchester, makers of machine tools. Keen to extend its activities into other areas, this firm had decided that the two-stroke engine would be particularly suitable for driving a dynamo for domestic lighting purposes, and accordingly the two young engineers were invited to design two sizes of engine capable of producing 2½kW and 5kW respectively. At that time, long before the establishment of the national grid, electricity generation was carried out on a local basis and individual consumers, be they households or factories, were responsible for providing their own supplies. In 1912, one of these 2½kW Britannia sets was installed at Halsey Ricardo's house at Graffham in place of the old pumping engine; Sir Harry recorded that, twenty-five years later, it was still going strong, providing the house with light and water and that it continued to do so until the public supply from the grid reached this remote region of the Sussex countryside, in the late thirties. The Two Stroke Engine Company had also envisaged this purpose for its product, of course, and had advertised the availability of a 4½hp generator unit, in which the Dolphin engine was coupled to a 2kW Westinghouse dynamo. But so far as is known today not one example was ever sold to a paying customer.

The outbreak of the First World War brought the career of the two-stroke Dolphin engine to a sudden close, and following the death of Lloyd, and the consequent demise of the Lloyd & Plaister company, no attempt was made to revive its production for any purpose after the Armistice. Neither Hetherington nor Ricardo could see any hope of ameliorating its performance, whereas that of the four-stroke was improving by leaps and bounds.

For Harry Ricardo, the Dolphin episode had been a great disappointment, but not a catastrophe. He had always considered that his future career lay in a different direction and had never viewed the Two Stroke Engine Company venture as more than an interesting sideline giving him the opportunity for practical, hands-on design and research work in a congenial location. Although he had hoped to see a factory established at Shoreham turning out his designs in large numbers, he had never sought to become caught up in its day-to-day management and, indeed, had drawn back from becoming too deeply involved in such responsibilities, preferring the role of counsellor and consultant, advising from a position of lofty independence. Yet there is no doubt that he felt a sense of responsibility for the failure of the venture and took the lessons to heart, not least that four loyal and highly skilled employees had lost their jobs through no fault of their own, a matter that weighed heavily on his conscience. Having observed the risks and difficulties of entrepreneurship at first hand, never again did he become directly involved in a manufacturing enterprise, or attempt to create an automobile that would bear his name, although – as we shall see – the Dolphin was by no means the last car that he was to design as an entirety.

CHAPTER 10

The Walton Years

It was in his small two-seater Dolphin car that in June 1911 at the age of twenty-six Harry Ricardo set off on his honeymoon, a motoring tour of the West Country. His bride was Beatrice Bertha Hale, a 29-year-old former art student whom he had met for the first time some two years previously when they were both guests at a Rendel family gathering at Rickettswood. A skilful artist who had already shown her work at a number of exhibitions, and who continued painting for pleasure until she was well over eighty, Beatrice had studied at the Slade School of Art with Harry's sister Anna, but since leaving the school she had become closely involved in Rendel family affairs, by helping Harry's aunt Edith Rendel with her welfare work. Beatrice happened to be the daughter of Halsey and Kate Ricardo's long-standing friend and family physician, Dr Charles Hale, who had actually attended at Harry's birth, and who had looked after him and his sisters ever since.

Beatrice, or Betsy as she was known among her family and friends, was also a keen and accomplished dancer; in his autobiography, Sir Harry recorded that he must have been hard hit indeed on her account, for to pursue their courtship he had been forced to endure the agony of a course of lessons in ballroom dancing. Like her sister Cecily and many of her fellow woman students at the Slade, Beatrice was also a fervent supporter of the suffragette movement, though her activities stopped short of chaining herself to railings and setting fire to pillar boxes. Even so, she could proudly claim that she had carried a banner at the first of the militant suffragette demonstrations, held in Hyde Park in the summer of 1908 and led by the founders of the Women's Social and Political Union, Emmeline Pankhurst and her daughter Christabel.

The issues of the woman's movement and female emancipation in general were fervently debated and supported by all who gathered at Rickettswood. Like their relations the Wedgwoods, the Rendels were members of the group most responsible for the social, industrial and political changes of late Victorian times, the *nouveau riche* industrialists and engineers who voted Liberal and supported Gladstone, and who had succeeded in wresting parliamentary power from the old landowning nobility and gentry, the class into which the Ricardos had been assimilated. Progressive and enlightened, they had brought about many radical social and constitutional reforms, including the modernisation of an electoral system based solely on property-owning qualifications, which until the General Election of 1885 had denied representation even to the majority of male citizens. Actually, on the question of universal suffrage, Harry's immediate family supported Millicent Garrett Fawcett, President of the National Union of Woman's Suffrage Societies, in her more constitutional and non-militant efforts to gain the vote for women. Dame Fawcett (as she later became) was their near neighbour; she lived at 2 Gower Street, just round the corner from 13 Bedford Square.

Sir Alexander Rendel regarded his own wife as an equal partner in every respect, and the status of women seems to have been at the root of the rift that occurred between him and his brother Stuart, Lord Rendel. The Liberal politician was considered by the Rickettswood clan to have betrayed the cause of female emancipation and also to have made excessive demands on his own spouse. Although she bore him four healthy daughters and suffered many miscarriages in addition, she failed to provide him with the longed-for son and heir who would carry on a dynasty of Rendel peers. None of Sir Alexander's family could condone this thoroughly old-fashioned behaviour on the part of their rich relation. For all of them, marriage meant far more than a property contract in which women were regarded as their husbands' goods and chattels or – worse still – merely as child-bearing machines, and in his own very happy and long-lasting marriage Harry Ricardo upheld this belief in the essential partnership between the sexes.

On his return from honeymoon with his new wife, he forsook the comforts of Bedford Square where

In 1911 Harry Ricardo married Beatrice Hale, the daughter of his family doctor. Their marriage lasted for over sixty years.

he had resided since his birth, and took lodgings in a house beside the river at Walton-on-Thames, before moving one year later to a small flat near Hammersmith Bridge at Barnes, again very close to the river. Here they remained for a further year until July 1912, when their eldest daughter, Cicely Kate, was born, after which they returned to Walton-on-Thames where they rented a house standing in a large garden; this was to be their home for the next six years.

Although Harry's stockbroking uncle Arthur Ricardo had commissioned Halsey Ricardo to design and build a substantial country house, Fox Oaks, at Walton-on-Thames in 1886, there was no other previous family connection with these riverside areas; it was just that Harry and Beatrice could think of nothing better than being near to water and to boats, in places where on long summer evenings they could hire a punt and drift off for a spot of fishing, or maybe even a swim, followed by a picnic supper on the banks of the Thames. Also a deciding factor in their choice of homes was the fact that here they would be only a few miles away from the newly opened Brooklands racing track, a venue which boasted that it attracted 'the right crowd, but with no crowding'; although he never competed there, Harry was not averse to making an occasional high-speed spin around the course. For entertainment in the evenings the couple would often go into town to join Halsey and Kate Ricardo for an evening at one of the variety theatres such as the

Alhambra or the Palace, where they saw such famous singers and comedians as Dan Leno, Marie Lloyd and Harry Lauder and the other great personalities of the Edwardian music hall. On other occasions they would all go to the Gilbert and Sullivan operas at the Savoy Theatre, the music of which Sir Harry, no highbrow, confessed that he could understand and enjoy to the full. He also admitted enjoying such productions as *The Merry Widow*, *The Chocolate Soldier*, *The Geisha* and the other compositions of Johann Strauss and Franz Lehár staged at the Gaiety Theatre, not just because of the lovely lilting and sensuous music, but also because of the beauty and charm of their leading ladies and chorus girls, with whom, as a young man, he had inevitably fallen in love. In his bachelor days, the mantelpiece of his room at Bedford Square had been adorned with postcard photos of Marie Lohr, Gertie Miller and the other famous stars of the Edwardian theatre.

Sir Harry described his years at Walton-on-Thames as being the happiest and most carefree of his life. The weather during the summer of 1911 in particular was the finest and warmest that he could ever remember, and throughout July and August the sun shone daily from a cloudless sky. These halcyon days must truly have been the high point of the Edwardian epoch; never again would the outlook be quite so bright and sunny for the British upper classes and their households.

Every weekday during these early years of married life, Harry Ricardo would set off in his little Dolphin to drive the few miles to his office at Great George Street (and later, Dartmouth Street), Westminster, where he had taken up his place with Sir Alexander Rendel's firm four years earlier. As related previously, Sir Alexander had always hoped to keep his firm a family affair and had taken into partnership two of his sons, first William and later Harry, who were both fully qualified civil engineers. Sadly, William Rendel died in 1898, leaving Harry Rendel alone to carry on the tradition. And in the

Harry and Beatrice on honeymoon in the West Country.

up-and-coming generation, there was only Sir Alexander's grandson, Harry Ricardo, of course, who had shown any interest in, or aptitude for, engineering.

Sir Harry Ricardo described his uncle Harry Rendel as being his favourite uncle, 'a really brilliant engineer and a perfectly charming companion'. During his childhood he had seen little of him, as Uncle Harry was constantly abroad. But on his return to the London office to take up his partnership after William's death, they became close friends and, throughout Harry Ricardo's undergraduate years, they frequently went out shooting together when staying at Rickettswood. The future looked promising indeed; as senior partner, Harry Rendel would look after the civil engineering side of the business, while Harry Ricardo would take care of the mechanical developments, including the adoption of the internal combustion engine to provide motive power, which both were convinced would assume an ever-greater importance in the firm's activities during the coming years. That way, as Sir Harry wryly put it, no client would ever be expected to entrust him with the design of a bridge or dam!

But then, in 1904, Harry Rendel died suddenly from septic pneumonia after only two or three days' illness. To all the family, and old Sir Alexander Rendel (now in his middle seventies and close to retirement) in particular, this was a terrible tragedy, not least because it completely upset the plans for his succession. Earlier, on the death of William, Sir Alexander had taken into partnership his long-serving employee Frederick Robertson, of whom Sir Harry always had a very low opinion, considering him to be nothing more than a dull and unenterprising bureaucrat, an administrator quite unfitted to the challenging task of guiding his grandfather's firm into the twentieth century. Within a few days of Harry's death, however, another senior member of the staff, Seymour (later Sir Seymour) Tritton, was offered a partnership, though Robertson assumed effective control of the firm and its name was changed to Rendel & Robertson. This arrangement lasted until 1912 when Robertson died also. A new partner, Frederick (later Sir Frederick) Palmer, then Chief Engineer of the Port of London Authority, was brought in to take his place and the name of the firm was changed yet again to Rendel, Palmer & Tritton, and so it remained until recent times.

With the death of Harry Rendel, the prospect of a secure and remunerative career as a partner in his grandfather's firm lost its appeal for Harry Ricardo, particularly in the light of the very great satisfaction that he had gained from his internal combustion engine research work at Cambridge with Professor Hopkinson. Nevertheless, the plans for his future as first envisaged by Sir Alexander had gone ahead and he had joined the firm in the summer of 1907, having left Cambridge the previous autumn to cram for the professional examinations required for associate membership of the Institution of Civil Engineers. In his first years at Great George Street during Robertson's regime, however, he felt somewhat neglected. As he confided in his autobiography, he thought that his potential contribution to the firm had been overlooked and that the senior partner regarded him as a playboy, far too frivolous to be entrusted with any real responsibility. Moreover, he firmly believed that both Robertson and his grandfather took a very poor view of mechanical engineers in general. In their eyes the civil engineer was an artist in an exalted position of supremacy, while the other was a mere mechanic belonging to a lowly position in the hierarchy.

Fortunately for Harry Ricardo with the arrival of Palmer in 1912 this situation changed. The new partner took the view that as time progressed the civil engineer would become ever more dependent on the work of the mechanical engineer and so he encouraged the inventive young Ricardo to develop and eventually to take charge of that side of the firm's activities. He even allowed Harry to begin designing new items of specialised construction machinery in a drawing office that the firm set up for this purpose. It was hoped that this equipment might prove rather more suitable for its purposes than much of the inferior and inadequate machinery that the company was then obliged to purchase in the UK for its bridge- and dock-building activities in India and Africa.

Hitherto Ricardo's duties had involved supervising the procurement of mechanical plant and equipment, such as steam, gas and oil stationary engines, cranes, hoists, jacks, air compressors and a wide variety of pneumatic and hydraulic apparatus, contemporary electrical equipment being unsuitable for service in hot climates due to the problem of maintaining insulation in tropical conditions. This work often took him out of London on liaison and inspection visits to the various suppliers and manufacturers approved by the India or Colonial Office, and it was during these trips to Manchester and Glasgow that, for the first time in his life, he came into contact with some of the leading lights in the field of engine building and mechanical engineering at the premises of such famous British companies as Crossleys, Mirrlees, Bickerton & Day, Mather & Platt, and Hornsby-Ackroyd. His fact-finding missions on his firm's behalf were not confined to the United Kingdom either. In the course of the first of many journeys on the Continent, in 1911 he also visited many of the most significant German engine-building companies, including Deutz at Cologne, Korting at Hanover, Benz at Mannheim, Daimler at Stuttgart, MAN at Augsberg and BMW at Munich, and what he learned there made a deep impression on him.

Many British stationary engine manufacturers were then producing designs licensed from foreign companies such as Deutz, MAN or Korting on a royalty basis, in the belief that it was much cheaper and far less risky to buy know-how from elsewhere than to invest in long-range product research and development on their own account. Alan Chorlton (later Sir Alan Chorlton MP), Chief Engineer of Mather & Platt, was particularly scathing about this mistaken and short-sighted policy and his criticisms seem to have awakened Harry Ricardo's youthful dreams that, in the years to come, he might one day open a research laboratory of his own to cater for the needs of British engine builders, a place where he could carry on the kind of work begun with Professor Hopkinson at Cambridge. The establishment of his imagination would be a kind of independent University of the Internal Combustion Engine, staffed by the very best brains in that field and fully equipped to undertake long-term research and development investigations on behalf of both government and industry. Working on a commercial fee or royalty-earning basis, this laboratory would undertake design, development and other experimental work for individual clients, or design and build special experimental engines for use as laboratory equipment by the research departments of universities and oil companies.

At that time, Ricardo's dream was a unique idea, and one that would take another ten years of his life to bring about. In the meanwhile, he would have to carry on his engine design and research activities on his own in his spare time, in the two large inter-connected wooden sheds that he built himself at the far end of the garden at his rented house in Walton-on-Thames in 1912. These buildings, which served as a machine-shop and test-shop, were paid for and fitted out by a present of £100 given to him by his grandfather and by the royalties that were still trickling in from Messrs Lloyd & Plaister and the Britannia Company in respect of his Two Stroke Engine Company patents. Over

The garden workshop at Walton-on-Thames that Ricardo built for himself in 1913. It was here that he continued his experiments into the internal combustion engine and its fuels begun at Cambridge. It was also the place where he built his first research engines. The car to the left of the picture is Ricardo's own Dolphin.

a period the machine-shop was equipped with four lathes, a milling machine and a drilling machine, together with other, smaller equipment, while the other shed was set as a test-shop with two electric dynamometers that could be coupled to the engines under test. This shed also housed the Dolphin engine that had formerly been used for pumping water at Graffham.

Ricardo was by now a first-class mechanic, well able to machine and assemble the component parts of an engine without assistance, working from his own drawings. So it was that in 1913 he proceeded to design and build a completely new experimental supercharged single-cylinder engine incorporating many novel features which were later used in several of his most successful full-scale commercial designs. The so-called Walton engine was a water-cooled poppet-valved unit of 110mm bore and 140mm stroke with a swept volume of 1,330.5cc, but its main feature was its cross-head piston, so arranged that the underside of the piston could be used to compress a charge of air into the chamber surrounding the cross-head guide barrel, from which it escaped to the working cylinder through holes uncovered by the descending piston at the bottom of its stroke.

From this working prototype, Ricardo evolved a design scheme for a supercharged twelve-cylinder, four-stroke aero-engine of about 300hp, with the cylinders arranged in a narrow-V configuration. The supercharged air produced by the downstroke of the piston could be employed either to boost performance – so as to maintain ground-level output from the engine when flying at high altitude around 10,000 ft – or as a stratified diluent to improve fuel consumption by up to 10 per cent under cruising conditions at lower altitude. This work was inspired and encouraged, of course, by Professor Hopkinson, with whom Ricardo had remained in touch since leaving Cambridge some five years earlier. Even then, Hopkinson had repeatedly stressed his belief in the military and commercial viability of the aeroplane, provided that a really suitable engine could be supplied for its propulsion. The aircraft of the future, he maintained, should be capable of carrying heavy payloads over long distances, so that low fuel consumption was an even more important design consideration than achieving the combination of high power and low weight. The small, featherweight but altogether thirsty 50hp engines currently being built by the French were simply inadequate for the task, he believed.

When this V12 design scheme had been completed, Hopkinson arranged an appointment for Ricardo to meet a high-ranking officer at the War Office, with a view to obtaining official backing for the production of the engine, but to no avail. After listening courteously to his proposals, the officer announced that the young engineer was wasting his time; the only use that the army had for aviation of any kind was for target spotting for artillery and for this purpose an altitude of only a few hundred feet was quite sufficient. There was no requirement at all for a high-flying, far-ranging aeroplane; the captive balloon tethered to the ground was a far better proposition, since it remained in direct telephonic communication with the guns below. In the Whitehall brass hat's view, moreover, the aeroplane was far too fragile for the rough and tumble of military service. Ricardo recalled that he was disappointed by this verdict, but not entirely discouraged, for he decided to press on regardless with his aero-engine work.

During this same period Ricardo continued with the experimental work begun at Cambridge, using the optical indicator instrument that Hopkinson had given him to analyse the combustion process and investigate the mechanism of detonation or knock. This work also led him to examine the behaviour of different varieties of petroleum fuels in the single-cylinder version of the supercharged aero-engine, and to discover that the tendency to detonate increased as the fuel became more paraffinic and less aromatic; pure aromatics such as benzene and toluene seemed almost immune to detonation. Accordingly by 1913 he had satisfied himself that 'the incidence of detonation was the most important factor limiting the compression ratio and therefore the efficiency and power output of the spark-ignition engine' and that this phenomenon was related to the chemical composition of the petrol and thus an entirely different matter from pre-ignition, initiated by some hot surface within the combustion chamber, which had previously been held to be the culprit. Thus it was that, working alone on his own initiative and in a laboratory of his own making, he became one of the first engineers to distinguish between knock and pre-ignition, the two most important abnormal combustion phenomena in the petrol engine. As we shall see, this discovery was to be of the very greatest significance in the later development of the internal combustion engine and its fuels.

Since leaving Cambridge, Ricardo had kept in close touch also with his automobile club friend Harry Hetherington who had married and moved to live in London. Together the pair spent many hours scheming out imaginary engines for automobiles and aircraft. To keep abreast of new developments in the internal combustion engine field, they also made it their business to go to the lectures given at the Institution of Mechanical Engineers in London by distinguished experts and exponents such as Frederick Lanchester, Laurence Pomeroy (the Chief Engineer of the Vauxhall car company) and, of course, Sir Dugald Clerk, whose memorable talks Harry had often attended as a schoolboy. At the conclusion of these lectures there would usually be an open forum in which the audience was invited to participate and as a result of Ricardo's contribution to a discussion that followed one of Pomeroy's talks, he was invited to visit the Vauxhall works at Luton where, at lunch, he met the firm's well-known Managing Director, Percy Kidner. A robustly extrovert personality, Kidner was an early motoring enthusiast who had joined Vauxhall as its Engineering Director in 1904. He later became more famous as a competitor in motor-sport events, particularly those held at the Brooklands Racing Track, where he raced the cars that Pomeroy had designed, most notably the celebrated Vauxhall 30/98 model. Powered by a 4.2-litre, small-bore, long-stroke engine embodying Pomeroy's advanced ideas, this car could reach a speed of over 100 mph. When driven by Kidner at Brooklands, it was well able to keep its end up in competition with the bigger Napier, Fiat and Mercedes racers fitted with giant engines of more than three times its total cylinder capacity. Some twenty years later, Percy Kidner was to play an important part in Ricardo's affairs, when he became a director of the Shoreham company, having sold his interest in Vauxhall Motors to the American General Motors organisation in 1927. Sir Harry described his visit to Luton in 1910 as the first time that he ever came into personal contact with any of the leading members of the automobile industry. But through his growing friendships with men like Lanchester, Pomeroy and Kidner (and later, of course, Sir Henry Royce and Montague Napier) it was not to be long before he was accepted as an equal member of this fraternity of motoring pioneers and an authority on automobile engineering in his own right.

But in gaining the respect and confidence of his fellow engineers, he had first to overcome the natural diffidence and shyness which, in truth, affected him all his life. An engaging and convincing talker when in conversation with small groups of like-minded professionals or when relaxing among his own family circle, Harry Ricardo disliked large crowds and congregations which made him feel awkward, uncomfortable and tongue-tied. Although he was in no way introverted, gauche or anti-social and could express himself with great charm and lucidity when in the company of friends and colleagues, he avoided noisy gatherings of strangers such as cocktail parties and formal banquets, particularly in his old age when he became very deaf. Although throughout his career he was often called upon to read papers at professional conferences or to address important committees, he always declined to give extemporary lectures or to speak off the cuff in public, even on his own home ground at assemblies of his staff. As he put it himself, when describing his attempts to join in the exchanges that followed a lecture given by Sir Dugald Clerk: 'I longed to take part in these discussions . . . but at first had not the courage to do so. Noting that Sir Dugald's replies to his questioners were invariably kindly and courteous, and that he was particularly encouraging to the younger and more timid members of his audience . . . at long last I screwed up my courage and timidly questioned him about his advocacy of the stratified charge in petrol engines.'

So impressed was Sir Dugald Clerk with what his youthful questioner had to say on this arcane subject, especially with regard to Ricardo's own experiences with the Dolphin two-stroke engine, his research work with Professor Hopkinson at Cambridge and his most recent experiments at Walton-on-Thames, that at the end of the meeting the great man invited him to call at his London office to discuss the youngster's future ambitions and career plans. 'I told him that the height of my ambition was to follow on the research that Hopkinson had initiated and to design a really light and efficient aeroplane engine. He wished me well and told me not to hesitate to ask him for any help or advice I needed,' Ricardo recalled in his autobiography.

This, of course, was his first face-to-face meeting with Sir Dugald, although, as we have seen, he had already been an ardent disciple of the distinguished mechanical engineer for many years. 'As with Hopkinson, I fell a victim to the charm of his personality,' he admitted. After this first meeting he paid several more visits to Clerk's office, when they talked about their respective experiences of the internal combustion engine. Being mindful of the differences in their ages (Clerk was then about sixty-five and Ricardo twenty-five) this curiosity on the part of his senior and mentor he found very flattering indeed. The upshot was that Sir Dugald invited him to lunch at the Athenaeum Club in Pall Mall to introduce him to a number of its members including Sir Charles Parsons of steam-turbine fame and Parson's friend and associate, the electrical engineer and pioneer of wireless telegraphy Alan Archibald Campbell-Swinton, who also happened to be an old family friend of the Rendels. As a founder-director of the Parsons Marine Turbine Company, Campbell-Swinton had actually been on board the SS *Turbinia* when it made its spectacular appearance at the Diamond Jubilee Naval Review at Spithead in 1897.

This occasion was truly a red-letter day in Ricardo's life, for, as we shall soon discover, in his other capacity as an entrepreneur, venture capitalist and industrial talent-spotter, Campbell-Swinton was destined to play a vital part in his career, by becoming in due course a founder-director of Ricardo's engine research company Engine Patents Ltd, the precursor of Ricardo Consulting Engineers Ltd. Some twenty years later, in 1932, Harry Ricardo was himself elected to the Athenaeum, a club which has always numbered a high proportion of the country's leading academics, scientists and engineers among its members; he remained a member until 1965. His candidature was proposed by Mervyn O'Gorman, formerly the first Director of the Royal Aircraft Establishment at Farnborough, the cradle of British military aviation, and seconded by Sir Dugald Clerk who died shortly afterwards at the age of seventy-eight. During that same period, another very important formative event in Sir Harry Ricardo's life took place. One day during 1913, a tall man with a broad Scots accent turned up at his office in Great George Street and introduced himself as Mr John Blackie, senior partner in the Glasgow publishing firm of Blackie & Sons. The Scotsman announced that he and his partners considered that the time was ripe for the publication of a new book on the subject of the internal combustion engine, for although Sir Dugald Clerk's book *The Gas Engine*, first published in 1886 and subsequently revised and reissued in 1909 as *The Gas, Petrol and Oil Engine* was still regarded as the classic work, its long run as a best-seller could not last much longer. The purpose of his visit, made on the recommendation of Professor Bertram Hopkinson no less, was to invite Ricardo to be the author of such a book.

'The invitation took my breath away,' said Sir Harry. 'I pointed out that I was a mere amateur; that I had never for one moment dreamt of writing a book, nor had any idea of how to set about it, but the publisher was not deterred.' Immediately, he sought out Sir Dugald Clerk who told him that he considered Blackie & Sons to be a first-rate firm, adding that in his experience there was nothing like the work of producing a book for exposing gaps in the writer's knowledge and forcing him to fill them in, and his advice was that Ricardo should go ahead and accept the offer. The terms agreed were that the author should receive a lump sum payment of £500, which was a far greater sum than Ricardo had expected as it amounted to considerably more than a year's salary from his current employers; needless to say, he had no private income or allowance from his father to help defray the expense of raising a family.

As things turned out, Sir Harry's lack of confidence in his ability as a writer was misplaced; the venture was a great international success and the resulting book, *The Internal Combustion Engine*, originally published in two volumes in 1923 and 1924 respectively, eventually ran to five editions and was translated into many foreign languages. Undoubtedly, his other achievements aside, this classic work helped to establish his reputation as a leading international authority on the internal combustion engine, since it soon found its way on to the library shelves of the world's leading universities and technical colleges. After being revised, reissued and retitled as *The High Speed Internal Combustion Engine*, it remained in print for almost fifty years until the early 1970s, and was required reading for at least three generations of mechanical engineering students. Years after publication, Sir Harry was pleased and proud when the President of St Catherine's College, Cambridge, T.R. Henn, included a passage from the book in a compilation of the very best examples of scientific writing to be found in the English language, ranking Ricardo's prose with that of such authors as Francis Bacon, Robert Hooke and Sir Isaac Newton.

There can be no doubt that Sir Harry's gifts as a writer and communicator were a major contributing factor in his success as an engineer. His ability to avoid obfuscation by expressing himself clearly and concisely in simple English, often describing the workings of intricate machinery or the action of complex physical processes with a brilliantly illuminating turn of phrase, made the many reports, articles and papers that he was called upon to produce transparently understandable, even to a non-technically minded readership. Not only that, as Sir Harry was not slow to recognise and acknowledge himself, it also made for keener observation and clearer thinking on the part of the writer. Many were the young would-be recruits to his laboratories who were startled to find that the first question he would ask them at their interview was whether or not they were any good at writing decent English.

Due to unforeseen circumstances, however, it was several years before Mr Blackie's commission could be completed and published. Although the first part dealing with heavy, low-speed engines was delivered to the publishers within a year of the commission being received, its appearance was suspended until the second part dealing with light, high-speed engines was ready. By all accounts, this part was eventually written during long winter evenings at home, with the author lying on the floor with his manuscript and pencil, surrounded by his young children and their toys. By then he was the father of three daughters, for Cicely, born in 1912, had been joined by Angela Edith in 1915 and Camilla Bertha in 1921. Sir Harry explained the delay with the following poignant words: 'I had made a start on the book and was getting on nicely with the first volume when the 1914 war burst upon us, and all our plans were changed.'

CHAPTER 11

The First World War

E arly in 1914, Sir Alexander Rendel expressed his decision to retire later that year and, as had always been his intention, he offered his grandson a partnership in his firm as his successor alongside Palmer and Tritton. In order to broaden Harry's experience and bring him up to date with the latest developments in the civil and mechanical engineering fields, the young man was sent to America for four months to visit various engineering establishments there.

Unfortunately, no record survives of his activities on this trip, his first visit to the USA, although it seems most unlikely that while there he would not have made his way to Highland Park, Detroit, where two years previously Henry Ford had opened the world's first sequential moving-belt production line for automobile engines and chassis. If so then, like many other visitors from Europe, he would surely have been bowled over by the sheer scale of American engineering enterprise, and by the enormous increase in industrialisation that had been achieved there in so short a time.

However, it is known that on his return from America he was immediately dispatched on a similar tour of European firms in Holland, Italy, Sweden and Germany. It was during his visit to Sweden in July 1914 that the First World War broke out. This development came as a very great surprise for up to that point neither he nor his colleagues had considered a conflict with Germany as being even the remotest possibility. And in any case, the general view in those days was that wars were events carried out by armies and navies in remote locations and in which the civilian population was not involved. Similarly, scientific and engineering research was a matter that knew no national boundaries and had no particular political significance or bias. Many eminent British engineers occupied leading commercial positions on the Continent and vice-versa and, similarly, in academic circles there was a constant interchange of teachers and students between the universities of England, Germany and France. Consequently, information could be freely exchanged between members of the engineering community without governmental restraint, even on matters having important actual or potential military applications. Engineers considered that they belonged to a brotherhood whose professional interests and responsibilities transcended normal barriers and frontiers; in any case, the Official Secrets Act was unknown and travel throughout Europe was virtually unrestricted. No passports or visas were required, and the English sovereign was recognised as an international currency, accepted everywhere.

It had long been Ricardo's ambition to visit a Swedish engineer who was engaged in internal combustion engine research work that paralleled his own. This was the diesel pioneer Dr Hesselman, the Chief Engineer of the Atlas company which was currently building a new type of high-speed diesel engine to power the submarines of the Swedish Navy. Consequently, plans had been arranged for Harry and his wife to spend some time with Hesselman in Stockholm in early July and then to take a short sailing holiday in the

Baltic before returning to England via Berlin and Aachen, where he was due to call on Professor Hugo Junkers to view the diesel engine research that was currently under way in the German engineer's magnificent laboratories.

During his holiday in Sweden, he had seen no English newspapers, nor had he received any letters from home containing disturbing news of the kind that might have led him to change his plans. Hearing nothing from Krupps, therefore, he made straight for Aachen arriving on 1 August to be welcomed with great cordiality. While being shown round the laboratories, however, his host was suddenly called to the telephone, and on his return he asked Ricardo when he was planning to return to England. Learning that his guest was in no particular hurry, Junkers replied that Ricardo and his wife would be well advised to head for home as soon as possible, as he had just been informed that Russian troops were mobilising on Germany's eastern frontier, and he shuddered to think what that might portend. 'That was the first hint I got that serious trouble was brewing,' said Ricardo in his autobiography. 'We returned to England the next day, August 2nd 1914, by way of Ostend. The boat was crowded with English travellers returning hurriedly from holiday, having been warned that war might break out at any moment.' Two days later – with German troops pouring into Belgium – the United Kingdom, France and Russia declared war on the aggressor and the two engineers, Junkers and Ricardo, found themselves on opposing sides of the greatest military conflict in history. 'I suppose we must have been very unobservant but at no time during our three days in Germany did we see any sign of military activity or of popular excitement,' Ricardo confessed.

In his autobiography, Sir Harry admitted that he found it hard to recall the emotions that he felt on the outbreak of the First World War, but thought perhaps the word bewilderment best summed up his feelings. As an educated Englishman who had been brought up to respect the civilising achievements of German culture and science, and who admired the country's great technological and industrial achievements, he must have been perplexed to find that this mighty nation had abandoned rational conduct in the pursuance of its political aims by resorting, once again, to militarism. Doubtless he was put in mind of Bismarck's dictum that the great questions of politics could never be solved by speeches and votes, but only by iron and blood.

It was widely predicted in the newspapers that the affair was a storm in a teacup, and that the fighting would all be over by Christmas. It was sheer madness on the part of the Kaiser to challenge the combined power of Britain, France and Russia, said the press and politicians, and the ordinary citizen should carry on his or her business as normal and prepare a rousing yuletide welcome to the victorious Allied armies and navies on their return. This wishful thinking was sadly misplaced, however, and within a matter of weeks the greatly outnumbered British Expeditionary Force of professional soldiers, hastily dispatched to France to halt the German advance through Flanders, was forced to retreat following the Battle of Mons at the end of August 1914. After this defeat it became apparent to the civilian population at home that, in Ricardo's words; 'a long, grim and deadly struggle lay ahead of us, and that it was up to all of us to play our part, either in the actual fighting or in the support of the active services. The call went out for volunteers and for a time the recruiting offices were snowed under by the response.' At the same time, the reservists of the Territorial Army were also called up, while a survey was made of the country's manpower to identify those individuals with special technical knowledge or professional expertise who would be needed at home in a civilian role, to keep the war machine in operation behind the scenes. As the only mechanical engineer in his grandfather's firm (which had military responsibilities) Harry Ricardo was classified as being in a reserved occupation and instructed not to volunteer for active service abroad.

By October 1914 the first furious onslaught had ground to a halt and the two opposing armies on the Western Front had become completely bogged down in defensive positions. Along a 400-mile line from Belgium to Switzerland a continuous network of trenches had been dug by both sides, separated by a narrow strip of no man's land and protected by machine-gun nests and barriers of barbed wire. Across this gap the opponents regularly lobbed devastating artillery barrages in a futile attempt to smash their rival's defences and break the demoralising stalemate. From time to time an offensive was mounted, and to soften-up resistance prior to infantry attacks, a non-stop barrage often lasting over a week would be fired off, with over 1,000 guns discharging several million shells on to a few square miles of territory. Even so, throughout the next three years of the conflict it was never possible for the infantry of either side to advance and capture more than 100 yards of territory without sustaining appalling casualties inflicted by machine-gun fire.

For Ricardo, the early months of the war were a time of absolute misery. His instructions were to carry on as usual with his work at Rendel, Palmer & Tritton, but there was no work for him to do. Day after day he sat alone in his empty drawing office hoping that some use would be found for his services. 'To while away the time I went on with the writing of my book and putting finishing touches to my design of an aeroplane engine, but with a heavy heart,' he recalled. 'Most of the time I spent reading reports from the front which grew gloomier and gloomier every day, or scanning the ever-lengthening casualty lists.' By Christmas 1914, almost all of his inner circle of school and university friends, including Harry Hetherington, Oliver Thornycroft, Tony Welsh, Michael Sassoon, Keith Lucas and Erasmus Darwin, had enlisted as volunteers. 'By contrast with their fate I could but feel that I was a frightful shirker, but I buoyed myself up with the hope that I might yet have a chance to play a useful part in the war,' said Ricardo.

However, his sense of embarrassment, frustration and guilt was greatly relieved in the spring of 1915 when quite by chance he came across 'a very able young automobile engineer, T.B. Barrington, who had served an apprenticeship with Rolls-Royce, but who had recently joined the Royal Naval Air Service as a volunteer engineering officer'. As we shall see in following chapters, the Royal Naval Air Service, established in July 1914, was a curious formation, part fighting force and part research organisation, which maintained units staffed by regular naval engineering officers and volunteer civilian engineers serving with the Royal Naval Volunteer Reserve. As the Royal Flying Corps, formed in May 1912, was regarded purely as the aeronautical branch of the British Army, with its aircraft confined to a tactical battlefield role, it was the RNAS that had responsibility for the air defence of Great Britain. In addition to its coastal patrol duties, therefore, the RNAS pioneered the concept of strategic bombing, attacking German airship bases deep in enemy territory as early as 1914 in an attempt to prevent attacks on British airspace by the Zeppelins. This state of affairs continued until April 1918 when the Royal Air Force was created by a merger of the RFC and the RNAS, which were then disbanded.

Barrington's unit was led by a certain Commander Briggs, the man who, at the outbreak of war, had requisitioned a Mercedes Grand Prix racing car on display in the German firm's West End showrooms and towed it to Rolls-Royce's Derby factory where its engine was dismantled and inspected; the lessons learned were incorporated in Rolls-Royce's first aero-engine, the Eagle. His squadron was concerned with research into anti-submarine warfare problems and in particular the development of long-range flying boats that could patrol far out to sea to detect and destroy U-boats with depth charges and small high-velocity guns firing armour-piercing shells. Even at this early stage in the war, it was recognised that the greatest threat to national survival came from the torpedo attacks that enemy submarines were making on unarmed and unprotected supply ships, and the large flying boat with its relatively high speed and wide range of action in comparison with balloons and dirigibles was perceived as being the only way to deal with the menace.

On being introduced to Briggs by Barrington, Harry Ricardo learned that the plans to build this 'flying destroyer' were at an early stage, but that the aircraft envisaged was to be a far larger machine than had ever previously been contemplated. Moreover, it would have two propellers driven by chains or bevel gears from a single large engine located in the fuselage, just like the Wright brothers' earliest aeroplane. It had been estimated that to get this massive craft aloft, its engine would have to produce at least 600hp, a rather ambitious requirement since at that stage in the development of the aero-engine the most powerful unit available to the RNAS, the RAF Type 4 designed by A.J. Rowledge and built at the Royal Aircraft Factory at Farnborough, was rated at only 140hp.

In Ricardo's view, Briggs was 'a go-getter and an optimist' who lacked technical knowledge and thus relied on Barrington, his second-in-command, for engineering expertise. So when it was suggested that Ricardo might already have conceived exactly the aero-engine that the RNAS were looking for, its young designer was obliged to point out that although his supercharged 300hp design would certainly deliver low fuel consumption at cruising speeds, making it ideal for maritime work, at its best it would develop less than half the power output demanded. But Briggs was undeterred. 'He told me not to mind but just to get busy and design a larger version; after all it only meant increasing the dimensions by 30 per cent all round. . . . I told him that it was not quite as simple as that, but that I would certainly look into what could be done,' Ricardo recalled.

Two or three days later, Barrington came to Walton-on-Thames, accompanied by several other officers from his squadron, to see what Ricardo was doing in his workshop and to view the single-cylinder and Dolphin test engines in action. According to Sir Harry, Barrington was extremely interested in the experimental work that he was carrying out and was well able to understand the significance of his research into the combustion process, but was shocked at the shaky condition of some of the equipment being used, including the ancient 5-inch lathe which Ricardo had owned since he was seven and which had served him well for more than twenty years. The naval men insisted that he must have something better and from an Admiralty store they conjured up a brand new 6-inch precision lathe which Ricardo was allowed to borrow until the end of the war. A little later they also offered him the full-time services of a first-class mechanic named Doughty who, in fact, remained with him for the next fifteen years.

It seems that Barrington gave his commanding officer a glowing account of all that he had seen in the Walton-on-Thames workshops, and especially of the design of Ricardo's would-be aero-engine, for a day or so later Briggs invited the young engineer to accompany Barrington and himself on a visit to Peter Brotherhood's works at Peterborough. At that time Brotherhood was engaged on the design and manufacture of a wide variety of auxiliary machinery for the navy, such as air compressors, steam pumps and torpedo engines. In fact, its Chief Engineer and Managing Director, Commander Bryant, was an ex-navy man, a helpful and fatherly figure for whom Ricardo was soon to develop a deep affection, describing him as 'a guide, philosopher and friend'. Bryant clearly served as a role model in Ricardo's later life, for the Commander had 'an extraordinary grasp of every detail of the work in each department of his large works, and obviously inspired the loyalty and affection of all ranks of his employees', precisely the qualities that Sir Harry sought to emulate when he himself became an employer. The Brotherhood firm had only recently moved to its new and up-to-date Peterborough factory from London where it had previously occupied premises on the south bank of the Thames at Lambeth, the very buildings that Ricardo had observed as a boy when out walking by the river with his mother.

The purpose of the visit to Peterborough was to find out whether Brotherhood's would be prepared to develop and manufacture a much larger version of Ricardo's original aero-engine design. He had pleaded in vain with Briggs to employ two or more smaller engines mounted on the wings of the projected aircraft, but the Commander had insisted that in the interests of reliability and long endurance, it was essential to have a single large engine situated in an accessible position within an engine-room deep in the hull of the flying boat, where its needs could be constantly ministered to by a mechanic wielding a spanner and oil-can, as was the standard naval practice with engines of every kind. The aircraft itself, a gigantic biplane with a stepped hydroplane hull, was to be built by Messrs Short Bros of Belfast.

The visit was entirely successful. Bryant agreed with Briggs that the 'flying destroyer' was exactly the sort of new weapon that the navy needed, although it would require an engine at least five times more powerful than any so far developed by the British or French. Constructing it would indeed be a plunge into the unknown, but on the principle that 'nothing ventured, nothing gained' was the only appropriate course of action in wartime, it was agreed that they should proceed. 'We settled down to a long technical discussion from which it emerged that in the absence of a more challenging assignment that they could get their teeth into, Brotherhood's would like to have a shot at designing and constructing a much larger 12 cylinder version of my original 6 cylinder design, with its capacity expanded from 15 to 40 litres, and that they were ready to start work at once by building a single-cylinder test unit.'

It was also agreed that Ricardo should stay in Peterborough for a few days to supervise the layout of the new design and provide the data that he had been able to glean from two years' test work on his own experimental single-cylinder unit. Naturally, he was delighted at the prospect of collaborating with this famous engineering firm and making a positive contribution to the war effort. 'At last I could feel justified in being reserved as a key man, and this took a great load off my conscience,' he recalled.

During the next two or three months, Ricardo spent several days a week in Brotherhood's drawing office discussing the design and manufacturing problems of this much-enlarged version of his aero-engine, which reached the outer limits of contemporary engineering know-how and of casting techniques in particular. This area of the engine's construction posed particular problems, so much so that as time went by Ricardo's misgivings deepened as to the viability of the scheme. In those days materials such as low-expansion silicon aluminium alloys and high-expansion austenic iron or steel were simply not available to engine builders. On reflection Ricardo admitted that in embarking on this ambitious project the team was perhaps attempting the impossible.

By the summer of 1915 Brotherhood's had got as far as building and testing the experimental single-cylinder test engine and making trial castings for the full-scale version, activities that provided the young designer with experience that was to prove of great value in the years that followed. But then quite suddenly his work was stopped as abruptly as it had been started, when Bryant received a letter from the Admiralty instructing him to stop all further work on the flying boat project, for reasons that were never fully explained to him. Thus, Ricardo's association with Barrington was ended for a number of years. Similarly his collaboration with Commander Bryant was also halted for the time being.

After the winding up of the flying boat project Ricardo returned once more to his lonely London office. On weekdays he occupied himself with what little there was to do for his grandfather's firm and at weekends he continued with his experiments in his Walton-on-Thames workshops. At nights he continued to work on finishing the writing of his textbook for Blackies, only to hear that, due to a shortage of staff and other difficulties, its publication would be postponed until after the war. 'My four months of activity had done much to restore my spirits and to revive the hope that I might yet have a chance of playing a useful part in the war effort,' he recalled.

Before very long, a second opportunity to establish himself as an aero-engine designer did indeed come his way, though it was to prove no more fruitful and fulfilling than the first. His old friend and fellow internal combustion engine enthusiast Harry Hetherington had volunteered for military service at the outset of the war but on account of his short-sightedness had been classified as unfit for active duties. Instead he had been drafted into the Engine Branch of the Aeronautical Inspection Directorate (AID) of the War Office, an inspectorate that had originally been set up in 1913 after a series of fatal aircraft accidents, and had been given the task of supervising all aeronautical design and construction matters, military and civilian. Based at Farnborough, adjacent to the Royal Aircraft Factory, but with headquarters at Albemarle Street in London, it employed a number of engineers who were destined to go on to achieve great things after the war. Its Inspector of Aeroplanes was Geoffrey de Havilland while its Inspector of Engines was Colonel (later General) R.K. Bagnall-Wilde of the Royal Engineers. Here, Hetherington's duties involved inspecting and analysing captured German aircraft engines and writing technical reports on his observations, a task for which, according to Sir Harry, he was ideally suited.

Among Hetherington's fellow officers in the AID was a young twenty-year-old former flying instructor who, possessing a certain aptitude for engineering, had joined the department at its inception and had risen to become Bagnall-Wilde's second-in-command. This was none other than Captain (later Major) Frank Halford, a remarkable aeronautical engineer and engine designer whose handiwork appears again and again in the annals of British aeronautics, but whose name remains virtually unknown to the public at large.

Ultimately, his manifold achievements – including the Gipsy engine of the de Havilland Moth light aircraft of the 1920s, the Napier Sabre piston engines of the Hawker Tempest and Typhoon fighters of the Second World War, the Goblin engines of the de Havilland Vampire and Venom jet fighters of the Cold War era and finally, of course, the Ghost jet engines of the first de Havilland Comet airliners – stretched through four decades, from the 'stick-and-string' Bristol Boxkite of the early days through to the Bloodhound guided missile of modern times. He left an indelible mark on the British aircraft industry and as we shall see in later chapters, much of his life's work as an engine designer was accomplished either in the employment of, or in close association with, his friend and colleague, Harry Ricardo.

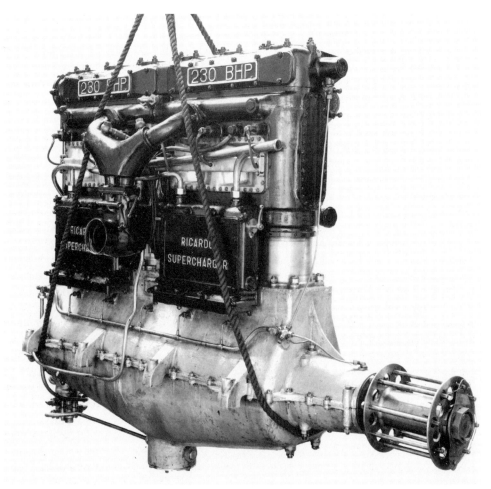

The 230hp Beardmore, Halford, Pullinger aero-engine incorporating Ricardo's ingenious supercharger, photographed at Farnborough, *c.* 1917.

Born in Nottingham in 1894 and educated at Felstead School, Halford set out to study engineering at University College, Nottingham but left the course in his second year without taking a degree. He had caught the flying bug and, having gained his pilot's certificate on a Bristol Boxkite at Brooklands, he immediately joined the Bristol Flying School as an instructor in 1913, at the age of nineteen. At the outbreak of war the following year he enlisted in the Royal Flying Corps and was sent to France with the rank of sergeant, but when his engineering talents were noticed by his superiors he was commissioned and drafted into the AID and posted back to the United Kingdom, where he was then seconded to the engine makers William Beardmore of Glasgow with the task of improving the performance and rate of production of the aero-engine currently being manufactured by that firm. This was a 120hp version of the 90hp, six-cylinder, water-cooled Austro-Daimler unit that Beardmore's had been building under license since 1912.

Halford soon succeeded in raising the output of this engine to 160hp, but as a still more powerful – though no less reliable – engine was urgently needed by the Royal Flying Corps, he was asked to design a suitable unit with an output of at least 200hp based on Beardmore's improved and modified version of the Austro-Daimler motor. The resulting engine (the prototype of which was actually produced by Beardmore's subsidiary Arrol-Johnston) was rated at 230hp and designated the BHP – from the initials of the men chiefly responsible for the project, Sir William Beardmore Bt, Frank Halford and T.C. Pullinger, Beardmore's Chief Engineer. This prototype first flew in August 1916, mounted in the prototype of the DH4 aircraft designed by Geoffrey de Havilland, thus beginning another of Halford's close and enduring aeronautical friendships.

During the winter of 1915–16 Halford continued to improve his BHP design with the aim of raising its output to over 300hp and increasing its high-altitude performance. This had now become a high priority in fighter aircraft design in order to combat the bombing attacks being made on British cities by monster Zeppelin airships which flew at a height of between 16,000 and 20,000 ft, well beyond the reach of existing anti-aircraft guns and fighter aircraft. To achieve this fast climbing ability, some form of supercharging would have to be employed, Halford realised, though this again was an aspect of aero-engine design that had scarcely been investigated at that time.

So it happened that, at Hetherington's suggestion, in the spring of 1916 Halford made his way to Ricardo's Walton-on-Thames workshop to examine Ricardo's proposed 300hp supercharged design, which then existed only on paper, and to witness tests on the related experimental single-cylinder unit. Halford immediately grasped what Ricardo was suggesting and agreed that with a 40 per cent supercharge to supply additional oxygen it would be possible for the BHP engine to propel a fighter aircraft to over 20,000 ft. He also agreed that Ricardo's original aero-engine proposal should never have been rejected by the authorities before the war, as it was sorely needed now.

The ingenious system of 'top-up' supercharging that Ricardo had devised involved using the lower part of the cylinders as an air pump, with a charge of air being drawn in on the upward stroke of a trunk-type cross-head piston through a non-return leaf valve located near the base of the cylinder. This air was then forced by the downstroke through an intercooler, from which it was released to the upper part of the cylinder through ports uncovered by the piston at the bottom of the stroke, to join the carburetted mixture admitted through poppet valves in the usual way and then to be compressed in the combustion chamber by the piston's upward stroke, as is normal. By this means the top-up air could either be utilised as a diluent to reduce fuel consumption at cruising speeds, or as a power boost for high-altitude flying.

Halford's report on this novel technique so impressed Colonel Bagnall-Wilde that Ricardo was immediately briefed to collaborate in the design of a supercharged version of the BHP engine and then to work on the design of an entirely new high-performance engine, similarly supercharged and based on his original proposals which had been turned down by the authorities before the war. This was to be a 14-litre twelve-cylinder engine with cylinders of 110mm bore and 125mm stroke arranged in a narrow upright 45° V, so as to offer minimal frontal area – an important aerodynamic consideration in fast aircraft. Its normal running speed was to be from 2,000 to 2,100rpm, and its compression ratio approximately 5.5:1. Bagnall-Wilde also agreed that to assist Ricardo in this work at his Dartmouth Street office he should have the temporary services of a very competent young draughtsman serving in the AID, Dennis Plunkett.

This event marked the starting point of two important and enduring relationships in Ricardo's life, each one lasting over forty years, for not only did he continue to collaborate with Halford almost constantly until the latter's death in 1955, but he also enjoyed the benefit of Plunkett's abilities for a longer period still. After the war the draughtsman joined his staff on a permanent basis, initially in London and then at Shoreham, remaining there until his retirement in 1963.

Writing in 1985, nine years before his death at the age of ninety-eight, Plunkett recalled their first encounter: 'I was driven from the AID headquarters in a long grey official RFC car driven by a smart girl in uniform to an address near Trafalgar Square where Halford was waiting to present me to a tall good-looking young man in his early thirties. As I remember him then he had a fresh complexion and a clipped fair moustache. As we shook hands, I little knew that he was to be my employer for the rest of my working life. Halford left soon afterwards and we were alone together. He [Ricardo] began at once to explain the nature of his project. I was very nervous, afraid that I might not be able to understand him, but as I listened I realised that he also was nervous. He spoke with a slight stammer but his explanation was lucid and clear and I found to my relief that I could follow him without difficulty.'

Having completed the drawings of the V12 design, Plunkett was recalled to his duties at the AID, and Ricardo was once more left alone in his empty drawing office, for there was nothing more that he could do until Beardmore's were ready to make a start on building the engine. Week followed week and news from the front grew gloomier and gloomier, with the list of the men killed in action filling not just a column in *The Times* but a whole page. Next came news that his Rugby schoolfriend Tony Welsh had been killed within a week of arriving at the front. 'And so the ghastly slaughter went on and on, with no end in sight,' he wrote. 'At both Charing Cross and Victoria stations a seemingly endless succession of hospital trains unloaded the wounded into mile-long queues of ambulances.' His despondency was greatly increased when it became apparent that virtually no progress was being made in producing a prototype of his new engine, although three experimental supercharged examples of the BHP engine rated at 260hp were actually built, one of which was flown at Farnborough in a prototype of the Sopwith Rhino fighter, some time in 1917. By then, of course, Ricardo's attention had been temporarily diverted away from military aircraft engines and pointed in a rather different direction, due to his increasing involvement in the production of a new and quite revolutionary form of land weapon.

Unfortunately, the ever-worsening situation at the Beardmore firm left Ricardo's V12 engine stuck on the shelf once again, until Halford made another bid to revive the project on his behalf. In the spring of 1917, the War Office placed a contract with Armstrongs for the construction of six prototypes of the engine, which was to be known as the RHA – the initials of Ricardo, Halford and Armstrong. But by then it was all too late. According to Sir Harry's account, by the date of the Armistice a couple of engines – their design now well over four years old – had been completed and tested and the remaining four were almost finished; in fact, it is now believed that a total of three examples were built, one of which was actually flown in a de Havilland machine at Farnborough in 1918. The performance of the RHA unit did not disappoint its creator; on its Type Approval test the first engine developed 260hp without supercharge, 300hp when using the supercharge as a diluent and 360hp when making full use of the supercharge at ground level. Nevertheless, the design was axed forthwith, never to be revived. The war was over, the urgency had passed and high-performance aero-engines no longer had top priority on the nation's shopping list.

Despite this setback, however, aircraft engines continued to play an increasingly important part in Ricardo's life. In the autumn of 1917, he had been surprised to receive a letter from his old Cambridge mentor Professor Bertram Hopkinson, who was now Director of the newly formed Department of Military Aeronautics. Hopkinson invited Ricardo to become his part-time deputy, with special responsibility for aero-engine research matters. 'This was a job after my own heart,' said Ricardo in his autobiography, and indeed the post provided him at last with a proper entrée into the world of aero-engine design and manufacture.

Firstly, this was his introduction to most of the greatest personalities and founding fathers of the British aircraft industry in its nascent days, designers and engineers such as Roy Fedden of Bristol and A.J. Rowledge of Napier (and, later, of Rolls-Royce) and, of course, constructors and industrialists such as Geoffrey de Havilland and Ernest Hives (of Rolls-Royce) and, in due course, Sir Henry Royce himself. It also led to his first meeting with another important man who was soon to join the ranks of his collaborators and thus to become perhaps his greatest personal friend outside his immediate inner circle of colleagues and fellow-engineers. This was Henry Tizard, an Oxford scientist then acting as Assistant Controller, Research and Experiments at the Air Ministry, who was destined to exert a profound influence over the development of the internal combustion engine and the formulation of British defence policy over the next two decades. Secondly, the Department of Aeronautics brought him into contact with other influential Whitehall officials who, later, were to be instrumental in awarding him long-term research contracts when he set up in business on his own account. And thirdly, it provided him, as Hopkinson's deputy, with his first involvement in the affairs of the Aeronautical Research

Penstone, Ricardo's Edwardian house at Lancing, where he and his family lived from 1919 to 1933.

Bertram Hopkinson FRS photographed at Farnborough during the First World War while serving as a major in the Royal Engineers, attached to the Department of Military Aeronautics. He was killed in a flying accident in 1918, aged only forty-four.

Committee (1920–45) which had originally been established in 1909 by Lord Haldane as the Advisory Committee on Aeronautics, and on which he was to serve for the greater part of his career.

Since the days of his and Ricardo's collaboration at Cambridge, Bertram Hopkinson had maintained his interest in the science of flame and explosion, serving as a member of various government research and advisory committees and as a consultant to both the army and the Royal Navy. At the outbreak of hostilities, however, he had joined the Royal Engineers with the rank of major and very soon became involved in experimental work on mines and torpedoes for the Admiralty. Later in the war he was transferred to the Department of Military Aeronautics, to conduct research into the design of bombs and bomb-sights for the aircraft of the Royal Flying Corps, and by 1917 he had been promoted to the rank of colonel. In due course, his responsibilities were widened to encompass the testing of complete aircraft, together with their engines, and also their bombs, guns and ammunition. Initially, this aeronautical research was carried out either at Farnborough or at the Central Flying School at Upavon, Wiltshire, but early in 1918, when the Royal Flying Corps was reorganised and reformed as the independent Royal Air Force, the armament experimental activities under his command were transferred to a station at Orfordness, Suffolk, while aircraft flight testing was based at an entirely new aerodrome at Martlesham Heath, Norfolk, built later that year on a site selected by Hopkinson personally.

At Farnborough, Orfordness and Martlesham Heath, Hopkinson gathered around him a team of young scientists who represented the most outstanding talent of their generation. Almost all of them went on to achieve the highest distinction in their respective fields. Popularly known as Hopkinson's Gang, the group included David Pye (later Sir David Pye FRS), Charles Darwin (later Sir Charles Darwin FRS), Frederick Lindemann (later Lord Cherwell FRS), Geoffrey Taylor (later Sir Geoffrey Taylor FRS), Richard Southwell (later

Sir Richard Southwell FRS), William Farren (later Sir William Farren FRS) and, of course, Henry Tizard (later Sir Henry Tizard FRS) of whom we shall hear much more in later chapters. Also, to be his personal assistant, Hopkinson picked Major Aubrey Evans, a former associate of Sir Dugald Clerk, who subsequently also became one of Harry Ricardo's closest friends and colleagues, acting as Chief Experimental Engineer of his Shoreham laboratories for over forty years from 1918 until his death in 1960.

The prospect of joining this distinguished scientific band in a renewed partnership with his erstwhile professor delighted Ricardo. But, sadly, their revived association lasted for less than a year. While based at Orfordness, Hopkinson had learned to fly and had become a skilled and enthusiastic pilot. His extensive responsibilities covered a wide variety of research spread out over many different locations, so he regarded flying as not only a highly enjoyable activity in itself but also as the best means of transport between the numerous aerodromes that he had to visit in the course of his duties. It was on one of these solo flights between Martlesham Heath and Farnborough in August 1918 that he ran into bad weather over London and lost control of his aircraft while descending through low cloud to establish his position. Attempting to make a forced landing from too low an altitude, he crashed into the ground and was killed instantaneously.

It was said that only those who knew something of the secret work that he had undertaken during the First World War could truly appreciate the magnitude of the nation's loss. At the time of his death, plans were afoot for the establishment of a national school of aeronautical engineering, of which he was to have been the head. In this capacity, he would have been responsible for organising, directing and overseeing all aircraft-related scientific research in the United Kingdom, a role for which he was uniquely well qualified by virtue of his ability to encourage and foster close cooperation among his colleagues, and to arbitrate between the abstract preoccupations of scientists and the tangible realities and priorities of fighting men. Had he lived to take up the post, the course of British military history might well have taken a quite different turn during the 1920s and with it the path of Ricardo's own career.

Certainly, Hopkinson's demise had considerable repercussions on the future combat fitness of the Royal Air Force. Writing of Hopkinson's death in his unpublished autobiography, Sir Henry Tizard said that 'in his position, and with his knowledge and character, he would have had a great influence on Government policy between the wars. I would go so far as to say that the chance of a second world war breaking out would have been greatly lessened.' At first sight this claim may seem extravagant, but in the light of the unhappy record of military scientific research in the late twenties and early thirties, Tizard's views (which Ricardo undoubtedly shared) may well have been fully justified.

In 1910, Hopkinson had been elected a Fellow of the Royal Society. Speaking as Master of Trinity in a Commemorative Sermon at the College, the President of the Royal Society, the eminent physicist and Nobel prizewinner J.J. Thomson OM, Cavendish Professor of Experimental Physics and founder of the Cavendish research laboratory, said of him: 'Our Roll of Honour contains the name of no one who has rendered greater services to his country.'

CHAPTER 12

Formation of the Ricardo Firm

A t the outbreak of the First World War in August 1914, Sir Alexander Rendel had been forced to postpone his plans for retirement in order to assist his partners Frederick Palmer and Seymour Tritton in the day-to-day running of their civil engineering firm. The workload must have been heavy, for in addition to its normal activities on behalf of the India Office, the partnership had been appointed consultants to the War Office and the Ministry of Munitions. During the First World War, Rendel, Palmer & Tritton was solely responsible for the design, procurement and supply of the locomotives, rolling stock and other railway materials employed on all the fighting fronts. These responsibilities, which involved supervising the laying of 9,000 miles of track and inspecting the working of 3,400 locomotives and 72,000 wagons, many of which were requisitioned from the main line railway companies, became all the more demanding when Palmer was called upon to resume his former post as Chief Engineer to the Port of London, a vital wartime function, leaving Tritton and old Sir Alexander together at the head of a skeleton staff.

In January 1918, at the age of eighty-nine, Sir Alexander died in his sleep, ostensibly as a result of a cold which had turned into pneumonia, but in all probability from the exhaustion produced by a lifetime of overwork and from the very great loneliness that he had suffered in his declining years, following the death of his beloved wife Leila in 1916. Both Rickettswood and 23 Russell Square were very soon sold, a decision that resulted in the complete disintegration of the close-knit family network, known as the Rendel Connection, over which Sir Alexander had presided for half a century. After his demise things were never again quite what they had been, either in the firm or in the family.

The slow decline and eventual death of his grandfather brought home to Harry Ricardo the fact that he had arrived at a watershed in his life and that, in all fairness to Palmer and Tritton, he ought to make up his mind as to what he intended to do when the war was over. The offer of a partnership in the firm remained open to him, but by this time he had fallen so deeply in love with the internal combustion engine that he could not bear the thought of parting from it. However, it was hard to see how the engine research activities in which he had by now become so deeply immersed could ever be combined with the normal business of a civil engineering practice, and although he was indeed a fully qualified civil engineer, in reality he knew little or nothing about the work. 'I could not see how, as a partner, I could ever take a useful part in the principal affairs of the firm,' he confessed. Moreover, his appetite for engine research work had been whetted by the investigations he had carried out in his garden workshop at Walton-on-Thames and by the recognition that his efforts were beginning to earn in official circles. 'My head had been turned by this praise,' he admitted.

However, it seems that well before the outbreak of war, the young Ricardo had already made up his mind about the future course of his career and had begun to take steps to bring his long-cherished ambitions into being. Ever since his association with Professor Hopkinson at Cambridge some twelve years earlier, his mind had returned again and again to the idea of establishing a laboratory of his own in which to carry out engine research, design and development work on behalf of industry. When discussing his ambition with the chief engineers of a number of leading engine manufacturers – men such as Windeler, Chorlton, Bryant and Kidner – he had been assured that such an establishment was sorely needed and would have their full backing and support. Indeed, it was apparent that if he was successful in establishing such an enterprise, he could count on such well-known firms as Peter Brotherhood, Crossley Brothers, Mirrlees, Bickerton & Day and Vauxhall Motors to retain him as a consultant. Ricardo had even gone so far as to mention his dream to his closest friends, Hetherington and Thornycroft, and both had indicated unequivocally that they

Alan Archibald Campbell-Swinton FRS (1863–1930) scientist, inventor, photographer and pioneer of television. He was the first Chairman of Ricardo's company.

would be delighted to join him in such a venture, providing he could find suitable premises and sufficient working capital to ensure the long-term viability of the scheme.

In 1913, to help fund the work that he was undertaking in his workshops at Walton-on-Thames, he had been able to arrange some temporary financial support from a small syndicate of investors and bankers. Known as Ricardo Developments, the syndicate's members included Harry Hetherington, Campbell Farrar (the solicitor who had earlier been involved in the Dolphin venture) and Frederick Goodenough, better known in financial circles as the first Chairman of Barclays Bank. But evidently by the following year moves were afoot for the syndicate to be re-formed as a small private company having a capital of 2,000 ordinary £1 shares, launched with the aim of exploiting the patentable ideas that were emerging from Ricardo's shed at Walton-on-Thames, and with the intention of raising sufficient funds to enable him to carry on with his work without hindrance. In fact, a draft prospectus for this company, to be known as Internal Combustion Engines Ltd was prepared but not issued by Campbell Farrar at some point during 1914. Moreover, the prospectus declared that 'the well-known engineer Mr Alan Archibald Campbell-Swinton has consented to be a director of the company and to invest money in it, having examined the drawings and specifications of a new four-stroke engine suitable for aeronautical purposes that Ricardo had recently invented, and also having discussed the matter with one of the greatest authorities on the subject.' This man, of course, was Sir Dugald Clerk.

Just a few months previously Sir Dugald had invited Ricardo to the Athenaeum Club to meet his friend Campbell-Swinton. During lunch the trio had talked about the lack of independent research facilities in the United Kingdom, and in the course of the conversation, Ricardo had been greatly encouraged to hear Campbell-Swinton declare that it would be much more difficult to find the right man to run such an establishment than to find the necessary finance.

In his autobiography Sir Harry explained that Clerk had prepared the ground by telling him that Campbell-Swinton was a very distinguished consulting electrical engineer who had done much important pioneering work in the field of wireless telegraphy and who had become the leading authority on radio communications and radiography in Great Britain. Actually, although Sir Harry did not mention the fact, for many years Campbell-Swinton had also been a close friend of the Rendel clan and a frequent guest at Rickettswood. In his capacity as an electrical engineer and contractor he had been responsible for installing electric lighting systems in many country mansions, including those belonging to Sir Alexander and Lord Stuart Rendel, and thus Sir Harry must surely have often met him as a boy. Campbell-Swinton was also something of an entrepreneur and venture capitalist who made a hobby of financing promising young inventors, and it was he who had taken the young Guglielmo Marconi under his wing on the Italian's arrival in the UK in 1896, introducing him to the Chief Engineer of the Post Office, Sir William Preece, who was then known to be on the lookout for an effective system of wireless telegraphy. With a wide circle of friends in the worlds of banking and business who relied on his sound judgement when evaluating the prospects of the many novel industrial and technical proposals being put before them, Campbell-Swinton was particularly adept in bringing inventors and investors together, Sir Dugald Clerk opined.

In truth, Alan Archibald Campbell-Swinton (elected a Fellow of the Royal Society in 1915) was a most remarkable man. Born in Edinburgh in 1863 he came from an ancient and well-connected lowland Scottish family, that could trace its descent back directly for more than 1,000 years to well before the Norman Conquest. The house in which he grew up, the family seat at Kimmerghame near Duns in Berwickshire, was a substantial country mansion built in 1851 in the Scottish baronial style, but Campbell-Swinton preferred to reside in London, at his magnificent house in Belgravia, 40 Chester Square, where he lived a splendid bachelor existence, attended by a butler. In the basement of this house he had installed his own electrical laboratory where he conducted research into the technology of wireless telegraphy and even television, of which he was the true progenitor. In 1904, while investigating the feasibility of a system of 'distant electronic vision' based entirely on electronic principles he conducted a number of experiments involving a home-made oscillograph which anticipated the use of the cathode ray tube as an image-display device. Unfortunately, as he failed to publish any account of these experiments at the time, he was denied the credit for having conceived the principles of television, which is generally held to have been invented and patented by John Logie Baird some twenty years later, in 1923.

Although he was entirely self-taught and had never passed, or attempted to pass, a single examination of any kind, Swinton's experimental work came to the notice of all the great men of science and industry at that time, many of whom also became his close personal friends. In Ricardo's eyes he seemed to be acquainted with, or even to be related to, all the people in London worth knowing. In fact, Campbell-Swinton had arrived at his enviable position not by nepotism but through his own unaided efforts, having begun his career in 1882 as an engineering apprentice at William Armstrong's Elswick shipyards, just like a number of Sir Harry's Rendel uncles. However, his interests had always lain in electrical rather than mechanical engineering, and while at Armstrong's he had specialised in applying electricity to naval architecture, for example by introducing electric lighting into the Fleet and by devising electrically powered gunnery control systems which enabled a warship's turrets to fire salvos simultaneously. At Elswick, Campbell-Swinton had become very friendly with another apprentice from an upper-class background, the Hon. Charles Parsons, the inventor of the steam turbine, so that when the Parsons Marine Steam Turbine Company was formed in 1894 to build the world's first steam-turbine-powered vessel, the *Turbinia*, he became a founder-director and major investor.

According to Ricardo's account (and he was certainly no stranger to affluence) Campbell-Swinton was a very wealthy man, his income deriving partly from his fees as a consultant to and director of many important companies, and partly from his acumen as a financier. Besides being a talented amateur photographer – in 1896 he took the first X-ray picture of the human anatomy to be made and published in Great Britain – he was also a pioneer motorist; as a director of the French Delahaye company he owned several examples of that make from 1908 onwards.

So it happened that, at some point towards the end of 1914, Campbell-Swinton invited Harry Ricardo to call on him at his offices located at 66 Victoria Street, Westminster, to discuss in detail the young engineer's plans for the future and to consider how his scheme to establish an independent research laboratory for the long-range study of the internal combustion engine and its fuels and lubricants might best be brought about. Despite the large gap in their ages – Ricardo was now twenty-nine while Campbell-Swinton was fifty-one – the two men had much in common besides their respective connections with the Rendels and they hit it off immediately. Indeed they were on the same wavelength. Both could be described unkindly as being typical representatives of that peculiarly British tradition of eccentric amateurism so reviled today. Yet though they may well have worn the Norfolk jackets and knickerbockers customary among Edwardians of their class, neither could be accused of being dilettantes, casual and uncommitted in their attitude to science. On the contrary, both were thoroughly competent and disciplined experimentalists who by dint of their insatiable curiosity and inexhaustible perseverance achieved discoveries that would probably have escaped the purely professional investigator, motivated by mercenary considerations rather than by sheer enthusiasm. In Ricardo's vocabulary the words amateur and enthusiast had no pejorative connotation; he was himself an amateur in the true and original sense of the word in that everything he did was done purely out of the love of it.

At that point in time, Ricardo had not yet become involved in the military engineering projects that would make his reputation and not one of his various engine designs had reached the point of being taken up for production by a commercial manufacturer. Nevertheless, Campbell-Swinton was evidently impressed by the young man's potential. Believing that Ricardo had a vital contribution to make to the advancement of the internal combustion engine and that he had the sheer determination and enthusiasm to see his ambitions through, the eminent electrical engineer agreed to talk things over with those of his friends, associates and fellow capitalists who might be interested in investing in the venture.

Campbell-Swinton was in the habit of photographing the guests who dined at his house in Chester Square, Belgravia. This group included Swinton (front row, third from left) and Harry Ricardo (front row, second from left) but, unfortunately, the identity of the others present is unknown.

There followed over the next few months a series of what Sir Harry described as 'select little dinner parties' held at Chester Square, at which he was presented to the leading members of Campbell-Swinton's circle, including Stuart de la Rue, Chairman of the famous firm of printers (and, later, Chairman of Bentley Motors Ltd), Frederick Goodenough, the leading light of Barclays Bank, Sir Eustace Tennyson d'Eyncourt, the Director of Naval Construction at the Admiralty, and Viscount Combermere, an officer currently serving in the Royal Artillery but whose ancestor, the first Viscount, had commanded the British cavalry under Wellington in the Napoleonic Wars with the rank of field marshal. Sir Harry observed that although the economies imposed by wartime food rationing greatly restricted the menu that Campbell-Swinton was able to offer his guests, these limitations were not permitted to affect the general opulence and elegance of his style of entertaining. Apparently, the Scotsman still clung to the Victorian splendour of his table with its superb silver and glassware, while a seemingly endless succession of dishes was served by his immaculate butler.

As Sir Harry put it, it was over the nuts and port at these dinner parties that his firm came into being, for in due course Campbell-Swinton's hospitality at Chester Square led to the establishment of Engine Patents Ltd, the precursor of Ricardo Consulting

Engineers Ltd. A private company with an issued share capital of £3,150, Engine Patents Ltd was incorporated on 8 February 1915 and registered on 10 August 1915. Although its objectives as set down in its articles of association were exceedingly wide-ranging (including the manufacture, assembly and repair of vehicles), its essential purpose was to provide the finance and facilities that would enable Ricardo to continue with his internal combustion engine design, research and development work unimpeded. The original directors were Campbell-Swinton (who acted as Chairman), Harry Ricardo (who was Technical Director), Campbell Farrar (who was appointed Managing Director and Company Secretary) and three others – Stuart de la Rue, Bertram Beale and R.H. Houston – all of whom were friends of either Farrar or Campbell-Swinton and were prepared to take shares in the new venture. Lord Combermere, who eventually served as a director from 1920 to 1962 was also one of the original investors. He was another of Campbell-Swinton's friends with engineering interests, having served a premium apprenticeship with him at Armstrong's shipyards. In August 1917, Harry Hetherington also joined the board, having been released from his duties at Farnborough. The company's anonymous-sounding name was chosen on the advice of Campbell-Swinton, who reasoned that, in the event of the venture proving unsuccessful, by not being directly associated with the company by name, Harry Ricardo would be free to start again without the disadvantage of having been associated with a failure.

Due to the uncertain military situation prevailing in 1915, when the full, horrific extent of the struggle being fought out in the mud of Flanders became apparent to the civilian population at home, the new company got off to a slow start, a situation that only served to aggravate Ricardo's sense of frustration and despair. Although licensing arrangements were negotiated that year with a number of major companies including Rolls-Royce and Armstrong-Siddeley, the plan to set up laboratory facilities was put on ice and for the time being the activities of the new company were centred on his workshops at Walton-on-Thames, where a small technical staff was now employed, and also on the offices of Campbell-Swinton's firm at 66 Victoria Street, London, where its administrative personnel were based; its first board meetings were held there that same year.

But within the next two years, the situation changed completely. Largely as a result of Ricardo's increasing aero-engine design responsibilities on behalf of the Air Ministry, and also his involvement with the Ministry of Munitions in the design and manufacture of the new engine ordered for the Mk V tank (a task that got under way in the autumn of 1916), by early 1917 his personal reputation and prospects had been transformed, and with it those of his firm. Indeed, in December 1916 he had reported to the board that orders for 600 tank engines had been placed by the Ministry of Munitions, with a probable further order for 300 more in the offing, all producing for Engine Patents Ltd a royalty income of 4 per cent of the manufacturer's selling price.

As a result of this increase in activities, suitable premises to house its ever-expanding drawing office and administrative departments had shortly to be found for the firm. This London office (which was occupied by Engine Patents Ltd and its successors for nearly forty years) was located at 21 Suffolk Street, Westminster, a little cul-de-sac leading off Pall Mall East near its junction with Trafalgar Square. The first board meeting to be held there took place in June 1917.

Throughout the earlier part of the First World War, Harry Ricardo remained in the employment of his grandfather's firm and on its payroll, although his services were loaned out to the military authorities – initially the Air Ministry and later the Ministry of Munitions – on a roving commission with no clearly defined position in regard to either. He considered this to be an admirable situation since, as a civilian he was free to criticise or even abuse his uniformed superiors without risk of court martial, nor could he be sacked from a position that officially did not exist.

Despite his increasingly tenuous connection with the family firm, however, he continued to keep Tritton and Palmer informed of his plans, and of the steps being taken towards the formation of Engine Patents Ltd. Both expressed the view that they would be very sorry to see him go and generously offered to keep open for him for a further two years the partnership that would inevitably become vacant on the death of Sir Alexander, in case the new enterprise failed and he wanted to return to them. For a young married man with a family to support, the thought that he had not burnt his boats entirely, and that if things went badly he could always resume his connection with the prosperous and long-established Rendel firm, must have been greatly reassuring.

Nevertheless, there was to be no turning back. In February 1917, almost a year before the death of Sir Alexander Rendel, Harry Ricardo formally tendered his resignation and left the employment of the family partnership, to join Engine Patents Ltd on a full-time basis, although continuing with his governmental work. Ricardo was agreeably surprised to find that his salary, which during his ten years' service with Rendel, Palmer & Tritton had risen from £150 to £400 per annum, but which currently was being defrayed by the Ministry of Munitions, was to be fixed at £2,000 per annum (approximately £50,000 in today's money), backdated to October 1916 in line with the heavy official responsibilities that he was now undertaking and, indeed, had been shouldering for some months past. 'I temporarily became a relatively wealthy man,' Ricardo recalled in his autobiography. 'In other circumstances I should have been blissfully happy, but over all hung the continuing ghastly nightmare of the war.'

Even so, there was still no go-ahead from the board on the question of building the laboratories and Ricardo had come to the reluctant conclusion that the matter would have to wait until after the end of the war, which was nowhere in sight. Not until his principal potential technical collaborators, Hetherington, Thornycroft, Halford and Evans, all of them serving officers, had been released from their military duties would there be any point in taking active steps in that direction. But then, quite out of the blue, an event took place that transformed the hitherto cautious attitude of the other directors, who had been inclined to wait for a successful outcome to the tank engine project before sanctioning further investment.

Sometime during the spring of 1917, following the events just described, Ricardo was asked to attend a high-level Whitehall committee whose purpose was to allocate the supply of petroleum fuel among the various services. Most of the members of this committee were high-ranking naval and military officers and strangers to Ricardo, but the chairman was a civilian. This 'huge and formidable-looking fellow' as Ricardo described him was none other than Sir Robert Waley-Cohen, the Managing Director of the Anglo-Dutch Shell Oil Company.

In the course of this meeting Ricardo pleaded that the new 150hp engines that he was producing for the Mk V tank (currently being built in large numbers and due to go into action in the offensive planned for the autumn) should be fuelled with a higher quality of petrol than the low-octane gasoline earmarked for the purpose; the policy in force at that time was that the best quality petrol was reserved for aviation purposes, the next best for

Sir Robert Waley-Cohen, the Managing Director of the Anglo-Dutch Shell Oil Company in 1918. His service as a director and, later, chairman of the multi-national conglomerate extended for over forty years, from its foundation in 1911 until his retirement in 1950.

staff cars and the lowest grade for tractors and heavy transport lorries – the category of vehicle in which the tanks were included. When this suggestion was refused, he asked that benzole should be considered as an alternative, but the rest of the committee threw up their hands in horror at the idea, saying that his proposal was quite out of the question since benzole was ruled out as an acceptable fuel for petrol engines, due to its high specific gravity. Ricardo replied that benzole was preferable to kerosene because it was less inclined to detonate, which meant that he would be able to raise the compression ratio of his engine and therefore realise a considerable gain in power and economy, thus improving the radius of action of the tanks. But the brass hats would have none of it. Ricardo remembered that he came away from that meeting feeling utterly defeated by his brush with the authorities, but just as he was about to leave the building the Chairman took him aside and asked, 'What's all that stuff about benzole and detonation. I would like to hear more about it!'

A few days later he received a letter from Sir Robert inviting him to dine with him at his home at Highgate. There the Shell mogul examined him closely about his knowledge of petroleum fuels and listened to his account of the experiments that he had carried out before the war, which had convinced Ricardo that it was the incidence of detonation that governed the highest useful compression ratio of an engine and therefore its power and efficiency. Ricardo reiterated his conclusion that detonation was a phenomenon quite distinct from pre-ignition, and that it was dependent on the chemical composition of the fuel, and went on to explain how he had developed a single-cylinder, variable-compression engine which could serve as a knock-rating test unit. Using this apparatus he had already tested small samples of paraffins, naphthenes and aromatics in his workshop at Walton-on-Thames during the course of 1913 and had found that, so far as the tendency to detonate was concerned, the paraffins were by far the worst offenders and the aromatics the best of all. Sir Robert ended the discussion by saying that he would very much like to send Ricardo some samples of petrol from the company's various oil-

Harry Ricardo, aged about thirty-five, in the twenties, shortly after the formation of his firm.

fields for evaluation in terms of their tendency to detonate, and that he would also like his Chief Chemist, Mr Kewley, to witness these tests.

Not long after this meeting, about half a dozen five-gallon drums of petrol from the Shell Haven refinery arrived on Ricardo's doorstep at Walton-on-Thames, each marked with an identifying number. In most cases Ricardo detected no significant difference in the tendency to detonate between individual samples, but one alone stood out as being far and away the best. Indeed, as it produced a 20 per cent greater power output from the test engine, its performance resembled that of benzole. Thinking that perhaps some of the latter fuel had accidentally found its way into one of the petrol drums, Ricardo had a fresh supply sent from Shell Haven, but the result remained the same. In the meanwhile Kewley had examined a sample from the errant drum in his laboratory at

Fulham and had discovered that its specific gravity was much greater than that of the other samples. His analysis revealed that this particular fuel contained an exceptionally large proportion of aromatics, which accounted both for its good performance and its high specific gravity.

On reporting their findings to Sir Robert, the researchers were told that the sample in question came from Shell's large oilfield in Borneo where thousands of tons of the fuel were presently being burned off as waste in the jungle, merely because, like benzole, its specific gravity was too high to meet any current specification. In other words, although in the present state of knowledge this heavy spirit was considered to be of an inferior quality, it was in fact far more efficient than other, lighter motor spirits and therefore worth a higher price.

Ricardo had made a startling discovery! Without further delay, Sir Robert cabled to Borneo to stop the wastage and to arrange for the aromatic-rich oil to be transported to England to be refined and blended with petrols from other sources, and thus to improve the quality of Shell's product – and profits – as a whole. As Sir Harry put it, 'Thus began my long and happy association with the Shell Company.' Very shortly after this discovery, Sir Robert approached Ricardo's fellow directors and promised that Shell was prepared to support the fledgling Engine Patents company by spending up to £10,000 per annum for a period of three years on a programme of fundamental research into the problem of matching fuels to the differing needs of engines, and also on the design of the specialist stationary engines that were becoming increasingly essential to the petroleum industry for laboratory research, for exploration and for drilling wells and pumping oil.

This was indeed a generous offer and on the strength of it Campbell-Swinton organised another dinner party, this time to discuss not whether but when and how to get going with the enterprise. Consequently, at an extraordinary general meeting held on 18 September 1917, the company's share capital was increased to £10,150 by the creation of 7,000 additional ordinary shares. The purpose of this extra finance, of course, was to build and equip the long-sought-after laboratory, and to acquire the plot of land lying on the west bank of the River Adur at Old Shoreham, West Sussex, on which this building, named Bridge Works, was to be constructed to a design commissioned from Halsey Ricardo. Sir Harry later confessed that this was the very plot of land that he had had his sights on for many years. At the time of the Dolphin venture some ten years earlier he and his cousin Ralph had fondly imagined that it would one day become the site of a great car factory, turning out his designs by the thousand.

Two years later, Ricardo's collaboration with Shell's Chief Chemist Kewley in investigating the properties of the company's Borneo fuel produced an interesting and important sequel. Following their discovery in 1917 of the high anti-knock value of this petrol, it occurred to both men that with further refining by the fractional distillation process it might be possible to produce a highly aromatic super-quality aviation fuel for special purposes such as long-range flights. Their experiments bore fruit and when samples were tested on the Walton engine the results were exactly as predicted. Samples were also sent to Farnborough and to Rolls-Royce at Derby, where it was concluded that by using the new fuel the compression ratio of the Rolls-Royce Eagle engine could safely be raised from 5:1 to 6:1, thereby gaining about 10 per cent in power output and about 12–15 per cent in fuel economy at the normal cruising speed. Unfortunately, at that time it was simply not possible to produce enough of this special fuel for general use by the Royal Air Force during the remaining months of the war.

Alcock and Brown of the RAF with the Vickers Vimy bomber in which they made the first non-stop transatlantic flight in June 1919. The special high-octane fuel they used was produced as a direct result of Ricardo's experiments for Shell.

However, shortly following the Armistice Ricardo and Kewley had a visit from two airmen, John Alcock and Arthur Whitten-Brown of the RAF, who were planning to attempt a crossing of the Atlantic in a Vickers-Vimy bomber, powered by two Rolls-Royce Eagle engines. In Ricardo's own words,

> They had heard of this special fuel and wanted to know more about it and what, if any, were the objections to its use. We told them that we knew of none, except its scarcity, and demonstrated on my little supercharging engine the improvement both in power and fuel consumption that might reasonably be expected. They said that even a small increase in power or fuel economy might make all the difference between success and failure for their enterprise, for it was touch and go whether they could take off with enough fuel for the crossing. Kewley said that now that the war was over and that he and his colleagues were once again in touch with Shell's large laboratory and refinery in Holland, he felt sure that his company could provide enough for both preliminary test flights and for the crossing itself. As all the world knows, these two brave men accomplished the first direct crossing of the Atlantic by aeroplane in June 1919.

Their flight from Newfoundland to Ireland took 16 hours and 27 minutes, and when they landed there was scarcely enough fuel in their tanks for a further mile of flight.

CHAPTER 13

The Engines of War

Ever since the American-born inventor Sir Hiram Maxim had perfected his fully automatic, quick-firing machine-gun in 1884, the more perceptive among military commentators had prophesied that his invention would change the face of infantry warfare. Capable of delivering a withering hail of shot that would mow down all advancing troops within view (it could fire ten rounds per second with considerable accuracy over a range of more than a mile), it was soon recognised as the ideal defensive weapon and adopted by the British Army (as the Vickers gun) in 1889, and by the Germans (as the Spandau) shortly after that. When it went into action for the first time in a major war, in Flanders during the autumn of 1914, its impact was decisive. For although its use had long been anticipated, by the outbreak of the First World War no one had as yet devised a satisfactory countermeasure to protect attacking troops advancing through barbed-wire barricades within its wide field of fire. Prior to any assault, therefore, the British Army continued to rely on a devastating artillery barrage to suppress enemy defences, thus obviating all chance of taking the Germans by surprise. What was required was a weapon with the firepower of artillery, the mobility of cavalry and the ability of the infantry to advance through machine-gun fire to capture ground and hold it against counter-attack.

This wonder-weapon, when it came, arrived from a most unlikely quarter, for it was the Admiralty rather than the War Office that championed the development of the mobile pill-box, crawling on caterpillar tracks and powered by an internal combustion engine, that we recognise today as the tank. Its progenitor, however, was most certainly a military man – the soldier, engineer, writer, author and Oxford academic Major General Sir Ernest Dunlop Swinton KBE, CB, DSO, the father of the Tank Corps. Acknowledged by military historians to have been the first serving soldier to advocate armoured vehicles and to devise appropriate tactics for their use on the battlefield, Swinton was, of course, a distant cousin of Alan Archibald Campbell-Swinton, a founder-director of Ricardo's company.

Born in October 1868 at Bangalore in Mysore, India, where his father was a judge in the Madras Civil Service, he was educated at the Royal Military Academy, Woolwich, and the School of Military Engineering, Chatham, and was commissioned in the Royal Engineers in 1888. On the outbreak of the Boer War in 1899, however, he was posted to South Africa where he commanded the 1st Railway Pioneer Regiment. Here he began to write a popular series of manuals of military tactics and stories about future warfare, which he published under the pseudonym 'Ole-Luk-Oie'. By 1913, he had been promoted to the position of Assistant Secretary of the Committee of Imperial Defence, holding the rank of major.

At the outbreak of war in 1914, Swinton was appointed Deputy Director of Railway Transport, but at the request of the Minister of War, Lord Kitchener, he was soon diverted from this task and on the strength of his literary talents he was sent to France to act as a

Major-General Sir Ernest Swinton, the father of the tank
and the first commander of the Tank Corps. He was a
distant relation of Alan Archibald Campbell-Swinton.

roving correspondent with the British Expeditionary Force. For the first few months of the First World War, tight censorship was imposed on the press and civilian newspaper reporters were banned from visiting the front line to witness the squalor and slaughter of trench warfare. Thus it fell to officers such as Swinton to act as official correspondents and his dispatches were regularly printed by British and Commonwealth daily newspapers under the pen-name Eyewitness.

Observing the horrific situation on the Western Front at the battle of the Aisne in September 1914, where a futile stalemate was killing men at the rate of 1,000 a day, he conceived the idea of a break-through mounted by armoured vehicles based on an adaptation of the Holt caterpillar-tracked agricultural tractor, an American machine that was then being used by the British Army for towing heavy guns. Inspired by a prophetic story written by H.G. Wells, these Land Ironclads would be, 'immune against bullets, capable of destroying machine guns and of climbing over obstacles and ploughing a way through barbed wire,' Swinton envisaged.

As is well known, when first presented with Swinton's ideas the military authorities were unimpressed; doubtless they abominated the thought that a mere sapper might have found the answer to the slaughter. The General Staff of the army was then dominated by cavalrymen, all of whom must surely have abhorred the notion that the dashing spectacle of the traditional 'death or glory' cavalry charge might soon be rendered redundant by the lumbering attack of Swinton's 'mechanical toys' as Lord Kitchener described them. But eventually the memorandum on 'The Necessity for Machine Gun Destroyers' that Swinton had submitted to the High Command in France came to the attention of Winston Churchill, then First Lord of the Admiralty, who had already begun to examine the matter of 'Landships' independently of the War Office.

Churchill was no respecter of inter-service jealousies and rivalries; although his responsibilities were entirely naval, he took a close interest in the development of mechanised land warfare and on learning of Swinton's idea he had no hesitation in authorising the use of £70,000 of Admiralty funds for the development of what was essentially a weapon for use on land rather than at sea.

Indeed, almost from the very outset of the war, Churchill had encouraged the Director of the Air Department of the Admiralty, Commodore Murray Sueter RN (later Rear

Admiral Sir Murray Sueter MP), to begin mechanised, land-based operations in France, using armoured cars manned by personnel of the Royal Naval Air Service to protect airfields and rescue downed pilots. Numerous RNAS squadrons were formed for this purpose, equipped with the famous vehicle armed with a heavy machine-gun turret mounted on a Rolls-Royce Silver Ghost chassis.

In addition, under Churchill's instigation and patronage, the RNAS also maintained a number of independent research and development units. Staffed by civilian technical volunteers and commanded by naval engineering officers, these squadrons were concerned with experimental work in various fields such as observation balloons and airships, long-range maritime patrol aircraft, anti-submarine devices and, of course, armoured fighting vehicles. This latter area was the responsibility of 20 Squadron RNAS, part of the RNAS Armoured Car Division. Commanded by Major T. Gerard Hetherington (actually a regular cavalry officer on secondment), it was based in London at the Talbot proving ground near Acton. Ricardo described this unit as 'a more or less lawless and independent group having a singularly inappropriate title since it had nothing whatever to do with either the sea or the air'.

To promote and progress the concept of armoured fighting vehicles, in February 1915 Churchill established the so-called Admiralty Landships Committee specifically to investigate the technical problems of armoured vehicle development, under the chairmanship of Sir Eustace Tennyson d'Eyncourt, Director of Naval Construction. A distinguished naval architect, Tennyson d'Eyncourt was later noted as the designer of the battleships *Royal Sovereign*, *Nelson* and *Rodney* and the battle-cruiser *Hood*. Other members of this committee included two men from 20 Squadron RNAS, Lieutenant Walter Gordon Wilson RN (later Major W.G. Wilson, Chief Engineer of the Mechanical War Department of the War Office) a leading expert in gearboxes and transmissions and the inventor of the Wilson epicyclic gearbox, and Lieutenant A.G. Stern RNVR, who acted as Secretary. An outstandingly energetic and enterprising personality, Lieutenant Albert Stern (later Colonel Sir Albert Stern) hailed from a wealthy merchant banking family and was actually a millionaire financier in his own right.

As a regular army officer still engaged on his reporting duties in France, Swinton played no part in the proceedings of the Landships Committee which was a naval body, but in July 1915, he returned to London to assume the position of Assistant Secretary to the Committee of Imperial Defence at the War Office and, later, Assistant Secretary to the War Cabinet under Sir Maurice Hankey, in which capacity he was well placed to follow up his memorandum and provide fresh impetus to the project.

In May 1915, when Asquith's Conservative administration was replaced by a coalition government, Churchill left the Admiralty and his position as First Sea Lord was assumed by Arthur Balfour. Fortunately, Churchill's successor also took a sympathetic interest in Swinton's proposals and preserved the experimental unit 20 Squadron RNAS which the Admiralty wanted to disband. Indeed Swinton's ideas continued to find favour in the highest political (if not military) circles and attracted powerful backing in the person of David Lloyd George, the new Minister of Munitions.

Immediately on taking over at the Ministry of Munitions, Lloyd George instructed Swinton to prepare a full report and engineering feasibility study for the construction of an armoured vehicle. To disguise the nature of this secret project, in his report Swinton referred to his brainchild as a mobile tank for carrying supplies of water to front line troops. By the end of July 1915, a contract had been placed with the agricultural engineers William Foster & Sons of Lincoln, and three months later the first prototype, an 18-ton vehicle christened Little Willie, emerged from its workshops, the creation of Foster's Managing Director William Tritton and Lieutenant William Gordon Wilson of the RNAS. Unfortunately, as its name might suggest, this version was found to be quite inadequate for carrying out the basic tasks set out in Swinton's specification, which were; to climb a 5-ft parapet, cross an 8-ft trench, flatten barbed-wire entanglements and to travel at 4mph across rough terrain while shooting at machine-gun nests and pillboxes with its own light quick-firing gun and auxiliary machine-guns.

Consequently, Fosters were asked to proceed with a larger and heavier prototype called Big Willie, also based on the engine and transmission of the Foster-Daimler agricultural tractor, but with two 6-pounder quick-firing Hotchkiss guns fitted in sponsons on either side. Also known as Mother, this second prototype – the forerunner of the first production Mk I tanks, with which it shared its familiar rhomboid silhouette – was demonstrated successfully before Lord Kitchener and members of the Army Council, the Admiralty and the Cabinet on Saturday 29 January 1916 at the Marquess of Salisbury's estate at Hatfield Park. One week later the demonstration was repeated in front of King George V, who expressed his great satisfaction at the abilities of this new, potentially all-conquering machine. In fact, this debut was considered such a triumph that a production contract for an initial experimental batch of fifty tanks was immediately agreed, some to be built by Fosters at Lincoln and others by the Metropolitan Carriage and Wagon Works at Birmingham.

A few days later, on 11 February 1916, a new body, the Tank Supply Committee, was formed to take over the work of the Landships Committee. Reporting to the Ministry of Munitions rather than the Admiralty, this committee included most of the original group of tank enthusiasts and advocates including Swinton and Tennyson d'Eyncourt, who served as a consultant, though Albert Stern now held the position of Chairman with the rank of colonel, all the officers and men of 20 Squadron RNAS having been transferred to army service. Officially, the tank was now army property, under the custodianship of the Inventions Department of the Ministry of Munitions.

Shortly after the order for the first production tanks was issued, Swinton was promoted to colonel and instructed to raise, train and command a unit to man the first tanks and also to produce a manual on battlefield tactics. The force that he created, recruited largely from the personnel of the disbanded RNAS armoured car units, was known until July 1917, when the Tank Corps proper was formed, as the Heavy Branch of the Machine-Gun Corps, in the interest of security.

In his memoirs and other writings Sir Harry Ricardo recalled that his first involvement with 'the matter that was to have such an important place in my thoughts for the rest of the war' occurred very early in 1916, when the tank was still a naval responsibility. On this occasion he was summoned to Seymour Tritton's office to meet a new client who was seeking the civil engineering firm's help and advice on a certain highly secret problem, so hush-hush, in fact, that it could not be discussed at the partnership's premises.

This client was Lieutenant Francis Shaw, another young RNVR officer serving with 20 Squadron RNAS. On accompanying Lieutenant Shaw to the squadron's headquarters, an office in Pall Mall, he heard for the very first time about the existence of the tanks, huge machines weighing over 28 tons that could only be transported from their bases in England to the battlefields in France on railway trucks, that area of military logistics in which Rendel, Palmer & Tritton had special responsibilities. Lieutenant Shaw explained that it was easy to drive a tank up a ramp and on to a flat-bed truck; the problem was, having done so, how could their drivers manoeuvre them into position exactly on the truck's centre line, given the somewhat erratic and imprecise steering of the earliest versions? As the overall width of a tank was only an inch or so less than the standard railway loading gauge, this accuracy would be critical when passing under bridges or through tunnels.

It seems that Lieutenant Shaw and his RNAS colleagues had already heard of the young Ricardo's mechanical engineering work at Rendel, Palmer & Tritton, including his design for hydraulic jacks with hydraulic intensifiers that were currently being used for manoeuvring the spans of bridges into position on their piers. Could a similar device solve the problem of transporting the tanks, they wondered?

In point of fact, as the tank drivers of the tanks became gradually more skilled, this particular difficulty diminished in importance only to be replaced by other more fundamental problems, and on these matters also Ricardo was able to give his client some valuable advice. In the weeks that followed he was invited to attend several more technical meetings when many other mechanical engineering matters relating to the tanks were discussed. Indeed, his contribution was very soon recognised to be indispensable and having been co-opted as an unofficial member of the Tank Supply Committee and appointed a consulting engineer to the newly established Department of Mechanical Warfare, early in 1916 he was taken to see the vehicles under construction at Lincoln and and later at a display held at Oldbury, near Birmingham, on 3 March 1916 before a large assembly of British and French military personnel. In Ricardo's words, 'I seemed to have insinuated myself into the technical affairs of the enterprise generally.'

Just as with the Hatfield Park demonstrations, the Oldbury event took place on a piece of wasteland that had been mocked up to resemble a typical fighting front in France, pock-marked with shell-holes and craters and strewn with obstacles and defences of the type over which the vehicles would have to pass. On both the British and German sides, these defences generally comprised three or more lines of trenches of various widths and depths, of which the outer one was protected by deep areas of barbed wire. In the company of Francis Shaw and Walter Gordon Wilson, together with other officers from the mechanical engineering department of the War Office, Ricardo witnessed a Mk I tank from the first experimental batch being put through its paces and was deeply impressed with what he saw. Clearly, the new weapon had the potential to break the stalemate on the Western Front. Yet as the first internal combustion engine specialist to have become involved in the project, he realised immediately that the British-built but American-designed 105hp Daimler 'Silent Knight' double-sleeve-valve engine currently fitted was woefully unsuited to the task, and that sooner or later a replacement would have to be found. Indeed, although it was the most powerful automobile petrol engine in production at that time, experience proved that the Daimler engine's power output was barely adequate to deal with adverse conditions in the field, when the tracks of the tanks became clogged by the glutinous Flanders mud or entangled with barbed wire.

Moreover, its mechanical design had several other fundamental drawbacks. Firstly, it lacked a proper pressurised lubrication system to cool the bearings – the big ends of the connecting rods merely dipped into a trough-like sump, splashing oil liberally around the crankcase but without necessarily supplying the bearings, which were consequently liable to overheat and fail under heavy load. Secondly, this trough system failed completely when the vehicle was tilted out of the horizontal as it climbed out of a ditch or over a parapet; in this position the oil ran back leaving the front con-rods turning in thin air, causing them to overheat. And thirdly, the purely reciprocating action of the Knight double-sleeve-valve system meant that seizure could only be prevented by supplying a very large quantity of lubricating oil to the outer sleeve. This tended to be carried into the exhaust port, with the unfortunate result that the tank's engine emitted a smoky exhaust at all times, making camouflage from aerial observation virtually impossible. Worse still, when the engine was accelerated during an advance after prolonged periods of idling, it gave off clouds of blue smoke visible for miles in all directions, betraying the vehicle's position to the enemy and presenting a virtually unmissable target to their artillery.

Ricardo's observations were confirmed when, some three months later, these drawbacks were exposed under battlefield condition in France. According to his account of the story, following the Hatfield and Oldbury trials the military authorities formed the misguided view that the only valid test of the tank's abilities would be to send a force into action, and at the earliest opportunity. So it happened that, against the advice of Colonel Swinton, who considered their deployment premature, at 6.20 a.m. on the morning of 15 September 1916 the first thirty-two tanks to arrive in France were thrown into the Battle of the Somme, though not under Swinton's direct field command. 'The whole operation was a tragic example of mismanagement, muddle and misunderstanding,' Ricardo wrote fifty years later, in his autobiography. 'Without any preliminary rehearsals, and without any clear plans for co-operation with the infantry (who were as ignorant of their purpose as the enemy) the tanks were instructed to cross no-man's land, knocking out any machine gun posts on the way, to get astride the enemy's front-line trench and then to carry on as seemed best to them'. Attacking on a relatively lightly defended sector of the front, the tanks had no difficulty in breaking through the barbed-wire defences and crossing the enemy's front-line trench. But on achieving their first objective, to their great dismay their crews found that no infantry were following them to capture the German positions that they had overrun, and that they were isolated in enemy territory unable to exploit the situation. Left to their own devices without clear orders, most of the crews had no idea of what to do next. Some turned round and returned to their base but others pressed on with their attack, driving straight ahead to cross the Germans' second and third lines of entrenchment and so out into open country, only to run out of petrol. After doing what they could to disable their machines, the crews abandoned the fight and attempted to escape back to their own lines on foot; most were captured, although a few did succeed in getting back to British lines.

'The whole affair was really a disaster of the first magnitude,' said Ricardo. The element of secrecy and surprise had been lost, with little or no territorial gain. With several captured tanks in their possession, the Germans now knew exactly what to expect in future and had ample time to prepare for the next major offensive by developing anti-tank guns and mines, armour-piercing bullets and other countermeasures, although they made little attempt to produce a tank of their own. Having entirely wasted its advantage, the British Army had no hope of building up a replacement tank force of new and better machines and crews with which to mount another attack for another year at least. On the other hand, important lessons had been learned which helped dispel any doubts that existed among the military authorities, who apparently resented having a weapon thrust upon them that had been developed largely by naval officers; certainly, in the light of the relatively low casualties sustained in the engagement, the British Commander-in-Chief in

France, Field Marshal Haig, could not ignore the fact that for the first time in the war a breakthrough had been achieved, and by only a handful of men and machines. On the strength of this achievement, therefore, orders were given that the production of an improved design of tank, the Mark IV, should proceed immediately, and on a large scale, to replace the losses sustained in the Battle of the Somme.

One month after the Somme debâcle, in October 1916, Ricardo's involvement in the tank affair was given a powerful impetus when his old Cambridge friend Oliver Thornycroft arrived on the scene. Thornycroft, who by coincidence had previously been serving as a lieutenant RNVR in another of the RNAS technical research squadrons had also been transferred to army duties and had managed to get himself posted to the Tank Supply Department of the War Office with the specific responsibility of organising the development and construction of a completely new and improved design of tank, the Mk V, which, it was planned, would eventually supersede the Mk IV currently in production.

'A charming, delightfully frank and forthright character of great ability and integrity,' Oliver Thornycroft undoubtedly played a major role in Ricardo's life, as a loyal friend and colleague. Born in April 1885, he was the son of the famous sculptor Sir Hamo Thornycroft and the nephew of Sir John Thornycroft FRS, the equally famous marine engineer. But oddly enough, although Sir Hamo was one of Halsey Ricardo's closest friends, their sons did not meet until they both arrived at Cambridge in 1903 and joined the University Automobile Club. There, as we have seen, the pair struck up a deep comradeship that lasted for over fifty years until Thornycroft's death in 1956. For a large part of that time – the twenty years between 1920 and 1940 – he was one of Sir Harry's most trusted collaborators at the Shoreham laboratories.

After graduating from Cambridge, Oliver Thornycroft served an apprenticeship in electrical engineering with the Westinghouse company (later Metro-Vick) at Trafford Park, Manchester, before joining his friend at Rendel, Palmer & Tritton where he acted as the firm's expert in electrical matters. At the outbreak of the First World War, however, he volunteered for active service and was accepted since, unlike Ricardo, he was not deemed to be in a reserved occupation. During the Second World War Thornycroft was recalled once more to naval duties, firstly to solve the urgent problem of magnetic mines and, later, to tackle the wider concern of anti-submarine devices. In all this vital work he played a crucial part; for example, the multiple mortar for throwing a pattern of depth charges, which proved so effective in combating the U-boat menace, was another of his achievements, in recognition of which he was ultimately awarded the OBE and promoted Director of Aeronautical and Engineering Research at the Admiralty.

According to Ricardo's recollection, on Oliver Thornycroft's suggestion Francis Shaw visited him at Walton-on-Thames later that month to discuss the question of a replacement for the 105hp Daimler engine, a matter to which Ricardo had already given much thought. He showed them the experimental 200hp aircraft engine that he was currently working on and explained its principal features such as its cross-head-type pistons and masked inlet valves, which he considered would be worth adopting for the new tank engine should he be asked to design it. Shaw was in full agreement with Ricardo's thinking and asked him to prepare a rough scheme which he would duly put before his colleagues; thereafter, he continued to act as technical liaison officer between Ricardo and the Tank Supply Committee.

It seems that, on the strength of these proposals, Shaw and Thornycroft very soon succeeded in impressing upon Colonel Stern, the Chairman of the Tank Supply

A cut-away example (made for instructional purposes) of the highly advanced 150hp six-cylinder engine designed for the Mk V tank by Harry Ricardo. Incorporating many novel and ingenious features, it represented the state of the art in automobile engine design in 1916.

Committee, that not only was it absolutely necessary to obtain a more powerful engine for the tanks, but also that this engine should be specially designed for the purpose, along the lines that Ricardo had set out. Indeed, they specifically recommended that Ricardo should be called in immediately to undertake the work, and that he should be given a completely free hand on the design. For a relatively young, unknown and untested engineer with only limited experience this responsibility represented an extraordinary opportunity and challenge.

At first, the senior members of the Tank Supply Committee were not convinced, preferring that the job should go to an established automotive engine builder such as Rolls-Royce or Napier, or even that Daimler should be commissioned to build a new engine. However, at the time most of the established and properly qualified manufacturers in the United Kingdom already had their hands full and were committed to other government contracts either for military transport vehicles or aircraft engines, which had top priority. However, through his work for his grandfather's firm, Ricardo had long been in regular contact with a number of the producers of large industrial engines, such as Mirrlees and Crossleys, and so he was asked to canvass these firms to find out whether they had the capacity to tackle the construction of the new engine for the tanks.

'I found them not only willing but eager to do this, but not to tackle the design, which they said was quite outside their range of experience,' said Ricardo. 'I reported this to Tennyson d'Eyncourt who replied: "You seem to have a pretty good idea of what is required. Will you undertake it?" I told him that although I had always been deeply interested in engine design, my experience was really very limited, but I should love to have a try at it provided that I could be assured of the good-will and co-operation of the would-be manufacturers, but that I was afraid that engineers of such firms with a hundred times my experience would regard it as an impertinence to be asked to build an engine designed by a little-known young man.'

The next step forward was that, early in October 1916, a meeting of the would-be constructors was convened under Sir Eustace Tennyson d'Eyncourt's chairmanship to discuss Ricardo's design proposals. According to Sir Harry, the meeting was a great success and his scheme was well received. All the manufacturers present wholeheartedly promised their full cooperation in the development of the new engine as a matter of the greatest urgency. At this meeting it was also agreed that Mr Windeler of Mirrlees would act as coordinator of the whole manufacturing group which consisted of Mirrlees, Bickerton & Day, Browett Lindley, Crossley Bros, Ruston & Hornsby and also, of course, Peter Brotherhood, so that Ricardo was able to renew his association with his friend Commander Bryant. Later Messrs Gardner and the National Gas Engine Company joined the list, making seven firms in all. To assist Ricardo in the detailed design work (which was to be carried out at Rendel, Palmer & Tritton's offices in London) he was loaned the services of two junior draughtsmen, Archibald Ferguson and George Holt. It is interesting to note that both these men joined Ricardo's company on its formation in 1919, and remained with him at Shoreham for the rest of their working lives.

It was decided that the output of the new six-cylinder engine should be roughly 150hp. Ricardo had originally proposed 200hp but this was thought to be rather too high by Major W.G.Wilson, who was doubtful that his new design could cope with so much power. Wilson, the designer of the transmission used in the existing tanks, was currently working on his famous epicyclic gearbox, which was to be used in the Mk V machine to simplify the problem of steering the vehicles. By applying a brake to one of the tracks, left or right,

Ricardo's 150hp six-cylinder tank engines under assembly at the Gardner Works at Manchester in 1917. Over 8,000 examples were built, making it Britain's first mass-produced internal combustion engine.

its driver could disengage the power to that particular track automatically, leaving the other side running free so that the tank pivoted around the braked and disengaged track, thus enabling the vehicle to be easily controlled and steered by one man. Hitherto, the steering action had relied on a cumbersome arrangement whereby the appropriate track, left or right, was disengaged by levers operating separate clutches and brakes, so that in practice it took three men to drive it, one man on either side to operate the clutches by pulling large levers and another to control the engine and change gear. Designated the Mk V, the new tank would also feature a modified hull as well as the new engine and transmission, which comprised a conventional clutch and a four-speed crash gearbox.

'Sir Eustace handled the gathering admirably,' said Sir Harry. 'Never in my life have I attended a meeting at which so much was settled in so short a time, for I came away with a mandate to go ahead with the engine design in detail, and to push on with all possible speed.' Indeed, so great was the priority given to the project that shortly afterwards, in December 1916, Albert Stern was able to demonstrate his faith in Harry Ricardo's design by persuading the Minister of Munitions, Lloyd George, to place an order for no fewer than 700 units of the completely new 150hp unit, not one part of which had yet got beyond the drawing board stage, let alone been built and tested. The intention was that the Mk V would be ready for action within a year, but in the meanwhile production of the Mk IV was to be continued to fill the gap, fitted with Ricardo's new 150hp engine as soon as it became available. However, such was the progress made on the Mk V version that further work involving the Mk IV was discontinued in June 1917. With Thornycroft's assistance and advice – aided and abetted by Hetherington when he could get away from his work at Farnborough – and toiling late into the night, Ricardo soon finalised the design of his new engine. Commencing work in November 1916 he was able to deliver the finished final detailed drawings to the manufacturers in January the following year.

In his book *Tanks 1914–1918, The Log-Book of a Pioneer*, Albert Stern recalled these events from his own perspective, saying that: 'It was clear at this time that if Mechanical Warfare was to make any real progress, an engine bigger than the 150hp (Daimler) engine would be necessary. Unfortunately, the Aircraft Production Department were seizing every possible source of supply [of engines, and also materials such as aluminium]. I found a well-known designer in internal combustion engines, Mr H.R. Ricardo, who knew of a certain number of gas-engine firms. These firms were got together under my presidency and agreed to work jointly to produce an engine specifically designed by Mr Ricardo, of 150hp, using no aluminium or high-tensile steel. As soon as Mr Ricardo had got out the designs, I submitted them to Mr Dugald Clerk, one of the greatest authorities in the world on internal combustion engines who considered that I was justified in ordering 700 of these engines before one had been constructed for test.' Indeed, in February 1917, directly against the orders of the Master General of Ordnance, General Sir David Henderson, who had instructed that all further work on Ricardo's 150hp engine should be suspended, Colonel Stern authorised that his original order should be doubled by another 700 units, making 1,400 engines in all, to provide a sufficient supply to power the large numbers of tanks and other armoured vehicles that he felt sure would inevitably be required in France.

Although the young Ricardo – he was then thirty-one – had been promised a free hand in the design of the engine, in the event he was forced to take into account a number of severe restrictions and constraints. It was stipulated by the Ministry of Munitions that the new engine had to develop exactly 150hp, maintaining its torque over a wide range of speed and without risk of stalling while on the move. It was to be capable of running continuously when tilted through an angle of 45 degrees from the horizontal, without losing oil pressure and under no circumstances was smoke to be emitted from its exhaust. It had to be capable of running for 100 hours without requiring any major adjustment or overhaul, and to operating on the low-grade fuel then allocated to heavy military machinery such as gun tractors; its fuel and oil consumption had to be as low as possible, of course, though no actual figures were set. All its working parts – especially the bearings – were to be easily accessible for maintenance or exchange and its overall weight had to be no more than that of the Daimler unit – 25 cwt. And finally the new engine was to be precisely the same width and length as the old Daimler unit, so as to be completely interchangeable with it. This meant, in effect, that Ricardo was required to design an engine producing 50 per cent more power than the Daimler engine but within the same external dimensions and total bearing surface area. Moreover, as all supplies of high tensile steel and aluminium were currently being allocated to the Air Ministry for aircraft purposes, the entire engine – with the exception of the pistons, induction pipes, valves and camshafts – had to be constructed from cast iron and mild steel. The assignment was indeed a challenging one and in Ricardo's own words, 'The restrictions as to dimensions made it necessary to resort to extraordinary means to obtain the power required.'

The need to avoid the large clouds of exhaust smoke given off by the Daimler engine was a severe test of Ricardo's ingenuity. 'In those days there were no such things as oil control rings for pistons and blue smoke in the exhaust of all motor vehicles was a prevalent nuisance,' Ricardo recalled.

Some two years previously I had designed and built in my small workshop an experimental single-cylinder four-stroke engine in which I used a cross-head type of piston employing the lower side of the piston crown as a supercharger. The crown of the piston was thus isolated from the crank-case and very effective oil control was obtained, the exhaust being completely invisible under all conditions of speed and load. I therefore decided to adopt this type of piston, but without employing it specifically as a supercharger. Use of the cross-head piston also made it possible to raise the temperature of the air entering the carburettors by about 25 per cent above ambient, sufficient to improve the carburation of the very involatile low-quality fuel that was available for the Tanks at that time.

Also by this means the oil was not exposed to heat from the piston crown, which dispensed with the need for an oil cooler. Worried about torsional vibration, he also fitted a Lanchester damper of the viscous type. The layout of the poppet-valve-type cylinder heads was exactly the same as on the single-cylinder Walton engine, while the compression ratio was a mere 4.3:1.

By the beginning of March 1917, some nine weeks after receiving the first detailed drawings from Engine Patents Ltd, the Peter Brotherhood firm had built the first hand-made prototype example of the 150hp engine at its Peterborough factory and the engine was ready for extensive test-bed trials. These trials provided the authorities with incontrovertible proof of Ricardo's skill and ingenuity as a designer; the new six-cylinder engine produced a 50 per cent greater power output than the Daimler unit from almost the same swept volume of 18.33 litres.

Taken at Wolverhampton in September 1918, this photograph of a Mk V (powered by Ricardo's 150hp engine) shows Harry Ricardo (third from left) with a group of colleagues, including Lieutenant Francis Shaw RNVR (to HRR's left) and Major Gordon Wilson (to HRR's right).

The first production engine, built by Mirrlees, followed five weeks later and was fitted in a Mk IV tank for service trials, in April 1917. The results were such that the entire manufacturing group was given the go-ahead to commence full-scale production; by the summer they were turning out the engine at the rate of 40 units a week so that by the end of the year some 500 or 600 units had been produced. Every single component part was interchangeable no matter by which firm it was made, a remarkable feat of manufacturing skill and cooperation for that era.

On 21 July 1917, just a few days after Ricardo's recently formed company Engine Patents Ltd held its first board meeting at its new offices in Suffolk Street, near Trafalgar Square, Albert Stern (now styled as Director General of the Ministry of Munitions) wrote to Ricardo as follows: 'On Thursday last, I witnessed some trials of a Mark IV Machine in which an 150hp engine was fitted. I was exceedingly pleased with the performance of this Machine and the increase not only in speed but in pulling power was most marked. . . . I should like to take this opportunity of thanking you very sincerely for this engine. I can assure you that I appreciate most highly your work, not only in designing the engine, but also in assisting so greatly in its production.' For his part, Sir Harry Ricardo considered that Stern was 'the most active driving force behind the whole project, a very capable organiser, and a tower of strength.'

Soon after the completion of the first engine, however, the Ministry of Munitions decided that the Ricardo engine was not to be fitted in the Mk IV tank after all, and that the 150hp unit would be reserved for the new Mk V machine exclusively, thus rendering unnecessary most of the limitations and handicaps that its designer had taken such pains to overcome!

The first production Mk V tank was completed early in June 1917, by which time, with even bigger and heavier tanks in view, the Ministry of Munitions had commissioned Ricardo to design a larger, scaled-up 225hp, six-cylinder engine with double the cylinder capacity of his original 150hp motor. This was not put into production until the summer of 1918, and thus did not see service in France. Similarly, the summer of 1918 also saw the first appearance of a lightweight chaser tank – the Medium Mk B Whippet, powered by a four-cylinder, 100hp adaptation of Ricardo's original six-cylinder engine – though this vehicle also arrived too late to play a significant role in the war.

The vindication of Swinton's concept came at the Battle of Cambrai in November 1917, when the entire current strength of the Tank Corps, a force of 476 vehicles – all of them Mk IVs fitted with the Daimler engine – were sent into action in an all-out attempt to breach the hitherto impregnable Hindenburg Line. Advancing on a broad front, the tanks seized their objective within a couple of hours, throwing the enemy into confusion. By the end of the day the most rapid advance of the whole war had been achieved. Previously it had taken 250,000 casualties sustained in weeks of bitter hand-to-hand combat to make so great a penetration. Unfortunately, however, once more the action was only a partial success; due to the speed of the advance and the resulting breakdown in battlefield communications, the cavalry failed to arrive in time to exploit the situation and the tanks were forced to withdraw. Nevertheless, the new weapon, previously regarded as something of a minor and irrelevant sideshow by the General Staff, had proved itself to be a major battle-winner, and in the most spectacular way.

Even so, Colonel Swinton was not involved directly in this action as, much to his dismay, he had fallen into disfavour and had been relieved of his command by the War Office the previous year. Replaced at the head of the Tank Corps by Lieutenant-Colonel (later Major-General) H.J. Elles, he was sent off on a public relations tour of the USA before being posted back to his old duties with the War Cabinet Secretariat in 1918 with the rank of major-general. It was not until many years later that he received official recognition for his pioneering work in establishing the mechanical and tactical principles of armoured warfare. After the war he retired from the army and turned to writing history, initially by undertaking research for Lloyd George's war memoirs. In 1925, however, he was elected Chichele Professor of Military History at Oxford University and held the Chair until 1939, remaining a fellow of All Souls College until his death in 1951. He was knighted in 1923.

As soon as the losses of the Cambrai battle could be replaced, the tactic of a massed armoured assault was employed again, this time with complete success. The new Mk V tank, fitted with Ricardo's 150hp engine, had its baptism of fire at Hamel on 4 July 1918; this minor engagement was a prelude to the decisive action that took place at the Battle of Amiens in August 1918. At Amiens a force of 600 Mk V tanks made a concentrated attack, smashing through the German defences at key points to penetrate 7½ miles into enemy territory within a day, taking 16,000 prisoners and capturing 200 guns. One hundred days later, enemy morale collapsed entirely under this and other similar armoured onslaughts; the Germans sued for peace, an Armistice being signed on 11 November 1918. In the words of a German commander, 'We had been defeated not by the genius of Marshal Foch (the Allied Commander-in-Chief) but by General Tank.'

Between March 1917 and the end of the war in November 1918, a total of well over 8,000 of Ricardo's 150hp and 225hp tank engines were produced and put into military service, many more than the actual number of vehicles constructed. This is because these engines soon found other employment, for example in railway shunting locomotives and auxiliary naval craft. Many more were used as stationary engines in France to provide electric power and lighting at base workshops, hospitals and camps, arduous duties that called for them to be operated continuously for very long periods without ill effect. Indeed there is evidence to suggest that many of these engines were still in service thirty years later, after the Second World War. In short, Ricardo's design was not only the most powerful and reliable automobile engine available to the British, French and American forces during the First World War but it was also the first British-designed and built internal combustion automobile engine to be mass-produced in truly large numbers, and there is no doubt that its efficiency and reliability had a significant influence on the successful outcome of the war.

In recognition of Ricardo's contribution to victory, immediately after the Armistice Engine Patents Ltd was awarded royalties of £30,000 by the Royal Commission on Inventions in respect of the 1,400 tank engines produced, funds large enough not only to cover the purchase of the land at Shoreham on which the Bridge Works laboratories would be built, but also to present a substantial bonus of £12,000 to Ricardo personally, about £170,000 in today's money; this must certainly have come as a welcome consolation after the disappointment of his aero-engine hopes. Thus, at the age of thirty-four he had become a relatively rich and successful man, whose reputation was recognised throughout the corridors of power in Whitehall and Westminster and whose opinions and expertise were widely sought after by both commercial engine manufacturers and the military authorities

The Mk V tank first saw action in France during July and August 1918. A force of 600 took part in the Battle of Amiens and won a decisive victory. Three months later, the Great War was over.

Ricardo's workshops at Penstone in the early 1920s. Note his customary trilby hat, hanging on the bannister!

alike. The internal combustion engine enthusiast had become a professional, and as a member of that small select band of pioneering technologists, his work was already proving to be crucial to the national interest. Indeed, his name, like that of Henry Royce, had become synonymous with progress in the automotive and aeronautical fields, and its appearance on the bonnet of a quality car to rival the Rolls-Royce was widely expected. All augured well for the expansion of his company, and on the ending of hostilities preparations for the move to Shoreham were put into effect without further delay.

With his new-found wealth, Ricardo was able to give up his rented house at Walton-on-Thames and purchase a country home, Penstone, at Lancing in West Sussex. Set in a large garden complete with an orchard and a tennis court, this imposing Edwardian gentleman's residence was situated conveniently near to the sea and just a few miles from the new Bridge Works at Old Shoreham. Here Harry Ricardo and his family were to remain for the next thirteen years.

At the same time he took the opportunity to upgrade the family's motor transport fleet, acquiring a second-hand Alphonso model Hispano Suiza sports tourer for his own use and a 12hp Humber saloon for his wife. His old Dolphin car, which had served him so well over the past decade, was handed over to his colleague Major Evans, who used it for several more years. 'Thus, with the nightmare of war behind us, we started out in the spring of 1919 on a new era of family life, this time on a more ambitious scale,' Ricardo later recalled.

CHAPTER 14

Bridge Works

The success of his tank engine marked the turning point in Harry Ricardo's life, and almost overnight his status was changed from that of an amateur pursuing an unusual but innocent hobby, to that of a serious person whose opinions carried weight. In the light of this transformation in his reputation and prospects, his fellow directors could no longer insist on a further postponement of his plans. Yet although the decision to proceed with the building of his much-longed-for design and research centre was taken by the board of Engine Patents Ltd on 1 January 1918, it was to be another year and a half before these premises opened for business. The experimental equipment needed for his engine research activities was finally transferred from Walton-on-Thames to Sussex in June 1919. For the time being the head office of his company, plus its technical department and design and drawing offices, remained at 21 Suffolk Street, at the Trafalgar Square end of Pall Mall in central London. However, in the spring of 1924, the design and drawing offices also moved to Shoreham, while the commercial offices continued at Suffolk Street until 1956 when they were relocated in more spacious accommodation at Ashley Place, Westminster, before finally moving to Shoreham in 1968.

It is known that an architectural design for the Shoreham premises was commissioned from Sir Harry's father Halsey Ricardo early in 1917 and that he completed the work during the course of that year for a fee of £1,200. The site, a 3-acre plot lying on the right bank of the River Adur just above the Old Shoreham Toll Bridge, not far from the location of the Two Stroke Engine Company's Dolphin Works some ten years earlier, was purchased from the Leconfield Estate in August 1918 for the sum of £250. Construction work began immediately and it was finished and ready for occupation in the spring of 1919, when the first locally recruited employee was engaged. By then the total cost of the project had reached £15,000.

The choice of this Sussex coast location, 60 miles from London, was perhaps quixotic and in the days before the widespread use of the telephone and telex machine it must surely have led to numerous delays or difficulties in communications between the laboratory and its headquarters, let alone with its clients. Yet Ricardo was determined to escape from the hurly-burly of the London scene and to live and work deep in the Sussex countryside, far away from the distractions of the metropolis and close to the sea where he could enjoy his chief recreations, boating and fishing. In those days, the West Sussex coast was completely unspoiled and undeveloped, as quiet and beautiful a place as any in the country. Although he was not a solitary or anti-social man, Harry Ricardo was far from being a gregarious party-goer and he always valued the company of his family and close friends far higher than that of strangers, no matter how famous or distinguished. He never joined a golf club, or frequented the saloon bar of his local public house. For him, an informal picnic on the beach was always preferable to a grand banquet or smart cocktail party in London. However, the more successful and sought-after he became in

Bridge Works, Harry Ricardo's laboratories at Shoreham, West Sussex, was designed by Halsey Ricardo and built in 1919. These buildings are very different today!

his later life, the more he was called upon to spend his time in town, attending conferences and committee meetings or dealing with administrative formalities; duties and obligations that he often found disagreeable.

In designing Bridge Works, Halsey Ricardo thought it appropriate to adopt the Sussex vernacular style, so that in its original form the Works resembled a linked pair of two-storey farm cottages fronting a group of single-storey outbuildings set around a courtyard or quadrangle. Their pantiled roofs were hipped in the local tradition while their walls were rendered and whitewashed. One of the cottages served as an office block and the other as a garage and caretaker's flat. In the outbuildings behind them adequate space was provided not just for the laboratories and test-shops of a research establishment but also accommodation for all the other essential functions of an engineering firm: workshops, pattern-shops, machine-shops and draughtsman's offices, together with a smithy and a coppersmiths, plus the usual stores, power-house and mess-room. It is said that, on seeing his splendid new buildings for the first time, marking as they did so great an improvement over his primitive wooden sheds at Walton-on-Thames, the young Ricardo was overcome by doubts that he would ever be able to fill them with revenue-earning staff and machinery, and that the place would become a white elephant.

Clearly, his worries were misplaced for within a short time the Shoreham research centre had acquired an impressive list of clients and was operating profitably, its income being greatly augmented by the substantial royalties that were beginning to accrue from his latest, recently patented, inventions – the slipper piston and the turbulent cylinder head. Consequently, the board of Engine Patents Ltd agreed that the time had come to acknowledge the fact that its founder's reputation was now fully established, by incorporating his name in the company's title. Thus in March 1920 its name was changed to Ricardo & Company Engineers Ltd. At this time Frederick Goodenough, then Chairman of Barclays Bank, retired as a director, his place being taken by Viscount Combermere, who remained a director until 1963. Seven years later, the company's affairs were entirely restructured under the new title of Ricardo and Company, Engineers (1927) Ltd.

Previously, in May 1924, Harry Ricardo and Harry Hetherington had taken over as joint Managing Directors, replacing Campbell Farrar who had resigned from the board the previous year. Campbell-Swinton continued as Chairman until his death in February 1930 whereupon Ricardo assumed this role, with Hetherington remaining as sole Managing Director until 1932 when he was given leave of absence due to ill health, and Ricardo took over the administrative reigns in addition to his technical responsibilities; Hetherington finally retired in 1935. As one of Harry Ricardo's oldest and dearest friends, a veteran of the Dolphin venture and the most senior among the active, technical, founding fathers of the company (he became a director in 1917 on his release from military service), his contribution to the firm's success was inestimable. Undoubtedly, his abilities as an ambassador and diplomat together with his fluent command of French were crucial in introducing the Shoreham firm to its many long-term clients in France and elsewhere on the Continent.

Similarly, as we have already noted, Harry Ricardo's other old Cambridge friend Oliver Thornycroft also remained with him throughout the interwar years, from 1920 to 1940, in his capacity as Chief Engineer and Works Manager, before rejoining the navy after the outbreak of the Second World War. But of the five key men who rallied to Ricardo's flag when his company finally got under way after the Armistice, the longest serving was Major Aubrey Evans who remained with the firm for no fewer than forty-two years, from 1918 until his retirement in 1960. Evans, whose title at Bridge Works was Chief Scientific Officer, had begun his career as an assistant to Sir Dugald Clerk, working initially in his internal combustion engine research laboratory and then, later, in his patent agency, before joining the Royal Flying Corps and becoming Bertram Hopkinson's assistant during the First World War.

Evidently, not least among Ricardo's gifts was his ability to recognise engineering talent in others, and then to gather these men around him in a happy and harmonious environment, singularly free of tensions and rivalries. His ability to attract, recruit and retain high-quality staff was a key factor in his success, for once admitted into the Shoreham fold the chosen men tended to stay with him for years, thankful for the chance to develop their potential to the full without undue pressure or interference from on high. Indeed, it was not unusual for graduates entering Bridge Works straight from university to remain there for their entire working lives. In planning his laboratories as a young man, Ricardo had hoped to create a self-financing research establishment that would also be a training ground for young engineers, a centre of knowledge with an ethos more akin to a university college than an apprentice school. Clearly, he succeeded in this aim. He knew how to get the best out of the people working under him, advising rather than ordering them about, and he treated his staff as pupils rather than servants. Indeed, it has been said by many ex-Ricardo engineers that HRR (as he was universally known among his staff at Bridge Works) was like a benign and benevolent headmaster, a much-revered and magisterial figure, profoundly respected but never remote or unapproachable. Even so, he preferred to address his staff and colleagues by their surnames, in the traditional way, and was on Christian name terms only with his oldest and closest friends such as Hetherington and Thornycroft. He would condone no impertinence or familiarity, nor would he suffer indifferent or indisciplined work that failed to reach his own high standards, yet he was respected as an unfailingly courteous and considerate employer who ruled his Shoreham empire by example and encouragement, and not by threat or coercion as did many other notoriously authoritarian leaders of the automobile and aeronautical industries in his day.

There was really only one exception to this rule of long service among the trusted band of friends and colleagues who formed Harry Ricardo's senior staff in those early days, and that was Major Frank Halford, whose stay as an employee was untypically brief. But in his case there was no suggestion of disloyalty or disregard; he was as devoted an employee as all the others. Unfortunately, however, Ricardo simply could not provide opportunities enough to hold the attention of this highly talented and ambitious man, or to satisfy the demands of his ebullient and energetic personality. On returning to civilian life after his demobilisation from the RFC, Halford joined Ricardo in early 1919, yet he stayed for only three years before leaving in late 1922 to pursue his own personal interests and activities as a consultant designer.

Halford's first assignment on Ricardo's behalf took place in the USA, where he was sent to establish the firm's American office in Cleveland, Ohio. Here, for the next two and a half years he was involved in negotiating licensing agreements for Ricardo patents, notably the slipper piston and the turbulent cylinder head. Little information has survived about this venture except an apocryphal story involving Henry Ford. It seems that after many attempts Halford managed to secure an interview at the Highland Park plant in Detroit, during which he attempted to interest the American motor magnate in manufacturing the turbulent head under licence. His joy in meeting the great man was short-lived, however, for the first question that Ford asked him was how much Harry Ricardo would be prepared to pay for the privilege of having his design incorporated in a Ford engine. The design was indeed taken up by Ford, but it was not until 1935, after much litigation (see Chapter 16), that any royalties were forthcoming.

Halford's work in the USA was not entirely unsuccessful, however, and during his stay there lasting links were forged with a number of US motor manufacturers and engine-building firms, most notably the Waukesha Motor Company of Wisconsin, a builder of proprietary side-valve automobile and industrial engines. But by 1921 the postwar slump had hit the motor trade on both sides of the Atlantic, making business practically impossible, and so it was decided that Halford should close the US office, pack up and return home. Because the US Patent Office continued to refuse to grant Ricardo a patent for the turbulent head in the USA, eventually he was forced to abandon the struggle; instead it was agreed that Harry Horning, President of the Waukesha Company and himself a noted pioneer of the internal combustion engine, should take out a US patent for the turbulent head in his own name and thus collect the royalties on Ricardo's behalf.

The two Harrys had first met in 1919 when the American visited the newly opened Bridge Works and, having identical interests and ambitions, they became close friends, keeping in touch both by regular correspondence and by an exchange of visits. At Horning's instigation, in 1922 Ricardo made a trip to the USA to read a paper before an assembly of the Society of Automotive Engineers in New York, and they met again in 1932 when Ricardo crossed the Atlantic on board the SS *Liverpool* to inspect the

Waukesha factory; and finally he visited the USA again in 1955 to honour the memory of his friend who had died in 1936, by delivering the SAE's Horning Memorial Lecture in Atlantic City, New Jersey. 'He was a great crusader, his battle-cry the marriage of the engine and its fuel,' said Ricardo in his lecture. 'Horning's ambition was to create a world-wide co-operative research between the oil companies and the engine builders, an ambition which he achieved with triumph, thanks to his energy, his enthusiasm and the charm of his personality.' Clearly, the Waukesha man was one of the few American businessmen that Ricardo trusted absolutely, and in whose company he felt completely at ease. While he admired the boundless energy and enterprise of the American industrial scene, he could never quite come to terms with its aggressive wheeling and dealing.

In his Horning Memorial Lecture, entitled 'Some Early Reminiscences', Sir Harry Ricardo (as he was by then) described the nature and origins of his turbulent head, which had evolved from the combustion chamber design of the larger and later of his two First World War tank engines.

'I was so pleased with the behaviour of this [tank engine] combustion chamber that I was anxious to see if I could apply the same principles to a small car engine,' he recalled. 'In those days the side-valve rather than the overhead-valve engine was the popular favourite among automobile manufacturers on grounds of convenience and cost, though it could not compete with the overhead valve type in terms of performance.' On testing a typical example in his Walton-on-Thames workshops he found that its combustion chambers were lacking in turbulence or swirl, a factor that he had already identified to be essential for optimum combustion of the fuel. In fact, the flow of flame and hot gases resulting from the ignition of the fuel mixture was inadequate to the point that the early side-valve engine was extremely prone to harmful detonation (also known as knocking or pinking) which in extreme cases could rapidly damage it beyond repair. After further experiments he designed a replacement head with offset combustion chambers that increased the essential condition of turbulence and speeded up the process of combustion by allowing the flame front to spread more rapidly through the incoming mixture and burn the maximum amount of fuel. This 'squish effect' allowed the engine's compression ratio to be increased, thus improving its performance to the levels of a good contemporary overhead-valve engine. On witnessing a demonstration of this turbulent head, the distinguished engineer Laurence Pomeroy of Vauxhall Motors lost no time in putting it into production on a new side-valve engine that he had designed. 'Others quickly followed; the side-valve engine came into its own again and held sway for many years after,' Ricardo observed. This achievement exemplified Ricardo's ability, unique in that era, to combine science and engineering. After reaching by experimental analysis an intellectual understanding of an internal combustion engine phenomenon, he was able through his skill as a mechanical designer to produce an improvement that would exploit his discovery to the full in practical terms.

As for Frank Halford, on arriving back on British shores in April 1921, he based himself at Ricardo's London office and returned not only to designing engines but also to his pre-war hobby of motorcycle racing. Thanks to his skilful riding, early that season he scored some notable successes at Brooklands on his old 500cc single-cylinder side-valve Triumph machine, but later that year he switched to another Triumph fitted with a new overhead-valve racing engine of advanced design produced by Harry Ricardo at Shoreham. This bike, which had a bore and stroke of 80.5 × 98mm, was first raced in the 500cc Solo Championship at Brooklands on 21 October, but without success, due to various mechanical problems. After further development was undertaken to eliminate overheating difficulties, however, Halford and Ricardo were able to raise the engine's power output to 20hp and in the last meeting of the 1921 season, success was achieved at last when Halford was second across the line in the 500cc Solo Handicap race.

Another factor in Halford's success on this occasion was his use of a new 'super racing fuel' which had been concocted by Shell to Ricardo's and Kewley's prescription. An incidental outcome of the fuel research programme then being undertaken at Bridge Works for the Shell Company, this fuel was a mixture of ethyl alcohol, benzine, acetone and water plus a 2 per cent additive of castor oil for upper cylinder lubrication. Rated at 100 octane, it gave a 10 per cent increase in power output without modifications to the engine, except for the fitting of larger carburettor jets. In his autobiography, Sir Harry revealed that to prevent analysis by competitors and to produce a peculiar and characteristic smell that would give it an appealing mystique in the eyes (and noses) of the racing fraternity and thus assist its sales, the fuel was given an extra, secret, additive of finely powdered bonemeal. 'When burnt in combination with the castor oil, this produced a distinctive and, I am afraid, a rather repulsive smell,' he remembered.

Their first test of the special fuel so delighted Halford and Ricardo that for the coming 1922 season they decided to redesign the single-cylinder Triumph engine once again, to exploit the potential of Shell's new racing spirit to the full, by raising the Triumph's compression ratio, as was now possible without risk of detonation. The revised motor – which incorporated a new cylinder, an improved pent-roofed cylinder head cast from bronze and a very light aluminium slipper piston with a domed top, plus several other features borrowed from the RHA aero-engine – had a compression ratio of 8:1, thus producing a 30 per cent increase in power output, about 25hp at a speed of 5,000rpm.

Frank Halford in the saddle of the Triumph-Ricardo motorcycle, on which he competed so successfully at Brooklands.

The machine shop at Bridge Works in the 1920s.

At the opening meeting of the next Brooklands season, Halford entered the new machine in the Open Class and scored an easy win against twin-cylinder machines of considerably larger capacity. When he continued to do so at subsequent meetings it soon became known that he was using one or other of two special fuels of secret composition that had just come on to the market, either Shell Racing Spirit or its rival, Discol R, supplied by the Distillers Company. Speculation was rife as to which of these two supposedly rival preparations was actually in Halford's fuel tank but, in fact, the liquids were identical and came from the very same source. According to Sir Harry much amusement was derived from hearing the theories on the secret ingredient expounded in the members' enclosure by various Brooklands competitors and spectators. 'The general consensus of opinion appeared to be that some form of high explosive developed during the war had been dissolved in petrol or alcohol and blended with standard motor spirit,' he recalled. The immediate effect of Halford's victories was that, very soon, all self-respecting motorcycle riders had their tanks filled with either the Shell or Distillers product. When the use of these special racing fuels was eventually banned at the Brooklands circuit, large quantities continued to be bought by enthusiastic amateurs for ordinary road use despite the high cost, so that what started off as a joke proved quite a profitable venture for the suppliers, and also for the Bridge Works firm, which earned a substantial sum in royalties.

In 1922, two machines modified for ordinary road use and fitted with detuned 498cc Mk IIA engines with a 6.4:1 compression ratio were entered by the Ricardo company in the Isle of Man TT motorcycle race, but although Halford rode with great skill and courage he finished down the field in eleventh place. Perhaps this disappointment was due to the bike's rudimentary braking system; though sufficient for the oval Brooklands track, it was quite inadequate for the many twisting corners of the Isle of Man circuit. The second machine ridden by Walter Brandish came second, however.

Naturally, Frank Halford's racing exploits soon brought Ricardo and his firm to the attention of the Triumph Company and in 1921 he was commissioned to design an 85×88mm single-cylinder, overhead-valve standard production engine employing many of the same features as the racing unit, but detuned for ordinary road use. At the same time, designs for a series of four-cylinder, side-valve engines all featuring the turbulent head were ordered from Bridge Works for use in the new range of small cars that the Triumph Company was planning to produce. The resulting 499cc motor cycle unit, known as the Triumph–Ricardo engine, used Ricardo's patented aluminium slipper piston, but this time in conjunction with a cast-iron cylinder head and would run happily on standard commercial petrol. Over the next decade the Triumph–Ricardo motorcycle proved to be a very popular machine indeed, selling in large numbers and bringing in several thousand pounds in royalties, not to mention considerable kudos for its designers, Halford and Ricardo. In fact, for an all-too-brief period during the twenties, together with the turbulent head, this motorcycle made the name Ricardo a household word for advanced automotive engineering and design among the public at large.

The same type of cylinder head employed on the racing Triumph was also used with great success on an exciting new automobile project that came Ricardo's way in 1921 – the 3-litre, four-cylinder, sixteen-valve double overhead camshaft Vauxhall racing engine designed at Shoreham specifically for a high-performance competition car that the boss of the Luton firm, Percy Kidner, planned to campaign in Grand Prix events; the vehicle made its first appearance in the Isle of Man TT race the following year. Although designed for maximum reliability and simplicity of manufacture, this engine was exceptionally advanced for its time and contained many novel features. Its performance was quite outstanding, maximum output being 129hp at 4,500rpm (3.7hp per sq in of piston area) and its maximum speed 115 mph using the normal touring car fuel of the day. The bore and stroke were 85mm and 132mm respectively with a compression ratio of 5.8:1. The cylinder heads were cast in pairs in hard bronze, with two inlet and two exhaust valves per cylinder set in a pent-roof combustion chamber, as in the Triumph engine, and there were two shaft-driven camshafts mounted in aluminium housings above the heads. Steel wetliners were used for the cylinders, set in a very rigid aluminium crankcase; the big-end bearings of the built-up crankshaft were of the dual roller type. The crankshaft main bearing caps were fastened to the block by massive vertical through-bolts, which made for an exceptionally rigid structure. Masked inlet valves and a divided induction manifold also contributed to the engine's high performance. Three spark plugs per cylinder were also provided, the outer pair acting as a standby in case of failure of the main, central, plug.

Three of these cars were built by Vauxhall Motors, which was then a quality marque ranking with names like Aston Martin and Bentley, and which therefore had high aspirations to succeed in the Grand Prix field. The Isle of Man TT race was regarded by Kidner and Ricardo as a proving run. In the event, only nine entrants took part, the others being three Sunbeams and three Bentleys. Unfortunately, the race was run in appalling weather and the result was a disappointment for the two friends, as two of the cars had to retire due to minor mechanical trouble. Two Sunbeams finished first and second, with the remaining Vauxhall third, and a Bentley fourth. A handwritten letter from Harry Ricardo to Laurence Pomeroy Snr (the former Vauxhall designer then working in the USA), now preserved in the Bridge Works archives, records his feelings: 'It is awfully nice of you to be so sympathetic over our failure in the T.T. race,' he wrote. 'This was a bitter disappointment but I had a presentiment that it would happen, simply from a superstitious dread of things that go too well at the start. The race was run in blinding rain, so that it became a test of drivers rather than of cars . . . and I really think that a malignant providence was to blame.' Later, these Vauxhalls redeemed themselves and proved their worth by winning numerous events at Brooklands, and also at the Shelsley Walsh hill-climbing event in 1929, but they never participated in any Grand Prix event due to the unexpected cessation of the 3-litre formula.

Though not a driver in the 1922 Isle of Man car event, Frank Halford was also disappointed by the outcome of the Vauxhall racing venture, for other, more personal reasons. At that point in time the wavering compass needle signalling the future path of the Ricardo firm began to swing away from such adventurous projects and to settle down in the direction of sober long-range research and the design and development of industrial engines, fields in which Halford took little interest. At the outset, the way forward for Ricardo and his team could have taken many routes – even towards the

The team of three Ricardo-engined Vauxhall 3.3-litre racing cars, entered in the Isle of Man Tourist Trophy race in 1922.

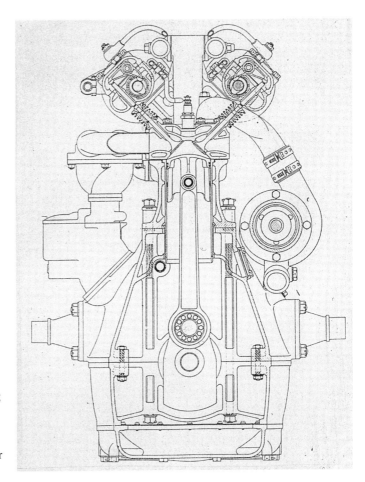

A cross-sectional drawing
of Ricardo's 1922
Vauxhall 3.3-litre six-
cylinder racing engine,
exceptionally advanced for
its time.

design and manufacture of a car bearing Harry Ricardo's own name. But in the currently
depressed economic climate, any expansion requiring a major investment was ruled out
of the question, at least if Ricardo's vital independence was to be preserved. A designer
and conceptualist by ability and inclination, rather than a research scientist or
development engineer, Halford grew impatient with this situation and sought other, more
challenging, outlets for his talents. A somewhat mercurial character who scorned the
security of pensionable employment, he was the archetypal freelancer, temperamentally
unsuited to working the routine hours of a regular salaried job, and so when the
opportunity arose to join his old Farnborough colleague Geoffrey de Havilland in a new
aircraft engine venture (on a consultancy basis) he resigned from Ricardo's company.
Even so, the parting was entirely amicable and the two men remained on the friendliest
of terms for the next thirty years, meeting regularly to consult each other on every aspect
of engine design. 'We were sorry to see him go,' said Ricardo, in a characteristic
understatement.

Indeed, when a few years later Halford's consultancy was retained by D. Napier & Son
to design a series of large-power high-performance aero-engines for high-altitude duties,

Harry Ricardo once more became his mentor and adviser albeit this time in a consulting role himself. Their renewed collaboration in 1928 eventually resulted in a classic of aero-engine design, the Napier Sabre which first appeared in RAF service in 1940, on the Hawker Typhoon. This complex water-cooled engine, which ultimately was made to develop 2,600hp, featured twenty-four horizontally opposed cylinders mounted in an H configuration, the pistons driving two crankshafts geared together. It also incorporated single-sleeve valves of the Burt & McCollum type, thus returning to a system that Halford and Ricardo had first worked on together at Shoreham twenty years previously, and which Ricardo had championed ever since. This system will be more fully discussed in following chapters.

In January 1920, Ricardo's collaborator in the ill-starred 'Flying Destroyer' project, Lieutenant T.B. Barrington of the RNAS (who by then had achieved the rank of colonel in the army) made a reappearance on the scene. After the First World War he had returned to Rolls-Royce at Derby as Assistant Chief Engineer, this being before the arrival of A.J. Rowledge from the rival Napier firm. Anxious to resume his personal collaboration with Ricardo, he visited Bridge Works to instruct the firm to produce an experimental version of the patented slipper piston design, suitable for fitting in Rolls-Royce's standard 40/50hp engine as fitted to its famous Silver Ghost car, and also another piston suitable for its new Condor aero-engine.

Ricardo had already been associated with Rolls-Royce since 1916, of course, and his relationship with the Derby firm lasted throughout the interwar years and beyond, with the Bridge Works firm acting as consultants on both automobile and aircraft engine matters. Even so, it took some time before Ricardo had the opportunity to meet the great man, Frederick Henry Royce, in person. As is well known, Royce was then in poor health and, on the orders of his doctor, from 1911 onwards he lived far away from the inclement climate of the Midlands, either on the south coast of England or in the South of France, surrounded by a small design team led by A.G. Elliott, and supervising business by remote control. Contact with his Derby factory was maintained by a constant stream of letters and drawings, and by the presence of Barrington, who acted as a link-man in the chain of command. According to Rolls-Royce historians, Barrington was a gifted engineer whose diplomatic skills matched his great engineering talents.

At the end of February 1920, Ricardo wrote to Royce (who was then residing at Elmstead, his seaside house at West Wittering, near Chichester) inviting him to pay a visit to the new laboratories at Shoreham, which was a mere thirty miles or so eastwards along the Sussex coast. 'We have got a lot of experimental apparatus here that I think will interest you,' he said. Royce replied within the month accepting the invitation, but giving the disappointing news that he was under great pressure of work at that moment and that it would be some time before he would be able to make the drive over. After numerous postponements, the two men finally met for the first time on Thursday 13 May 1920 at Bridge Works. The meeting marked the start of a particularly cordial friendship and shortly afterwards, on 14 June, Royce wrote to Ricardo saying: 'The country is now looking its best and I thought it would be a good time for you and Major Evans to visit West Wittering. Perhaps you could come next Saturday afternoon, and I should be delighted if you would bring your wives and children with you.' Apparently Royce had a bathing-hut on the shore which he often put at the disposal of his guests.

Ricardo described Royce as being by far the most brilliant mechanical designer that he ever met: 'He was also the finest example of intuitive genius, an artist to his fingertips and a perfectionist. He had the reputation of being somewhat of a dragon who breathed fire on anyone at Derby who dared to interfere with or modify any part of his design without his approval. All his staff, I gather, both feared and worshipped him, but he was always charming to me and to my children, who loved him. His gracious manner captured us all. He discussed his engine designs with me and listened to any suggestions I might have to make on technical matters almost as though I was a fellow artist, which I found very flattering.'

In Ricardo's estimation, the piston aero-engine represented the finest achievement ever reached in any sphere of mechanical engineering, for it constituted the best example of what could be achieved by the cooperation of scientist and the practical engineer working in harmony. Those who created these mechanical masterpieces were artists in the fullest sense of the word, he believed. Writing in the fifth edition of his book *The Internal Combustion Engine*, published in 1967, he said; 'In every successful example it will be found that the actual designer of such an engine is neither a great scientist nor an expert mechanic but an artist with an artist's temperament and intuitive genius, though none the less ready to appreciate and accept all the aid that the scientist and the practical mechanic can give him, and competent to blend his and their conflicting demands into a perfect picture. Such men are rare and, in any one country, can be counted almost on the fingers of one hand. Without doubt, the greatest of them all was Sir Henry Royce.' Not surprisingly, a deep rapport was established between the two artist-engineers, and their occasional, informal social meetings went on for many years, Royce's health permitting. On more than one occasion, while on holiday in the South of France, Ricardo and his family visited Royce's home, the Villa Mimosa, overlooking the Mediterranean at Le Canadel, and were taken for scenic drives along the coast in his experimental Phantom tourer.

In April 1922, Ricardo wrote to his hero saying, 'We have been hammering away at the question of combustion chamber design for a long time . . . and as a result we have found that we can produce a form of combustion chamber for side-valve engines which will show a very substantial improvement in power output and economy over the conventional form. . . . Quite recently we have put our theories to the practical test of altering a number of different engines in service and have been able to show a gain in power ranging from 10 per cent to 15 per cent and in economy of, in some cases, slightly over 15 per cent.' This invention, of course, was Ricardo's turbulent head, which by then had become the standard way of improving the performance of side-valve engines. '. . . I hope you will not think it impertinent if I suggest that we may perhaps be able to improve upon the combustion chamber of your ordinary car engine. I make this suggestion with all humility and reserve, because I appreciate to the full the amount of thought that you always put into every detail of design. . . . I hope that you will soon be able to find time to pay us another visit here – we have quite a lot of new toys I should very much like to show you,' he concluded.

It took a while for a reply to be received at Bridge Works but, on 7 June 1922, Royce duly wrote to Ricardo explaining that he had been away in the South of France on his doctor's orders for the earlier part of the year. However, having recently returned he would like nothing better than to come over to Shoreham to see what had been going on there during his absence abroad. 'Can I bring Miss Aubin, who will keep very quiet in the office?' he asked. Miss Aubin was his nurse and companion, and some say his mistress too. Another letter lodged in the Bridge Works' files reveals that later that month Royce wrote in his own handwriting to apologise for not being able to call on Ricardo at his home at Lancing as arranged, and to invite him and Major Evans to tea at Elmstead once again. 'Naturally, we more than hope that you will bring your ladies and children with you,' he added.

Evidently, these visits were still continuing many years later. In the last of his letters surviving in the Bridge Works archives, dated 26 June 1929 when he was aged sixty-six, Royce wrote to Ricardo inviting him over to West Wittering for another of their regular chats. A handwritten postscript reads: 'Bring Mrs Ricardo and your daughter . . . don't make it too serious or formal.' Doubtless the talk soon turned to gardening, a topic dear to the hearts of both these great artist-engineers.

It seems that by the mid-1920s the ubiquitous Barrington had departed from Derby and that Ernest Hives and A.J. Rowledge (who had recently moved from Napier) were now in charge of the experimental and design departments at Rolls-Royce in its founder's continued absence. However, another file of correspondence preserved in Bridge Works' archives reveals that some years later, having joined Bentley Motors Ltd to become its Chief Engineer, Barrington once again played a significant role in Ricardo's career. On 24 August 1929, a letter arrived at Shoreham from Captain W.O. Bentley enquiring if the Ricardo firm might be interested in entering into a consulting agreement with his firm, with a view to jointly designing and developing an entirely new engine capable of producing a higher specific output in terms of horsepower per litre and pound of weight than had been possible in previous Bentley engines. At this time, the Bentley range comprised the well-known 4½-litre four-cylinder engine and the two six-cylinder engines, the 6½-litre and the 8 litre, all of which had been developed from the original 3-litre engine that was by now out of production.

Evidently, Ricardo and Hetherington had not seen anything of W.O. Bentley since the Isle of Man TT races in 1923, but they had kept in touch over the intervening six years. Replying on 2 September, Hetherington affirmed that: 'We shall be delighted to do anything we can to help you.' Later that month Bentley paid a visit to Shoreham and by early October, Ricardo had prepared a scheme for a special cylinder head to be fitted to the new, 4-litre, six-cylinder engine of 86mm bore and 115mm stroke that was already under development at Cricklewood in single-cylinder form. By June 1930, two full-scale prototype six-cylinder engines were running on the Bentley test-beds.

The Ricardo design was a variation of the high-power head (itself an improvement of the original Ricardo turbulent head), which had been developed in association with the Société Industrielle et Commerciale de Gennevilliers in France, the owners of the Chenard et Walcker marque, which was already employing it in a 1.5-litre engine. This cylinder head was therefore subject to a joint patent. Under the management of M. Jean Donnay, the Société had been one of Ricardo's earliest and most friendly collaborators and, in fact, at that time it controlled the licences for all Ricardo's patents on the mainland of Europe, just as the Waukesha Motor Company did in the USA. With the full consent of the French company, therefore, Bentley Motors was awarded a licence for the manufacture of the high-power head later in October 1930.

The high power head differed from the turbulent head in that it allowed for the use of an overhead inlet valve located in the cylinder head immediately above the piston and working in conjunction with a side exhaust valve, situated in the engine block, rather than a conventional twin side-valve arrangement. This enabled a much higher compression ratio to be employed.

Exactly what use W.O. Bentley had in mind for his new high-revving, push-rod, 4-litre engine is unknown, although it seems that he was much concerned by the need to introduce a smaller, less overtly sporting car to compete with the Rolls-Royce 20/25hp model. But by the time that its development had been completed in late 1930, his company had been overtaken by the financial difficulties that brought about its downfall and, ultimately, its takeover by its great rival Rolls-Royce the following year. The onset of the Depression had led to a marked reduction in demand for the traditional 6½- and 8-litre Bentleys, and with sales almost at a standstill a large stock of chassis had built up. In an attempt to generate cash, of which the company was by now desperately short, against W.O. Bentley's wishes the board of directors voted that fifty examples of the short- wheelbase version of the 8-litre chassis were to be hastily fitted with the new engine (which produced 120 bhp at 4,000rpm) and marketed as the 4 litre.

As is well known, the results were disappointing, for the Ricardo engine, good as it was, was quite inadequate for the task of propelling a chassis intended for a unit twice its size. The vehicle lacked the performance traditionally associated with the marque, and W.O. Bentley refused to be associated with it, saying that it was not a car that could be recognised as a Bentley at all. Consequently, for many years the 4 litre was held in contempt by Bentley enthusiasts, who believed, quite erroneously, that the great W.O. Bentley himself had played no part at all in its creation.

When Rolls-Royce took over Bentley Motors, it also acquired the services of T.B. Barrington, who returned to Derby taking with him Ricardo's high-power head design. Although all work on the Bentley engine had ceased at Bridge Works in July 1931, a further derivative of this design was incorporated in the Rolls-Royce B series six-cylinder engines, employed in the postwar Rolls-Royce and Bentley standard models of the 1946–60 era, until the arrival of its American-inspired V8.

The files at Shoreham throw further light on the plight of the illustrious Bentley firm. In February 1931, Barrington wrote to Ricardo saying that a suggestion had recently been made that the use of the hallowed 8-litre engine for bus and commercial work should be considered, and inviting Ricardo's opinions on the matter. Ricardo's reply shows all the patience, tact and diplomacy on which his reputation as a consultant was founded. 'I take it that you wish me to be quite frank,' he began, 'and if I cast doubts on the suitability of your engine, please remember that my criticisms are directed not against the engine for the purpose it was designed to fulfil, but against its use for another . . . very different purpose.' After three pages of carefully reasoned argument in demolition of the proposition he gently concluded, 'I am awfully sorry to be so sceptical, but I feel it is quite unlikely that an engine designed for pleasure car work [i.e. in propelling a high-performance sports car] will suit a lorry or bus.' Whatever would Ettore Bugatti have said to that!

CHAPTER 15

Sussex by the Sea

In founding his laboratories at Shoreham, it had been Ricardo's firm belief that their role would be to carry out research, design and development work on behalf of the many small engine-building firms and motor car constructors that existed at the time, but which lacked the necessary resources or experience that he and his team could provide. He later admitted that in this aim he was utterly wrong, and that his firm had paid heavily in its early years for this error of judgement on his part. His experience in attempting to do business with such clients, by supplying them with designs for small automobile or industrial engines on a royalty basis, soon showed that his efforts were both unproductive and unprofitable. Thereafter, his activities as a designer were concentrated on collaborating with much bigger companies, while his research work gravitated towards long-term projects on behalf of official government bodies such as the Air Ministry or large corporations such as the Anglo-Dutch Shell company.

Before the First World War, the design and manufacture of aircraft and automobile engines in Great Britain had – with a few exceptions such as Lanchester, Royce, Rowledge and Pomeroy – been in the hands of men who had begun their careers as makers of bicycles or agricultural implements. In Ricardo's view, such men were 'superb mechanics, well versed in the art of light mechanical design, but for the most part, abysmally ignorant of thermo-dynamics or the many other factors upon which the performance of their engines depended'. Sometimes, rather more by accident than by design, they overcame this ignorance and produced engines with a satisfactory standard of performance and reliability, in which case they were regarded as 'wizards, possessed of some magic and mysterious secret known only to themselves'. But more often than not their lack of scientific knowledge told against them and their endeavours failed for reasons that they could not begin to explain or understand. Nevertheless, in those early days, the scientists and researchers who enquired into these mysteries with precise and systematic experiments were apt to be regarded as freaks, mere boffins isolated in remote worlds of their own, completely lacking in practical experience and quite out of touch with commercial realities.

After the war these attitudes began to change, thanks to the introduction of methodical scientific research into military matters that had taken place during the conflict, and to the long-overdue introduction of science into the civil aircraft and automobile industries that came about as a direct result. These trained enquirers, of whom Ricardo himself was a prime example, quickly set about rationalising the development of the internal combustion engine and debunking the notions of witchcraft that had held sway hitherto. Nevertheless, the influence of the old pragmatic metal-bashing school of thought still persisted in certain quarters, and for very many years to come the presence of fully qualified graduate engineers was hard to detect in the design departments of many well-known British motor-manufacturing firms, controlled as they were by hard-nosed

LA NOUVELLE 10 CV. ZÉBRE

Torpedo Série
5 Places

AGENT RÉGIONAL:·

In 1924 Ricardo was invited to design a 12hp (10CV) car for the French Le Zèbre company of
Suresne, near Paris. It was the only occasion on which he undertook complete responsibility for
every aspect of design – engine, chassis and bodywork together.

businessmen who had begun their working lives without the benefit of a university
education, or even a recognised technical apprenticeship. Among such men, product
research, design and development ranked a long way behind production itself in the list
of priorities, and in the buoyant seller's market of the times, these sins of omission on the
part of motor magnates, such as Herbert Austin and William Morris, went unnoticed by
the eager and undiscriminating car-buying public at large. Such firms built their products
down to a price, not up to a standard and, needless to say, they were rarely numbered
among Ricardo's clients.

Apart from Rolls-Royce and Vauxhall, the earliest among his automobile and engine-
building clients included such names as Bean, AEC, Albion, Triumph and Dorman, all of
whom adopted the turbulent head, but it was as much among Continental as native
British companies that he built his reputation. The turbulent head became particularly
well known in France where the first company to employ it was Automobiles Le Zèbre,
based at Suresnes, near Paris. Ricardo's work for this firm included a number of designs,
the best known being the Type Z, a 2-litre car for which his Shoreham firm designed not
only the engine but also the chassis, running-gear and bodywork, making it the only
vehicle that he was ever responsible for *in toto*. Founded in 1911 by Jacques Bizet (the
son of the composer) and Jules Salomon (the engineer who was later to design André
Citroën's first car, the Type A of 1919), the Société Anonyme des Automobiles Le Zèbre
had initially specialised in building small and inexpensive cycle-cars. When the company
was reformed after the war under new management (both Bizet and Salomon had long
since departed) its directors continued this policy for a while, producing a number of

Ricardo duly acquired a Type Z Le Zèbre as his own personal transport and used it for a touring holiday with his family through the Loire Valley in France, in 1925.

Remarkably, these family snapshots of the trip have survived – perhaps the only photographs ever taken of a car designer on a motoring holiday in one of his own creations – to show that even Ricardo suffered the kind of mechanical misfortunes that ordinary motorists meet with when touring abroad!

small cars in the 6, 8 and 10hp categories, including a 10hp car which was actually an Amilcar design built under licence. The success of this model led them to decide on building another in that class. Being without a resident designer, therefore, in 1922/3 they appointed Harry Ricardo to produce a scheme for a new, larger, more powerful and expensive car, the Type Z, which was produced in limited numbers between 1924 and 1930 when the firm ceased trading. No more than 550 examples are believed to have been produced, of which only two or three have survived, one of them in the possession of Ricardo Consulting Engineers Ltd at Shoreham. The Type Z came in a variety of body styles including a five-seater torpedo or open tourer, a four-seater sports tourer, a four-seater saloon and a coupé-de-ville, though later a de luxe six-seater tourer, a landaulet, a taxi and a light truck were added to the range. Powered by a 2-litre, four-cylinder, side-valve engine of 69mm bore and 132mm stroke, the Type Z Le Zèbre also featured Ricardo's patented slipper pistons and was rated in France as a 10CV and in the UK as a 12hp RAC.

Two examples of this car found their way to Shoreham in 1924, where they were used for many years, well into the thirties, one serving as Harry Ricardo's own personal and family transport, and the other as a general works car. In addition, there was a third, much smaller Le Zèbre at Shoreham during the twenties, a little open tourer powered by an advanced 1,100cc, four-cylinder overhead valve, push-rod engine. This unique vehicle, which was used at first by Oliver Thornycroft and later by Jack Pitchford (then a young and recently recruited engineer but who was destined to rise through the ranks and become the Ricardo company's Managing Director in 1950), was the prototype of an aborted design project that came somewhat later than the Type Z, and that was also designed entirely at Bridge Works. Apparently, this 'Little Le Zèbre' ended its days in the late 1930s, having become by then the property of Harry Ricardo's eldest daughter Kate, who used it to travel from Lancing to Brighton every day when she was studying at Brighton Art School.

A remarkable series of snapshots has survived in the Ricardo family album showing Sir Harry on a motoring vacation in France in his Le Zèbre during the summer of 1925, touring in the Loire Valley with his wife and daughter Kate. These are perhaps the only photographs extant in which a famous automobile designer can be seen driving his own creation in an informal, off-duty, holiday situation. Not only do they present a charming picture of a motoring expedition across rural France in those bygone days, with the tourists picnicking by the side of a ruler-straight road lined with tall poplar trees, utterly devoid of passing traffic; they also show that even so great an engineer as Ricardo was not entirely immune from the pitfalls that beset ordinary motorists in similar circumstances. In many of these snaps he can be seen tinkering beneath the bonnet of his car, or crawling under its chassis to mend a puncture.

These and other photos of the period show that at the age of forty Ricardo was in his prime. He had lost the gawky, gangling appearance that had characterised him as a young man and had become quite a distinguished-looking figure, still tall and spare, but no longer so thin and lanky as before. His success had filled him out and brought him a measure of self-confidence, but he was still by no means self-assertive. His hair, never thick, had all but disappeared, throwing his high-domed forehead into prominence. His clipped moustache, which he maintained throughout his life, was neatly trimmed in the military fashion, while from his mouth there invariable protruded a slender pipe which he puffed constantly, thereby adding a professorial air to his personality. His three-piece, single-breasted suits

were well cut in a conservative, Edwardian style that flattered his lean physique. He never
went hatless, and always wore a soft felt trilby or, in summer, a straw hat with a striped
band, the latter teamed with a buff-coloured linen jacket, grey flannels and club or
university tie. He was never a stickler for formality in matters of dress and it seems that he
followed his father's example and never donned evening clothes if it could be avoided.
Despite his fame and prestige, in his manner and deportment he remained diffident and
unassuming though by this point in his life he had acquired the *gravitas* that served him so
well when dealing with officialdom. Here was a man who knew exactly what he was talking
about but who never talked just for the sake of hearing his own voice, a decent and reliable
chap who could always be trusted to do the right thing. To the decision-makers in Whitehall
and Westminster, other technical experts could seem awkward or tiresome characters, spiky,
abrasive and thoroughly difficult to deal with. But not the urbane and civilised Ricardo. In
short, he was *persona grata* with the upper echelons of the establishment, but far too liberal
and independently minded a man to be a hidebound member of it.

Enjoyable though it was, the work of designing the Vauxhall and Le Zèbre cars was a
minor matter for Ricardo and his colleagues in comparison with the demanding
programme of research work that underpinned the existence of Bridge Works at its
outset, the offer of which had been the crucial determining factor in the Shoreham
laboratory's foundation. This, of course, was the research contract carried out on behalf
of the Asiatic Petroleum Company (a subsidiary of the Shell group) between 1919 and
1923, to investigate the problems of matching petroleum fuels to engines. As mentioned
in Chapter 12, in 1918 its Managing Director, Sir Robert Waley-Cohen, had promised
Ricardo that he would provide the sum of £10,000 a year to fund this research and to pay
for the design and manufacture of the necessary test equipment.

The project amounted to an exhaustive inquiry, both theoretical and practical, into the
ways in which the performance of the internal combustion engine is affected by
variations in the composition of its fuel. To the lay motorist, petrol is an immutable and
invariable substance derived from crude oil, itself a liquid of fixed and consistent
composition when pumped out of the ground, so that it has only to be lightly treated at
the refinery prior to its sale at filling stations as a branded product. In fact, gasoline is a
blend of many different chemical ingredients and additives, and its composition and
properties can be varied widely in the refining process, according to the source and
nature of the raw materials used in its production, as well as to its ultimate intended
purpose and the performance expected of it.

As Ricardo put it, he had long been convinced that the onset of detonation or knock
was the most important factor in limiting the performance of the spark-ignition petrol
engine, and had satisfied himself that it arose from the spontaneous ignition of a small
part of the fuel charge due to compression by the advancing flame front ignited by the
spark, and that its tendency to do so depended on the shape of the combustion chamber,
the movement of the gases within it, and, above all, on the chemical composition of the
fuel. Therefore, the next stage in the understanding of the phenomenon of combustion
was to carry out a thorough scientific analysis of the physical and chemical properties of
the very many types of light hydrocarbon fuels that were then being discovered and
extracted by oil companies such as Shell.

For this work Ricardo sought out the part-time help and collaboration of a research
chemist and a research physicist, both of the highest calibre, and his choice fell upon two
gifted academics whom he had met earlier through his work on the Aeronautical Research

Committee during the final stages of the First World War, and who, like himself, were disciples of Bertram Hopkinson; indeed it was Hopkinson who had actually introduced him to these two scientists, during his visits to the Martlesham Heath research station where the pair, both of them trained pilots, were based as Experimental Officers and engaged on the flight testing of aircraft. The first of the duo was a Fellow of Oriel College, Oxford, Henry Thomas Tizard (later Sir Henry Tizard FRS) and the second was David Randall Pye (later Sir David Pye FRS) who was a Lecturer in Engineering at Cambridge University and a Fellow of Trinity College. Both men subsequently went on to reach the highest levels of distinction in scientific research and administration, in both the aeronautical and the academic spheres, Tizard as Rector of Imperial College of Science and Technology and Pye as Provost of University College, London.

Henry Tizard in particular was destined to play a crucial role in national and world events, and his contribution to the defence of the United Kingdom can be claimed to have changed the course of history. Like Ricardo, he was Hopkinson's protégé and disciple, especially in the way that, from 1920 to 1929, he worked untiringly at the Department of Scientific and Industrial Research to promote the close cooperation of the military, scientific, administrative and industrial communities in the national interest, particularly in the realm of aviation. In common with Hopkinson, he had the gift of stimulating an interplay and understanding between research scientists and the serving officers of the Royal Air Force. As Hopkinson's successor at the Ministry of Munitions in 1918, he took over his responsibilities with the rank of lieutenant-colonel, joining the Aeronautical Research Committee (and also its Engine Subcommittee) in 1919, becoming Chairman in 1933, and serving until 1943, alongside his friend Ricardo. But, as we shall see in Chapter 19, his greatest achievement was as Chairman of the Committee for the Scientific Study of Air Defence (the Tizard Committee) between 1935 and 1940, when he took the steps that led to the setting up of the Radio Direction Finding (Radar) network. This development, of course, had a profound effect on the outcome of the Battle of Britain, by making it possible for the RAF to detect the course of attacking enemy aircraft and intercept them at long range. It was Tizard also who first took notice of Dr Barnes Wallis's scheme to attack the reservoirs of the Ruhr with a 'bouncing bomb' and who encouraged the RAF to take up the idea, the result of which was the famous Dambusters raid in 1943. In an obituary notice published by the Chemical Society on Tizard's death in 1959, the eminent physical chemist Sir Harold Hartley wrote: 'Tizard was at his best in throwing out challenging questions that forced people to think. He had no respect for accepted dogma and often saw things in a new light. . . . No scientist has ever made a more valuable contribution to Britain at a time of crisis.'

As soon as Tizard and Pye were released from their military duties after the Armistice they retired to the cloistered calm of Oxford University where they compiled what Sir Harry described as 'a really monumental analysis' of the physical and thermal properties of all the light hydrocarbon fuels together with other possible volatile liquid fuels such as alcohol, acetone and ether, using samples provided by Kewley of Shell as in the Walton experiments. Not only did their thesis set out such obvious data as specific gravity, boiling point, calorific value and latent heat of evaporation, but it also recorded more abstruse factors such as the total internal energy in terms of ft lb per standard cubic inch of a fuel–air mixture in the proportion required for complete combustion. No such analysis had ever been attempted before. For this work they drew on all the known data available, supplemented by their own researches at Oxford.

The original E35 variable compression ratio experimental engine, installed at Bridge Works in about 1920. Operating it are, from left to right, Harry Ricardo's colleagues Oliver Thornycroft, Major Evans and Dennis Plunkett.

Meanwhile, Ricardo set to work to design and produce the two single-cylinder test engines that would be required as scientific apparatus in the practical experiments which were to follow. The first of the pair (which had identical cylinder dimensions of 4.5-inch bore and 8-inch stroke) was known as the E35 and was ingeniously designed so that its compression ratio could be altered between 3.7:1 and 8:1 while it was running, without disturbing its temperature and other variables; this facility enabled the experimenters to determine the highest useful compression ratio that could be obtained with any given fuel, that being a measure of its efficiency. The other, suggested by Tizard, also employed the variable compression principle, but was so constructed that, on ignition, its piston would make only one rapid stroke and then become locked in its top-dead-centre position, by means of a sliding toggle arrangement. This unit was known as the E19, or alternatively, by virtue of its odd shape, the Sphinx. Both engines were built at Peterborough by Peter Brotherhood Ltd where Ricardo's old friend Commander Bryant was still in charge of affairs.

By the summer of 1919 all was ready for the experimental work to begin at the new Bridge Works laboratories and both Tizard and Pye came down to Shoreham to take part. Throughout the next eighteen months, the team examined and tested literally hundreds of fuel samples, including nearly all brands of gasoline then available worldwide, to prove or disprove the conclusions that had been reached in the theoretical analysis at Oxford. As Ricardo explained, 'as expected, we confirmed that the incidence of detonation was the most important single factor limiting the performance of the petrol engine, and at Tizard's suggestion we expressed this factor in terms of a fuel's Toluene Number, the number indicating the proportion of toluene in the blend, toluene being the least prone to detonate of any hydrocarbon fuel we had tested. During the course of this research we learned a great deal about the behaviour and appetite of the petrol engine and were able to advise the Shell company as to its diet,' he concluded. Indeed, for the next few years the Toluene Number was the standard measure used to express the quality or suitability of any fuel intended for petrol engines, though later, as a result of developments in the USA, it was agreed to substitute iso-octane for toluene as the recognised yardstick of resistance to detonation, and thus the expression 'Octane Rating' became universally accepted as the measure of quality in any blend or brand of petrol. Moreover, in 1926 two scientists working for General Motors in the USA, Charles Kettering and Thomas Midgeley, discovered that the use of tetra-ethyl-lead as an additive had a remarkable effect in reducing the tendency of petroleum fuels to detonate, thereby allowing higher compression ratios to be employed by automobile manufacturers.

It had been agreed with the Asiatic Petroleum Company that the results of this classic investigation could be made public eighteen months after the company itself received the Ricardo report. Thus, in due course the results were published by the Empire Fuels Committee and also in two papers that appeared in the *Automobile Engineer* during 1921, entitled 'The characteristics of various fuels for internal combustion engines' by Tizard and Pye and 'The influence of various fuels on the performance of the internal combustion engine' by Ricardo and Thornycroft. The appearance of these papers marked a landmark in the understanding of the internal combustion engine, and were fundamental also to the development of the petrochemical industry during the 1920s. At last, fuels for aircraft and automobiles could be marketed with some knowledge of their likely behaviour in an engine, a fact that helped vastly to establish the reputation and credibility of Ricardo's infant organisation among potential clients and the general public alike. This achievement Sir Harry modestly dismissed by saying that he was merely reaping the harvest that Hopkinson had sown, some twenty years previously.

The fuel research project had another important consequence. As a result of the Shoreham experiments, Ricardo's variable compression ratio engine became the standard apparatus for checking fuel samples at laboratories and refineries all round the world. It

Left: Sir Henry Tizard FRS (1885–1959) the distinguished scientist and administrator who was Harry Ricardo's close friend, colleague and collaborator over a period of forty years. *Right*: Sir David Randall Pye FRS (1886–1960), chemist, administrator and academic. As Deputy Director and subsequently Director of Scientific Research at the Air Ministry from 1925 to 1943, he exerted a profound influence on the direction of aircraft development. Together with Ricardo and Tizard, he served on the Aeronautical Research Committee continually throughout the interwar years.

was produced in a form approved by the Cooperative Fuel Research Committee of the USA, and was built and supplied by the Waukesha Motor Company by arrangement with Harry Horning.

The work on fuels for Shell was immediately followed by another three-year contract for research into lubricants, this time financed jointly by Shell and the Air Ministry, the former being interested primarily in the behaviour of its proprietary engine oils and greases in a motoring environment, while the latter sought information on the properties of the bearing materials used in aero-engines. For this work, Ricardo once again designed and made the necessary test equipment for use both at Shoreham and at the National Physical Laboratory at Teddington, the most important piece of apparatus being an ingenious machine for testing the endurance of big-end bearings in conjunction with different lubricants. Much important data was collected over this period but the findings were never published due to objections from the Air Ministry. Ricardo considered this to be a great pity as, had the information been made public, a great deal of duplication of effort elsewhere would have been avoided in the years that followed. The principal conclusion reached was that the characteristic 'oiliness' of vegetable and animal oils, such as castor oil and sperm-whale oil, to which so much importance had been attached in the past, was, in fact, of little or no significance in preventing wear in an internal combustion engine. Indeed there was no difference in this respect between the performance of vegetable or animal oils and that of straight mineral oils. 'This was the end of any serious use of vegetable oils as engine lubricants, although they continued to be purchased by amateurs for many years,' Ricardo observed.

In those days the pace of life at Shoreham was serene and tranquil in comparison with the frenzied urgency of the modern world, and as he often proudly recalled, Harry Ricardo and his colleagues rarely missed a meal through pressure of work. On the principle that all work and no play makes for a dull life, it was always his chief priority to devote as much time to his family and his off-duty hobbies as to his regular business activities. Overtime was unknown, and when his working day was over he made straight to his workshop at Penstone, where he delighted in making toys and models, or to his boat in Shoreham harbour for a spot of sailing and fishing. His work with Tizard and Pye had been 'the most interesting and fruitful research with which I have ever been concerned. . . . At the same time, at Shoreham I returned to the sort of home life my wife and I had enjoyed so much before the outbreak of war, and I took up once again the hobbies – boating, fishing and butterfly collecting – of our earlier days. With the work I loved best in the world only five minutes drive away, with more spacious surroundings, with the sea close at hand, and with more money to spend and more leisure time to enjoy my wife's and my children's company, I had everything that the heart of man could desire, except that we never again recaptured the sense of security or the carefree light-heartedness of our pre-war days. Although the politicians and press assured us that never again would there be a major war, yet in our hearts we knew this to be wishful thinking.'

Certainly, Tizard enjoyed himself greatly in Ricardo's company at Shoreham, then and for many years to come. During the summer of 1919 he stayed as a guest with the Ricardo family at Penstone, joining in all their activities and enthusiasms, boating in particular. Tizard returned to the area again and again, often renting a house on the outskirts of Worthing, and in due course he became perhaps Harry Ricardo's closest friend beyond the intimate circle of colleagues and associates at Shoreham. 'He was, I think, the most brilliant of my contemporaries [they were born in the same year], a delightful companion with a pretty sense of humour,' said Ricardo in his autobiography. 'His wit charmed us all and my two young daughters adored him.' Seventy years later, Sir Harry's third daughter Camilla, born in 1921, still retains fond childhood memories of the great man, and recalls her father's deep affection for his fellow scientist, which lasted for over forty years, until Tizard's death in 1959.

Henry Tizard came from a naval family (his father, Captain Thomas Henry Tizard FRS was Assistant Hydrographer to the Admiralty) and until his short-sightedness prevented it, he had been set on a career in the navy himself, so it was not surprising that he shared Ricardo's passion for the sea, and for messing about in boats. As we saw in earlier chapters, Ricardo had been initiated into the delights of sailing and fishing by his father Halsey as a boy when on family holidays in Dorset, Devon and Cornwall, so as soon as he became established at Penstone, he began a search in the local harbour for a suitable motorised sailing dinghy, in which he could recapture these pleasures and introduce his own children to the nautical life. Soon he had found such a boat, equipped with a little single-cylinder, four-stroke petrol engine which, with its shallow draft and light weight, could safely be navigated through the powerful current at the harbour entrance, and out into the open sea beyond at most states of the tide. At weekends or in the long summer evenings, he and Tizard would set out together in this craft, which he had named

The Mudfish, to fish for mackerel with rod and line, but although they had great fun, they had little luck. To improve their catch, they therefore decided to try their hands at trawling with a 5-ft net, which turned out to be a far more difficult exercise than either man had bargained for. With practice, however, they became quite skilled and on good days when the sea was calm they were able to catch quite a lot of skate, plaice and Dover sole, in addition to crabs, squid and octopus. Being scientists, they calculated that they could reckon on catching 1 lb of edible fish per pint of petrol used by the boat's little engine. 'For these fishing trips, Tizard was the ideal companion, and I think he enjoyed them as much as I did,' Ricardo recalled.

So much fun was had on board *The Mudfish* that very soon Ricardo commissioned a local boatyard to build him a larger motor boat and, later, two small sailing dinghies as well, for his two eldest daughters to use in Shoreham harbour at high tide. This 18-ft launch, which he christened the *San José* proved a great success as she had ample room on board to allow the entire family and guests to make a voyage up the River Adur,

As a keen yachtsman, in 1924 Ricardo acquired the *Pearl*, a former Bristol pilot cutter that had been converted for use by the Brixham fishing fleet. She was to be his pride and joy for almost fifteen years.

Like his father Halsey, Harry Ricardo enjoyed nothing more than a simple family holiday by the seaside with his wife and children.

which was navigable as far as Steyning when the tide was right. Here on summer evenings, it was their delight to enjoy a picnic supper spread out on the river bank, and to watch the birdlife in the rushes. At weekends, if the weather was favourable, they sometimes made the open sea passage to Littlehampton, and thence up the River Arun to Arundel or Amberley, where they would visit the castles. The *San José* served Ricardo well for fishing purposes for nearly twenty years, but gradually he became more adventurous and longed to have a much larger sea-going boat in which he and his family and their guests could all sleep on board and make longer holiday voyages.

By the spring of 1924 he had acquired and refitted the *Pearl*, a splendid 48-ft yacht of uncertain age that had started her life as a Bristol pilot cutter before being converted into a trawler, and which he had discovered at Brixham. As her keel was too deep for her to lie at Shoreham at low tide, during the summer months she was kept at a mooring at Poole, and from there over the next twelve or so years the Ricardo family and their friends including Henry Tizard regularly made long runs under sail, westward along the coast to such harbours as Dartmouth, Plymouth and Fowey, before old age overtook the *Pearl* and she became unseaworthy. 'During her life she gave us a great deal of pleasure and the thrill of adventure,' Sir Harry recalled.

'So far as I can remember, we never got into any dangerous situations for she was an excellent sea boat and seemed to enjoy rough weather, but being amateurs, we did get into several humiliating and undignified situations,' he wrote in his autobiography. One of these in particular stood out in his memory. In 1929, the Admiralty had allotted him an anchorage in the Solent, off Ryde on the Isle of Wight, where he planned to watch the second of the three Schneider Trophy seaplane races, which followed a course round the island. Unfortunately, his boat dragged its anchor in the strong tide, and during the race he kept drifting on to the course of the race, which was supposed to be clear of shipping, with the result that he suffered the indignity of being severely ticked off by a naval patrol boat. To make matters worse, after the race was over he met a sister ship to the *Pearl* and started to race her. Seeking to steal a march on his opponent, Ricardo took the risk of steering a course to cut inside the buoy marking the end of Ryde Sands, only to run hard aground in full view of the smartly dressed owners and crews of the assembled craft of the Royal Yacht Squadron. As the tide fell, his boat was left high and dry on her side and became the laughing stock of the assembled shipping, all the more so because the *Pearl* was stranded on the wrong side of the buoy to her owner's great embarrassment. There she lay for hours, the object of ridicule and scorn, until well after midnight when she was refloated on the rising tide. Needless to say, the next and final Schneider Trophy race, held in 1931, he watched from the shore.

In 1929, however, when Ricardo and his friends on board the *Pearl* saw the British team achieve its second victory in the biannual Schneider Trophy series, they saw the winning aircraft, a Supermarine S6B seaplane (designed by R.J. Mitchell, the designer of the Spitfire) passed overhead at a speed of 328.65 mph, a clear 40 mph faster than the nearest competitor. Like the Supermarine aircraft that won the trophy in 1927, this machine was powered by the high-performance Rolls-Royce R Type racing engine, a water-cooled supercharged V12, 36.7-litre unit designed for sustained high power, and producing 1,900hp at 3,000rpm, three times that of current standard production Rolls-Royce aero engines. Designed by A.J. Rowledge, the R Type was based on Henry Royce's Kestrel and Buzzard designs dating from 1927, both of these engines having been developed in association with Ricardo's Bridge Works laboratories.

But to win the Schneider Trophy outright for 1931, a third successive victory was required. Due to the effects of the Depression, however, the British government decided not to enter the third contest, until a private intervention by the heiress Lady Houston (who put up the then enormous sum of £100,000 to guarantee British participation) finally shamed it into action with only six months to go before the race, which was to be held on 13 September 1931. Working flat out at Derby, Hives and Rowledge and their engineering team managed to

Sir Frederick Henry Royce (1863–1933). Ricardo considered him to be the finest engineer that he ever worked with, 'an artist to his fingertips'.

In addition to Chrysler, Caterpillar and, of course, the Waukesha Engine Comapny, Harley-Davidson was numbered among Ricardo's earliest American clients.

increase the output of the R Type engine to 2,350hp at 3,100rpm, allowing Flight-Lieutenant John Boothman of the Royal Air Force High Speed Flight to win the event at an average speed of 340.8 mph, and to gain the world's most prestigious aviation prize in perpetuity. Undoubtedly, this victory also served to establish the credentials of the Rolls-Royce company as a builder of high-performance aero-engines.

Almost immediately afterwards, on 29 September 1931, the same pilot and aircraft achieved a new world speed record of 407.5 mph, thanks to a special sprint version of the R Type engine capable of producing 2,783hp at 3,400rpm, when fuelled with an exotic cocktail of methanol, benzole, acetone and tetra-ethyl-lead concocted by Wing Commander Rodwell Banks. It was a proud day for British aviation, and an occasion not without satisfaction for Harry Ricardo either. As a consultant to the Rolls-Royce firm throughout the previous decade, he had been closely involved in the design and development of the R Type engine and its predecessors (in particular, by advising on the redesign of the R Type's con-rod and crankshaft assembly to withstand the enormous loads imposed in the record-breaking runs). And not only that, the special aviation fuel used in the flight had also come about as a direct result of his research activities – the programme of petroleum investigations and experiments that he had carried out with Tizard and Pye at Shoreham, ten years earlier.

CHAPTER 16

Ricardo's Comet

By the middle of the 1920s, Harry Ricardo's turbulent cylinder head had really caught on with car owners, so that for a while at least he became a well-known figure among the general motoring public. Realising how greatly his invention improved the performance of the side-valve engines that powered the inexpensive popular family cars of the time, they began to demand it by name. Consequently it soon became widely available both in Great Britain and in France as original equipment fitted to many well-known makes and models of private and commercial vehicles, and as an accessory produced by proprietary manufacturers, such as H.R. Pope, which enthusiasts could purchase and fit themselves to hot-up their cars. Actually developed and patented as early as 1917, the turbulent head yielded substantial royalties for the Shoreham firm throughout the lean years of the Depression, helping to keep it afloat when normal consultancy and research work was in short supply. It is estimated that between 1919 and 1932 approximately £40,000 was earned from this source, of which nearly £25,000 was received between 1927 and 1930.

Unfortunately, not every car builder who made and sold Ricardo's brainchild acknowledged the fact. While his British and Continental patents were respected for the most part, this was not the case in the USA where several leading automobile firms such as Ford, General Motors and Chrysler employed the turbulent head but declined to admit their debt to its inventor, or rather to Harry Horning of the Waukesha company who held the US patent rights. And as Horning was unwilling to fight a patent action against such formidable opponents, there was nothing that the Ricardo firm could do about the situation.

By the end of the decade, an ever-growing number of American-built cars equipped with the turbulent head were being imported into Europe. And not only were their makers guilty of ignoring Horning's US patent, they also openly incited their European agents to challenge the validity of Ricardo's British and Continental patents. Indeed they even went so far as to offer to supply Ricardo's genuine and law-abiding licensees with technical evidence that would 'bust his patent wide open', thereby relieving them of any further obligation to pay. The Ricardo company was therefore faced with the harsh reality that, sooner or later, it would be forced to take legal action in defence of its turbulent head patents, not merely to protect its interest in that particular intellectual property, but also to safeguard the royalty income arising from any further inventions that might come about through its current and future research work. As Sir Harry said, 'It was all the more important for us to make it clear that we were prepared to fight for the sanctity of our patents, past, present and future.'

The issue came to a head early in the 1930s when Ricardo began to suspect that certain British and Continental firms had followed the Americans' example by disregarding his patents and introducing several new models equipped with side-valve engines featuring

Harry Ricardo being greeted by his American friend Harry Horning of the Waukesha Engine Company, on his arrival in New York on board the SS *Liverpool* in 1932.

the turbulent head without paying any royalties. Since there could be no external evidence of this fact, he called upon his old friend Percy Kidner to help ascertain the truth of the matter. As Managing Director and Chief Engineer of Vauxhall Motors, Kidner had been one of the first manufacturers to take up the turbulent head, on a legitimate basis of course, employing it on the Vauxhall 14/40 model.

In November 1928, however, Kidner had sold his interest in the Luton firm to the giant US General Motors Corporation, and with two partners he had acquired a car sales and service firm in Oxford, known as Hartwells Ltd, Automobile Engineers. In its garage at Park End Street, he was able to examine a wide variety of the suspect vehicles owned by his customers, removing their cylinder heads to take a plaster cast of their combustion chambers and reporting the details to Ricardo. One of the worst offenders was the Hillman Wizard saloon built by the Humber-Hillman firm of Coventry (then owned by the Rootes brothers) which had recently been introduced onto the UK market at the 1931 Motor Show. Its combustion chambers appeared to be almost an exact replica of the pattern described in Ricardo's patent specification, and when a brand new example of the car was purchased and stripped down for inspection at Bridge Works, this infringement was confirmed beyond all doubt. 'We wrote a polite letter to the Hillman-Humber firm pointing this out, to which we received a very terse reply to the effect that they had been advised that our patent was invalid, and that they were not prepared to pay any royalty. This was a direct challenge and my Board were unanimous that we must take it up, cost what it might,' Sir Harry stated in his autobiography.

Legal proceedings were instituted immediately and a writ was issued against the Humber-Hillman firm in November 1931, but it was not until October 1933 that the case reached the High Court, after many long months spent collecting and preparing evidence. This was a time of acute anxiety for Ricardo and his associates, not least because his legal representatives, led by the well-known King's Counsel Richard Stafford Cripps MP (later Sir Stafford Cripps), had decided that he should be called upon as a witness. It was most unusual for an inventor to be asked to give evidence in actions of this kind, lest he should get rattled under cross-examination or, worse still, become cocky and overstate his case, but Cripps and his deputy counsel, Mr James Whitehead KC, correctly believed that Ricardo could be trusted to do neither. Noted as a statesman and politician as well as a lawyer (he was the youngest King's Council of his day), Stafford Cripps was another important national figure who entered Ricardo's life on many occasions, particularly when Cripps served as Minister of Aircraft Production from 1942 to 1945. A lifelong socialist (his mother was a sister of Beatrice Webb) he became a leading advocate of the anti-fascist Popular Front in the late 1930s, and from 1940 to 1942 was Ambassador to Russia, although today he is best remembered for his service as Chancellor of the Exchequer in the Labour government of 1947–50.

The hearing before Mr Justice Farwell took nine days, of which Ricardo spent two full days in the witness box being examined at length and in great detail by Stafford Cripps who traced his work right back to his Cambridge days, and he was similarly cross-examined by Mr Trevor Watson KC, the Hillman company's leading counsel. As Sir Harry recalled, despite the weighty matters that were being tried, the proceedings resembled a high-level debate conducted in an atmosphere of friendliness and good humour. Whitehead's opening statement was a masterpiece of lucidity, he considered. 'He explained to the judge that we were not manufacturers but a research team and, as such, depended upon royalties from our patents to finance the research that we were carrying out on behalf of industry as a whole, and that our objective in bringing the case to Court was to establish the sanctity of one of our patents and that it was far from being our intention to hold-up the British motor-car industry to ransom.'

Clearly, the outcome of the case was vital so far as the future of Ricardo's company and his own career was concerned, not to mention the profound effect that the judgement would have upon the future conduct of the automobile industry as a whole. Even so, by all accounts Ricardo acquitted himself with distinction, impressing those present with his technical knowledge and his fluency in expressing complex matters under difficult circumstances. At the end of his evidence, Watson thanked Ricardo for his patience and courtesy and paid him some generous compliments which the judge endorsed. 'Mr Ricardo is a person of the greatest distinction in his profession . . . an engineer being concerned chiefly with internal combustion engines, and he has spent many years in various research work for the improvement of both of internal combustion engines and the improvement of fuels to be used in such engines. He has had a very large experience in these matters and has held, and still holds, important positions with regard to both the War Office and the Air Ministry in connection with this particular form of engine. There is no doubt that he is a person to whom this industry and, indeed, the public owes a considerable debt of gratitude for the result of his researches,' the judge declared in his summing-up.

In delivering his verdict, on 7 November 1933, Mr Justice Farwell pronounced in favour of the plaintiffs. His judgement was that there was no question but that the patent was the subject of a genuine invention which had been arrived at by long and painstaking research; that it was novel at the time of its registration; that the royalties demanded were not excessive and that the turbulent cylinder head had been of great benefit to the automotive industry. Nevertheless, he had some doubts about the wording of one of the claims set out in the patent specification which he found to be ambiguous, imprecise and insufficiently well expressed. If his judgement was to be in strict accordance with the law, he would have no choice but to declare Ricardo's patent void, but as he was allowed some latitude to exercise his own discretion in such matters, he proposed to declare that the validity of the patent should be upheld. In giving this verdict, however, he acknowledged that he was departing from established practice and precedent and that a higher court might take a different view. He therefore gave the defendants leave to appeal.

For the next few weeks, Ricardo and his friends were forced to endure a period of agonising suspense, while waiting for their next court appearance. According to family recollections, the month of December 1933 was the very worst period in Sir Harry Ricardo's life and the Christmas festivities at Penstone that year were dimmed by the gloomy and foreboding cloud that hung overhead.

In the event, however, the end of the matter was something of an anti-climax for when both sides assembled with their respective barristers and solicitors at the Court of Appeal on 15 January 1934, it was announced that the parties had come to an agreement and by consent the appeal was dismissed with costs being awarded to the plaintiffs. In other words, Mr Justice Farwell's earlier verdict had become final, to Ricardo's enormous relief.

There can be no doubt that the verdict marked a vital turning point in the history of Bridge Works, for if the decision had gone against the company its future progress would surely have been on a much smaller scale, and Ricardo's personal influence and credibility in the internal combustion engine industry would have been severely diminished. 'It now remained for us to let it be known that we had no intention of exploiting our victory by demanding excessive royalty payments on any of our patents; all we looked for was to recover the actual costs of our patent action and that without recrimination,' he wrote. 'To this end we obtained an order from the Court for the payment of arrears of royalties from the agents of those American firms whom we knew to be infringing Horning's American patent and to have been inciting British firms such as Humber-Hillman to infringement.' All the other transgressors were asked to pay a nominal sum of £1,000. Considering that the verdict had presented him with the opportunity of extracting potentially enormous damages from almost all the major motor car manufacturers in the world at that time, this generous gesture was proof of Ricardo's wisdom and far-sightedness as a businessman. But he was not an avaricious or vindictive man; he sought only to continue to serve his existing clients and licensees and to maintain cordial commercial contacts with the automobile industry as a whole.

Ironically, after the successful conclusion of this litigation, only a few months remained before the expiry of the turbulent head patent and before the reign of the side-valve engine itself was brought to a close. Even so, it took another year and a half before all the erring manufacturers settled their dues. Apparently, most of the British firms who had been infringing the patent paid up gracefully without delay, but two intransigent firms remained unwilling to agree with the judgement and further unpleasant litigation seemed unavoidable. These firms were Austin and Ford, whose bosses had always been adamantly opposed to paying royalties as a matter of principle. The job of dealing with these recalcitrants fell to Percy Kidner, who had been appointed to the Ricardo board in 1933.

As the current, much-respected President of the Institution of Automobile Engineers, Kidner exercised a considerable and benign influence among the upper echelons of the British motor industry, and he was able to prevail on Austin's then Managing Director Leonard Lord to persuade Sir Herbert Austin to change his attitude, to such an extent that Austin actually became quite friendly towards Ricardo and took up cudgels on his behalf in the battle to extract payment from Henry Ford. The latter had an unbroken rule that he would never on any account pay royalties on any patent and due to his extraordinary dominance of the auto-industry, reinforced by his vast financial resources which made him immune from any serious dissent or opposition, his disregard of the law had never previously been challenged. It seems that Austin was reluctant to pay up unless Ford was also compelled to do so and so he approached Sir Percival Perry (later Lord Perry), Ford's right-hand man in the UK and, as Managing Director of the Ford Motor Company, the creator of Ford's Dagenham factory, to take up the matter with the American motor magnate. By an amazing feat of persuasion, the facts of which we shall never know, Perry was able to convince his master of the advantages of reversing the habits of forty years and of falling into line with Austin to settle the royalties due from both his British and his US companies.

For Harry Ricardo, this was as great a victory as David's over Goliath and he never forgot his debt to Kidner in bringing it about. Thirty years later, in June 1968, following a luncheon held at Kettner's Soho restaurant to celebrate Kidner's ninetieth birthday, he wrote a touching letter to his old friend, saying:

> I am afraid that my performance at our lunch party was very inadequate. All my life
> I have suffered from the defect that, once my emotions are stirred, I become

completely tongue-tied, and quite unable to express my real feelings. There was so much I would have liked to say about all the help and encouragement you gave me in the very early days . . . but the words just wouldn't come out. . . . Ever since I first met you some fifty years ago, I came to regard you as a guide, philosopher and friend; throughout I have felt that you and I shared the same philosophy of life but you provided the experience and sound judgement which I lacked; more especially did I realise this during the anxious period of our Patent Action and its aftermath when you did so much to steer us through that difficult time. . . . All this I would have liked to enlarge upon, but too much emotion deprived me of speech.

Long before the turbulent head reached the end of its useful royalty-earning life, Ricardo had turned his attention towards the task of producing a new device that would take its place and generate the royalty income needed over the next decade and beyond. As early as 1923 he had identified the vast potential market that existed for a small high-speed diesel engine suitable for use either in powering road-going vehicles or for generating electricity, and had concluded that the development of such an engine represented the most promising of all the many directions along which he might steer his future research efforts. In reaching this conclusion he had the full support of his long-standing research partners among the Anglo-Dutch Shell Group who were keen to develop and promote the diesel engine in order to open up a new commercial market for its fuel stuffs and, in particular, a grade of oil produced in the refining process for which there was currently little demand. As with the earlier investigations into fuels and lubricants, Sir Robert Waley-Cohen agreed that Shell would fund this research in return for an interest in any resulting inventions. In an agreement reached with Shell's subsidiary the Anglo-Saxon Petroleum Company, signed in 1924, it was established that the royalties accruing from any patents or licensing agreements arising from Ricardo's current sleeve-valve diesel engine research programme were to be shared equally between the two parties. Later, in 1927, this agreement was extended to cover all forms of high-speed, compression-ignition engines, a high-speed diesel engine being defined as one in which the piston moved at a speed not less than 900 ft per minute.

History has treated Rudolf Diesel kindly for, just like William Hoover, his name has become a household word or generic term for an entire class of products. But the fact of the matter is that, were he alive today, he simply would not recognise the engines that bear his name. In the form that he conceived the compression-ignition principle when he took out his patent in 1892, the Diesel engine was a large, heavy and slow-turning machine, intended entirely for use in propelling ships or railway locomotives, or for stationary duties in electric power generation or water-pumping applications. He never expected that it would ever be employed as a prime mover for cars, tractors and trucks, and certainly not aircraft. Before it could be used on the roads, the engine to which he lent his name had to be refined and improved by other pioneering engineers, of whom Sir Harry Ricardo can be numbered among the most significant. Ricardo, of course, was one of the first to attempt to reduce the size and weight of the diesel engine and to increase its speed of revolution, so that it could be harnessed usefully in road transport applications.

Sir Harry did not subscribe to the 'Eureka!' theory of invention. Time and time again he remarked that inventors and inventions are two a penny, and that the only thing that matters is the ability to refine and develop a concept into a commercially viable product. Writing in 1931 apropos Rudolph Diesel he said: 'We are too fond, I think, of crediting a few particular individuals with a monopoly of inventive genius. The world is well stocked with men of scientific knowledge and wide imagination, and it is with no disrespect to the late Dr Diesel that I suggest that, had he never existed, an equally suitable engine to deal with these heavy oils would none the less have been developed and that at about the same time. Once the incentive is established, a way can always be found. Ripe seeds of invention everywhere abound, and it awaits only a certain combination of need, of circumstances and, above all, of chance, to decide which shall germinate.' On another occasion he remarked, 'Nothing, I think is more distasteful or invidious than arguing about who invented what and when, for most intelligent people come to much the same conclusion, at much the same time, when analysing the same evidence.'

In fact, Ricardo began his own investigations into the high-speed, compression-ignition engine shortly after the First World War in connection with a research contract awarded by the Air Ministry, which was interested in evaluating the potential of the diesel engine as a power plant for long-range transport and patrol aircraft. It was thought that the diesel engine would not only offer greater reliability and economy, but also a greatly reduced risk of fire compared with the petrol engine, not merely due to the relatively non-flammable nature of its fuel but also to the absence of an electrical spark-ignition system that might cause a petrol-engined plane to explode in a crash. This early experimental work was carried out on a number of single-cylinder research engines known as the E30 series, one of which featured single sleeve-valves. In this system, the fuel charge and exhaust gases entered and exited from the cylinder through ports in its side walls that were alternately opened and closed by the movement of the sleeve itself. This was positioned concentrically between the piston and the cylinder barrel, allowing the piston to move up and down in the normal way. For a number of valid engineering reasons, Ricardo considered that this type of valve-gear offered many advantages over the poppet-valve alternative, and advocated its use continually throughout his career.

The single-sleeve-valve system had been invented in 1909 by two engineers working independently of each other, Peter Burt a Scotsman employed by the Argyle motor car firm, and James McCollum, a Canadian. Burt and McCollum reached an agreement, filed a joint patent and saw their invention incorporated in the 130hp Argyle aero-engine that won the 1913 Naval and Military Aeroplane Engine Competition, where it first attracted Ricardo's attention. Its advantages over the double-sleeve-valve system invented earlier by the American engineer Charles Knight (and previously employed in Europe on Daimler, Minerva and Mors motor cars), was that by means of a bell-crank linkage driven off a layshaft the sleeve was made to oscillate from side to side as well as to reciprocate up and down. By virtue of this figure-of-eight motion, a thin film of oil was spread between the sleeve and the piston, thus curing the lubrication problems experienced in the American engine, which was notorious for burning oil and wearing out its sleeves.

However, after considerable work had been undertaken at Shoreham to refine the principles of this design (a project carried out in association with the Royal Aircraft Establishment at Farnborough), it was concluded that the diesel engine would always be at a disadvantage over the petrol engine for aircraft use, as the extra weight resulting from its necessarily stronger and more rigid construction (required to sustain the high cylinder pressures encountered in a compression-ignition engine) cancelled out its lower fuel consumption. The Air Ministry's research programme was wound down but not entirely terminated. Nevertheless, this research had shown that the sleeve-valve diesel engine had a considerable potential beyond aircraft use, and especially in industrial applications such as the stationary engines used for power generation at sea or on land, or for driving oil-drilling rigs in the petroleum industry – an application for which the Shell company itself had a considerable requirement. A successful 50-hour Air Ministry Test conducted in 1923 showed that the single-sleeve-valve diesel engine could combine a 10 per cent greater power output with a 12–15 per cent reduction in fuel consumption compared with other types, but although the Whitehall authorities were willing to finance continued limited long-term forward research on the concept, they were not prepared to authorise the necessary development work that would lead to its manufacture. The development of the single-sleeve-valve diesel engine therefore continued at Bridge Works throughout the first half of the decade but was funded by the Royal Dutch Shell Group. At the same time, steps were taken to acquire the rights to the original Burt and McCollum patents from the present owners, Wallace and Company of Glasgow, which had recently gone into liquidation.

As time went by, the Dutch side of the Royal Dutch Shell Group (in particular the De Bataafsche Petroleum Maatschappi (BPM) NV) became more and more involved in this project and research work was shared between Bridge Works and BPM's research station at Delft in the Netherlands. Two Dutch engineers G.D. Boerlage and J.J. Broeze became closely involved with the project and were frequent visitors to Shoreham, together with J.H.C de Brey and J.F. de Kok, both Directors of BPM. Indeed, at one point it was even contemplated that the Shell and Ricardo firms should collaborate in establishing a jointly owned company to manufacture industrial diesel engines, but after much heart-searching the idea was abandoned, much to Harry Ricardo's relief. Perhaps as a consequence of his experiences with the ill-fated Two Stroke Engine Company he had never wished to take on the role of a motor manufacturer or industrialist with all that that entailed in the way of commercial and financial responsibilities. Instead, it was decided to license his designs to suitable existing engine builders and let them take the risks.

The immediate objective of the original 1924 agreement with the Anglo-Saxon company was to develop an experimental 50hp, single-cylinder sleeve-valve diesel engine (the S50) for research purposes. This was intended to form eventually the basis of a complete family of two-, three-, six- and eight-cylinder industrial engines of varying capacities, all with interchangeable components. By 1927, five prototype full-size engines (all featuring Ricardo's new Vortex combustion chamber) had been constructed by Messrs Peter Brotherhood under Commander Bryant's supervision and were undergoing service trials in a variety of locations, including Brotherhood's own works at Peterborough, Bridge Works itself and the Worthing Corporation Power Station. By 1930, all the initial teething troubles had been ironed out and three more manufacturers in addition to Brotherhood had been awarded licences to construct and market the Ricardo sleeve-valve, high-speed diesel on a commercial basis, these makers being Mirrlees, Bickerton & Day, Vickers Armstrong and the Dutch firm of Thomassen based at de Steeg in the Netherlands, all of which produced a significant number of engines. Far in advance of anything else that had been achieved at that time, the design enjoyed a considerable commercial success; the Ricardo-Brotherhood version in particular was produced in large numbers, mainly for service as a stationary generating engine or an

The smallest (three-cylinder) version of the Ricardo-Brotherhood single-sleeve-valve diesel engine, a stationary unit generally employed for electrical power generation duties.

auxiliary marine engine. The prototype engine at Worthing remained in service for over thirty years until the early 1960s when the town was linked to the national grid and its power station was demolished.

By the late twenties, however, Ricardo had decided that the time had come to begin a study of the problems inherent in adapting the high-speed diesel engine to meet the needs of the mass-produced motor car and light commercial vehicle, exploiting all that had been learned about the diesel combustion process in his earlier research programmes at Shoreham. But despite the proven reliability and durability of his single-sleeve-valve design, the automobile engine-building industry at large remained decidedly sceptical about the virtues of this system, and it was only in the aeronautical field that the concept could be developed further. In fact, the general prejudice against it was so pronounced that in 1927 – when the Anglo-Saxon agreement was extended to cover all forms of compression-ignition engines and a start was made on designing a lightweight, high-speed diesel suitable for road transport use – Harry Ricardo was reluctantly forced to abandon the sleeve-valve principle in favour of its alternative, the traditional and widely understood overhead poppet-valve. Within the automobile industry in particular, the aversion to sleeve-valves (resulting from the poor reputation of the Knight engine) was considered to be virtually insuperable. According to Ricardo himself, potential customers in the road transport field were quite unable to discriminate between the single and double type of sleeve-valves.

Although forward research in this area began in 1927, Ricardo's serious involvement with what later developed into his famous Comet combustion chamber system actually began in 1929, and stemmed from his existing involvement with the Associated Equipment Company, better known as AEC, the bus-building subsidiary of the London General Omnibus Company (LGOC). For many years this firm had held a licence to employ the Ricardo turbulent head in its existing petrol engines. Although operational experience of the road-going diesel was extremely slight at that time – apparently there were only about eighty diesel-powered vehicles running in the whole of the UK in 1929, most of them of Continental origin – the Chairman of the LGOC, Lord Ashfield, recognised that, in theory, a switch to diesel engines in his fleet would produce considerable savings in his running costs and so he instituted a programme of research to design and construct a suitable high-speed diesel engine to power London's buses. The responsibility for this work was given to the company's Chief Engineer, C.B. Dicksee, already a well-respected engine designer in the commercial vehicle world.

Normally, stationary diesel engines run at a constant speed and load, so Dicksee's principal objective in designing a high-speed diesel engine for road transport use was to ensure that its torque was delivered over a wide engine speed range in order to offer the flexibility essential if a vehicle is to accelerate smoothly and vary its road speed according to changing road and traffic conditions. But in formulating his design, Dicksee had another important factor to consider: the need to choose between the two types of injection systems currently employed by the very few makers producing diesel engines at that time. These were the direct-injection or open-chamber type as employed by Gardner in England, or the indirect or pre-combustion-chamber type as favoured by German manufacturers such as MAN of Augsburg. In March 1930 the Gardner engine, fitted to a Lancia bus, was the first British high-speed diesel engine to go into regular passenger-carrying service in the UK. For his AEC engine, Dicksee elected for the indirect combustion option in the shape of the Acro-Bosch system which had been developed by the German firm of Robert Bosch. Dicksee incorporated this into a single-cylinder research engine of 115mm bore and 142mm stroke which was built by AEC at its Southall Works. Initially, the results seemed sufficiently promising for Lord Ashfield to order a batch of full-scale six-cylinder engines to be built and installed on a number of buses for extended service trials over ordinary routes throughout the metropolis. Unfortunately, however, the trials revealed a number of serious defects, not least of which was the fact that when accelerating or overrunning these engines emitted clouds of foul-smelling fumes which contravened the Metropolitan Police regulations regarding exhaust smoke.

In an attempt to overcome this problem, which clearly resulted from poor combustion, Dicksee decided to send his single-cylinder test engine to Bridge Works where Harry Ricardo and his team were given a free hand to improve the AEC unit's performance, utilising the experience already gained in their sleeve-valve diesel engine research programme. Immediately, Ricardo ruled out the use of a direct-injection system (in which the fuel is sprayed through injectors under high pressure straight into the combustion chamber to meet the air) as he considered that, in the current state of the art, the high-precision work required for the manufacture of reliable multiple-orifice injectors was beyond the capabilities of most engine builders. Instead, he chose to develop an indirect system (in which the air is made to seek the fuel, an approach first suggested to him by Dr Hesselman in Sweden some thirty years previously) but in doing so he attempted to improve the turbulence of the incoming air, the lack of swirl being the great defect or drawback of existing indirect systems. 'A new combustion chamber incorporating a spherical chamber connected to the cylinder by a tangential passage was grafted on to the AEC single-cylinder unit, and almost immediately gave results which were considerably in advance of what had previously been achieved, particularly as regards specific power output and flexibility of running over a wide speed range. An outstanding feature was the complete freedom of the exhaust from smoke or smell, a most important factor in ensuring the general acceptance of the diesel engine for urban service,' a contemporary Ricardo report relates.

Another batch of 8.8-litre, six-cylinder engines, this time with cylinder heads incorporating the Ricardo Comet combustion chamber (as it had been christened), was promptly built by the AEC firm and put into trial service in London in September 1931 on its LT class of Renown double-deckers. These poppet-valve engines, fitted with a CAV Bosch fuel pump which incorporated its own advance and retard mechanism, were an immediate success and thus were adopted by the LGOC as the standard engine for its entire fleet of sixty Renown red buses, which remained in service until 1935 and beyond.

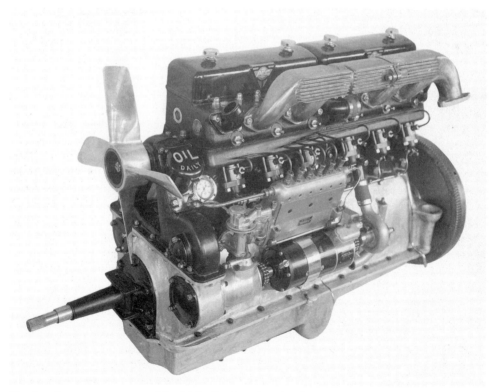

The first Comet-type commercial vehicle diesel engine, developed jointly for London Transport buses by AEC and Ricardo.

One of London Transport's LT Renown buses equipped with the AEC-Ricardo diesel engine photographed in Trafalgar Square in March 1937. Ricardo's London office was located just off the Square, in Suffolk Street, Pall Mall.

These buses soon achieved an enviable reputation for reliability and the number of involuntary stoppages or 'down-time' experienced on the company's routes was reduced by over 75 per cent.

The clean and flexible running of the AEC–Ricardo bus engine soon began to attract the interest of road transport operators not only in the UK but also on the Continent and further abroad. Before very long, it became apparent to Ricardo and his team that, in devising the Comet combustion chamber, they had created a innovative and easily patentable product with the royalty-earning potential to make good the shortfall in the firm's revenue income that had resulted from the ending of the turbulent head patents. Consequently, a very intensive development effort was put into action at Bridge Works, with the backing of the Anglo-Saxon Petroleum Company, which stood to benefit from its half-share in this income. In fact, under the benevolent eye of Sir Robert Waley-Cohen, throughout the existence of the agreement (which continued until 1953) Shell adopted the generous and far-sighted policy of ploughing back the proceeds of its collaboration with Ricardo into further research work at Shoreham.

Over the next five years the Comet system was further refined and developed so that it evolved into several different variations and alternatives, each suited to specific conditions and applications. Indeed the arrival of the Comet combustion chamber had an enormous impact on the automobile and industrial internal combustion engine industry since it made the production of a diesel engine a relatively inexpensive proposition for

Captain G.E.T. Eyston's diesel record car *Flying Spray*, which was fitted with Ricardo's single-sleeve-valve compression-ignition conversion of the Rolls-Royce Kestrel aircraft engine.

volume manufacturers, and by 1936 it had been licensed to a large number of companies for use in trucks, buses, tractors, cranes and earth-moving machinery and even private cars and taxis too, not to mention marine, railway and stationary industrial engines.

It is fair to say that, due to the success of Ricardo's Comet system, by the second half of that decade, Great Britain led the world in the field of high-speed diesels for road transport and nearly all the manufacturers of heavy commercial vehicles in the country had either turned over completely from petrol to diesel engines or were planning to do so at the earliest opportunity, with the consequence that ever bigger and more powerful engines were appearing on the market year by year; moreover British designs were being built under licence or copied in every European country, Germany included. But in the 1938 Budget, however, the Treasury decided to impose a heavy tax on diesel fuel, equal to that on petrol, which destroyed the advantage of diesels at a stroke. The result of this unfortunate action was to put a stop to the development of high-power diesel engines for road use in the United Kingdom. The initiative was lost, forward designs were either abandoned or licensed to foreign manufacturers, and, as we shall see in the following chapter, it was on the Continent that the advantages of the Comet system were taken up and exploited. Ultimately, by the 1980s around 90 per cent of the diesel passenger cars and commercial vehicles in the world employed the Comet combustion system, but the great majority of them were built by foreign firms.

Apart from well-known British commercial vehicle and industrial engine manufacturers such as AEC, Peter Brotherhood, Mirrlees, Bickerton & Day, Lister & Company, Thornycroft, Davy Paxman, Crossley Motors and Albion Motors, Ricardo's pre-war licensees were principally such famous Continental firms as Citroën, Berliet, Fiat and MAN, plus Waukesha and Caterpillar in the USA. Through the Shell connection, a number of leading Dutch engine builders such as Thomassen, Stork and Werkspoor also employed the Comet system. But no British passenger car builder took up the possibilities, and it was not until 1954 that the first British diesel car appeared, a Standard Vanguard saloon, powered, of course, by a 2-litre Comet-type engine.

The Comet combustion chamber, as fitted to the AEC–Ricardo bus engine, also had a competition career. In 1932 the well-known racing driver and record-breaking ace Captain George Eyston fitted an example in a special saloon car and established several world speed records for diesel-engined vehicles, which stood until challenged in the USA by a car powered by a Cummins diesel engine. A wealthy enthusiast who had begun his racing career at Brooklands driving Aston Martin and Bugatti cars, Eyston made his name with his 750cc MG Magic Midget streamlined car, in which he achieved many other speed records. Throughout the thirties he conducted a continuous duel with his rival record-breakers John Cobb and Sir Malcolm Campbell and eventually, in 1938 at the Bonneville Salt Flats in Utah, USA, he succeeded in raising the world land speed record to 357.5 mph in *Thunderbolt*. Fitted with two Rolls-Royce Kestrel aero engines totalling 73 litres and producing 4,700hp, this was the biggest and most powerful record car built to that date. Earlier, in 1934 he had set a new world one-hour endurance record, achieving an average speed of 162 mph in *Speed of the Wind* which was powered by a single Rolls-Royce Kestrel V12 petrol engine.

When his diesel speed records for the fastest flying mile and kilometre in the AEC–Ricardo-engined car were eventually overturned in the USA, he formed the idea of winning them back for Britain by fitting the *Speed of the Wind* with an experimental Rolls-Royce diesel aero-engine. This, of course, was the RR/D V12 cylinder single-sleeve-valve four-stroke compression-ignition unit fitted with a Vortex-type combustion chamber and developed from the Kestrel petrol engine by Ricardo at Shoreham in 1931, in connection with the aforementioned Air Ministry diesel research programme. After refurbishment by the Ricardo firm, this 19.2-litre engine was fitted in the *Speed of the Wind*, which was promptly renamed the *Flying Spray*. In April 1936, again at the Bonneville Salt Flats, this car (sponsored by the Wakefield Castrol Oil Company) duly set a new world achievement that stood until 1950.

CHAPTER 17

La Rosalie

In November 1932, two visitors from France stepped off the Dieppe ferry at Newhaven, *en route* to Bridge Works, Shoreham, on a fact-finding mission that was to have important and enduring repercussions for Harry Ricardo and his firm. The Frenchmen in question were Charles Brull, Director of the Research Laboratories of Automobiles Citroën in Paris, and Maurice Sainturat, the distinguished engineer who headed the *Service Moteurs* or Engine Design Department of the Citroën car factory.

It was Sainturat, of course, who had designed the engine of André Citroën's current great success, the 1,628cc C4 saloon (the first European car to exceed 240,000 units in production), and who was to design, in 1934, the engine for Citroën's revolutionary monocoque-bodied Traction Avant model, the world's first mass-produced, front-wheel drive car. This engine was destined to remain in production for almost fifty years until 1982, thus setting a world record for the continuous manufacture of an automobile engine.

André Citroën was an adventurous engineer-industrialist who, like Ricardo, had gathered around him a team of highly competent designers and engineers, to form a design and research department that was ultimately responsible for innumerable advances in automobile technology. Like Ricardo, André Citroën had a Dutch-Jewish ancestry, his father being a jeweller from Amsterdam who had settled in Paris in 1871 and adopted a French nationality. A graduate of the élite Ecole Polytechnique – the technical academy of the French military and civil services – Citroën was the first European car manufacturer to embrace American sequential assembly methods and to set up laboratories to investigate and control, with scientific precision, the quality of his products. With typical astuteness, long before most other car manufacturers had considered the possibility, he had foreseen a future need for small, economical, high-speed diesel engines for use in taxi-cars and light commercial vehicles and had taken steps to bring this development about. As early as October 1931, when addressing a conference of automobile and industrial manufacturers held at Columbia University in New York he had announced that: 'research work now under way . . . may in the near future open up markets . . . . where petrol supplies are costly and difficult to provide and where the use of indigenous fuels such as heavy oils and alcohols could greatly facilitate the development of the automobile'.

In this respect, Citroën's internationally minded thinking echoed that of the major petroleum producers of his era, who were seeking new markets for the heavy oil by-products of the refining process, for which no large-scale use had presently been found, and this search provided the commercial motivation behind early research into automobile diesel engines; the durability and high fuel economy that these engines promised came as a bonus. Indeed, as we saw in the previous chapter, the Royal Dutch Shell Group (through its subsidiary the Anglo-Saxon Petroleum Company) had actually funded Sir Harry's work on automobile diesel-engine research with that objective in mind.

André Citroën, the Henry Ford of France, playing backgammon with his wife at their apartment in Paris in 1934. When he visited Citroën at Passy that year, Harry Ricardo was invited to join his host in playing the French motor magnate's favourite game.

Currently at the height of his fame and fortune, and recognised worldwide as an international celebrity and socialite, André Citroën's reputation went far beyond the confines of the motor industry. Within ten years of having produced France's first mass-produced, mass-marketed car in 1919, this dynamic pioneer had overtaken all his earlier-established French and British rivals to become Europe's leading automobile constructor. By 1929 the rate of production at his Quai de Javel factory was exceeding 100,000 vehicles a year, twice that of other comparable Continental firms such as Renault and Fiat. This extraordinary industrial and technological achievement gave Automobiles Citroën its undisputed position as the fourth largest car firm in the world, and its proprietor his name of 'The Henry Ford of France'. In contrast to Ford, however, Citroën had no objection to paying royalties and spent a high proportion of his turnover in acquiring the rights to apply the latest technology in his products.

The arrival at Shoreham of André Citroën's two ambassadors was therefore regarded as a most welcome development by Ricardo and his staff, who had already identified the development of a diesel engine for cars as being potentially the most commercially promising of all existing lines of research and development. However, relations between the two firms had not always been quite so cordial. In 1922, through the recommendation of the French designer Jules Salomon (the founder of the Le Zèbre marque), Automobiles

Citroën had commissioned the Ricardo firm to design and build two sample versions of the turbulent cylinder head, with the intention of improving the performance of its side-valve-engined B10 and C3 models, the latter having been designed by Salomon. But although these heads gave good results in tests, and the appropriate research fee payment was made, nothing more was heard of the matter for two or three years and Ricardo and his colleagues concluded that André Citroën and Maurice Sainturat had let the matter drop.

Then, in the autumn of 1927, during a visit to the vast and palatial London showrooms that Citroën had opened the previous year at Devonshire House in Piccadilly, quite by chance Harry Hetherington overheard a salesman claiming that the cars on display there were fitted with Ricardo cylinder heads. Subsequent investigation revealed that Citroën's latest car, the B12, was indeed equipped with a close copy of the patented cylinder head that had originally been supplied in prototype form by Ricardo five years earlier. As no royalty agreement had ever been negotiated by Citroën to authorise series production of Ricardo's design, this development caused alarm bells to ring loudly at Bridge Works.

Initially, legal action was contemplated but, fortunately, was averted when André Citroën agreed to sign a series of patent agreements covering the use of the turbulent head on his cars; the first of these documents was dated 26 November 1928. Even so, for a number of years the Citroën firm was held to be in a state of disgrace by the Ricardo firm, to the extent that Sainturat and his colleagues were expressly forbidden from visiting Bridge Works, even though the French company made repeated approaches through the Anglo-Saxon Petroleum Company to repair the breach and thus gain access to Ricardo's increasingly valuable diesel-engine expertise. However, on the evidence of the correspondence that survives at Bridge Works today, it seems that by 1932 these earlier problems with Automobiles Citroën had been forgotten and that the two firms were collaborating on amicable terms once again, so that Sainturat's requests for admittance to the Bridge Works laboratories were no longer refused.

These letters also make it possible to set out a precise chronology for the historic Citroën–Ricardo diesel engine project, which in due course was to lead to the production and marketing of the world's first diesel-engined passenger car. On returning to Paris after their visit in November 1932, the French engineers reported favourably to *le patron* at the Quai de Javel. During their stay in England, the pair had been taken to London by their British hosts to observe the relatively clean and smokeless exhaust emissions given out by the large fleet of AEC buses equipped with Ricardo Comet cylinder heads that were then running on the streets of the capital city. Even then, such environmental considerations weighed heavily with André Citroën, and so one month later, in December 1932, a letter of intent was sent by Automobiles Citroën to Ricardo indicating the possibility of a research contract, 'if our intentions concerning the diesel engine are realised during 1933'.

This time there was to be no misunderstanding over the question of royalties, and eventually, after protracted negotiations, a licensing agreement giving Automobiles Citroën exclusive rights to the Comet combustion chamber system in the French market was duly drawn up and signed by both parties on 12 December 1934. In line with the terms normally demanded by the Anglo-Saxon Petroleum Company, which controlled the patents, the Ricardo firm was to be paid its standard royalty of 10*s* per litre on all engines manufactured by Citroën featuring the Comet combustion chamber, plus a flat annual consultancy fee of £500, which entitled Automobiles Citroën to call on the Bridge Works' staff and facilities for technical advice and assistance for a period of two years.

At last Harry Ricardo had achieved his aim of establishing a permanent consultancy relationship with a major volume-production automobile manufacturer – and, moreover, one with an unassailable reputation for engineering excellence and innovation.

In fact, this was not the first agreement in respect of the Comet cylinder head to be negotiated in France, for the previous year Ricardo had granted a non-exclusive manufacturing licence to the old-established firm of Chenard & Walcker, with which he had a relationship extending back to 1925. However, this agreement, effected as usual through the Anglo-Saxon Petroleum Company and dated June 1933, was amended in favour of Citroën with the full approval of Chenard & Walcker who were free to continue the manufacture of large-capacity engines for buses, heavy lorries and tractors – a market in which Citroën had no plans to compete.

The joint Ricardo–Citroën research project took some time to get under way, however, due to the very heavy workload then passing through the Bureau d'Etudes at the Quai de Javel in preparation for the launch of the Traction Avant, planned for the autumn of 1934. A letter dated 6 April 1933 signed by Maurice Brogly (the Technical Director of Citroën's research and design office) informed Sir Harry that progress on the matter would unfortunately be subject to a considerable delay. However, just three months later, in a further letter dated 21 July 1933, Brogly announced André Citroën's decision to proceed with the project by establishing a *Service Diesel* or Diesel Department, to be headed by René Wisner, a talented engineer who happened also to have been the former heavyweight boxing champion of the French Army and a member of the French team in the 1926 Olympic Games. Described by Jack Pitchford as being both 'formidably intelligent' and 'a natural athlete', Wisner was an Anglophile who spoke fluent English. Following the invasion of France in 1940, he escaped to England, where he spent the war years with the Ricardo firm before returning to Paris at the Liberation.

Later in 1933, during one of his regular trips to England to attend the October London Motor Show and inspect his own British factory at Slough, André Citroën visited Bridge Works in person to view the facilities and to meet Harry Ricardo and his team. Apparently during lunch Citroën entertained the staff assembled in the works canteen by making an impromptu speech in English while performing a series of conjuring tricks with a box of matches. Later that year, Harry Ricardo was invited to tour the Citroën factory in Paris, which lay almost under the shadow of the Eiffel Tower. By night, this gigantic structure was emblazoned with Citroën's name, picked out in huge letters by thousands of lightbulbs, visible for miles in all directions, a testament to the Frenchman's flair for marketing and publicity, which was often dismissed by his enemies as mere self-advertisement.

It seems that these meetings led to a brief but cordial friendship between the two engineers and that on various occasions during the course of their short collaboration, Ricardo dined with André Citroën, either at Citroën's favourite haunt, Maxim's restaurant (the unofficial club of the senior figures in the French motor industry) or at his apartment in Passy, where the two men played backgammon together. At first sight, this would seem to have been a most unlikely friendship for a greater contrast in personalities could scarcely be imagined. Ricardo was a diffident and retiring Englishman who abhorred personal publicity and avoided party-going, preferring the solitary relaxations of sailing, fishing and butterfly collecting. Citroën, on the other hand, was a gregarious socialite and *bon viveur* whose greatest pleasure in life was to gamble away his fortune on the turf or the green baize table and whose style of business

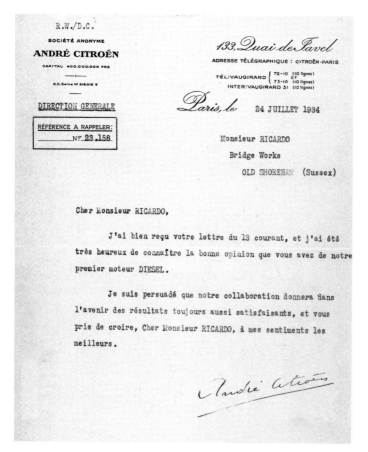

R.W./D.C.

SOCIÉTÉ ANONYME

ANDRÉ CITROËN

CAPITAL 400.000.000 FRS

R.C. Seine Nº 216.018 B

DIRECTION GÉNÉRALE

RÉFÉRENCE À RAPPELER:
Nº 23.158

133, Quai de Javel

ADRESSE TÉLÉGRAPHIQUE : CITROËN-PARIS

TÉL:VAUGIRARD { 72-10 (10 lignes)
                ET
                73-10 (10 lignes)
INTER:VAUGIRARD 31 (10 lignes)

Paris, le   24 JUILLET 1934

Monsieur RICARDO

Bridge Works

OLD SHOREHAM (Sussex)

Cher Monsieur RICARDO,

J'ai bien reçu votre lettre du 13 courant, et j'ai été
très heureux de connaître la bonne opinion que vous avez de notre
premier moteur DIESEL.

Je suis persuadé que notre collaboration donnera dans
l'avenir des résultats toujours aussi satisfaisants, et vous
prie de croire, Cher Monsieur RICARDO, à mes sentiments les
meilleurs.

André Citroën

In this letter, dated July 1934, André Citroën informed his friend Ricardo of his complete satisfaction in the performance of their joint achievement, Automobiles Citroën's first diesel engine.

was often criticised as being nothing more than showmanship. Ricardo was a research scientist with a gift for imaginative design, whose theoretical work was rooted in his practical hands-on skill and love of craftsmanship. Citroën was quite the opposite; although he was a highly accomplished production engineer and an expert at commercialising other men's designs, unlike Ricardo and the great majority of other automobile pioneers, he had no interest in practical mechanics and was never to be seen working at the drawing board or at the lathe, much less tinkering about beneath the bonnet of a car. Moreover, despite his ranking as one of the world's greatest ever champions and promoters of popular motoring, he actually disliked driving and rarely took to the wheel of any of his cars.

Initially, the Citroën–Ricardo diesel research programme involved an experimental 75×99mm single-cylinder engine fitted with a Comet Mk II head and the smallest diesel unit that the Ricardo firm had yet produced. A letter to Ricardo dated 5 February 1934 and signed personally by André Citroën records the Frenchman's satisfaction with the results currently being obtained from this experimental engine. On 9 April, Harry Ricardo was informed by Wisner that despite the pressure of work caused by the advent of the new saloon car model, the Traction Avant, all was ready for tests of Citroën's first diesel engine (a 94×110mm 4,578cc, 6-cylinder unit intended for use on trucks and light commercial vehicles) to commence at the beginning of May and that Ricardo's assistant, Jack Pitchford, would be welcome at the Quai de Javel to witness these tests.

Jack Pitchford, who had joined Ricardo directly from Cambridge University in 1926, was the first engineer who can be said to have risen through the ranks at Bridge Works, being promoted deputy to the Managing Director in 1939 and appointed to the Board of Directors the following year. He had taken a leading part in the high-speed diesel engine development programme since its inception and, as a fluent French speaker, it was natural that he should progress to the firm's client relations department, gradually taking over the role of Ricardo's roving ambassador on the Continent from Harry Hetherington whose health was failing.

On 6 July, a telegram from Pitchford in Paris was received at Bridge Works: 'Citroën Comet easily the best yet for smoothness and performance,' the message proclaimed. Following Pitchford's return to Sussex, on 13 July Harry Ricardo wrote to André Citroën congratulating the French firm on their achievement and singling Wisner out for special praise. This letter was answered by one from André Citroën on 24 July 1934; he recorded his pleasure at the good results then being achieved from 'our first diesel engine'.

Next, on 19 September 1934, Wisner wrote to Ricardo announcing that the first example of a second design, a 75 × 100mm 1,767cc, four-cylinder unit, had satisfactorily

The first Citroën–Ricardo high-speed diesel engine was actually this 4578cc six-cylinder unit, designed in 1934 for use in Citroën's light commercial vehicles and motor coaches.

completed a programme of bench tests in Citroën's research laboratories and that he was now proceeding to install this engine in an example of Citroën's existing taxi-car model, the 10CV Rosalie, to undertake road trials. 'The engine functions with complete silence . . . and seems to demonstrate all the qualities required from a passenger car engine,' Wisner declared. Naturally, Harry Ricardo replied right away, saying that he was delighted with the results being achieved at the Quai de Javel. Then, writing to Wisner in March 1935, he stated that he considered the Citroën versions of his design gave, without exception, the best performance of any Comet-type engine yet built in any country, an opinion he repeated on many occasions. According to contemporary Citroën publicity material, its three Comet diesel engines made possible a 70 per cent improvement in overall running costs compared with their petrol alternatives when fitted in identical vehicles. A complete interchangeability with the petrol engines fitted to its various different models was one of Automobiles Citroën's prime requirements for its diesel units, as was a wide speed range to ensure smooth and flexible performance on the road.

Throughout the spring and summer of 1935, three examples of Citroën's current base model, the 8CV Rosalie saloon, made countless circuits of the Montlhéry test track fitted with the 1,750cc diesel engine instead of their normal 1,452cc petrol units. The tests were observed by a party of Citroën and Ricardo engineers, including Jack Pitchford and Archibald Ferguson, Chief Draughtsman of the Shoreham firm, who had been with Ricardo since the tank engine days. Pitchford spent the greater part of that year based at the Quai de Javel as Ricardo's on-site project manager and link man, and during that time he met André Citroën on numerous occasions. 'Citroën was a charming man, always agreeable, approachable and amusing, totally without pretension and absolutely democratic in his relationships with his employees and associates,' Pitchford recalled shortly before his death in 1993.

Unfortunately, the tests took place against the backdrop of tragic events in the history of the Citroën firm and political turmoil throughout France. Early in 1932, André Citroën had received an invitation from his greatest competitor Louis Renault, to see the improvements that Renault had recently made at his Billancourt factory. To Citroën's great alarm he discovered that the Renault factory had grown to such an extent that it now covered not just 250 acres on both sides of the river, but also an island in the middle of the River Seine.

With his usual bold disregard of risk, Citroën immediately decided that, to remain on competitive terms with his arch-rival, he would also have to build a brand new factory, even bigger and better than Renault's, in which to construct his forthcoming all-new Traction Avant model, the world's first mass-produced front-wheel-drive car. Accordingly, between March and July 1933, a third of the entire Quai de Javel site was torn down and reconstructed, before being re-equipped with the latest machine tools from America. Not surprisingly, weighed down by the burden of the huge expenditure imposed by the simultaneous work of rebuilding his factory and producing a radically new model, in February 1934 André Citroën ran into a severe financial crisis that was made even worse by an unexpected fall-off in sales revenue caused by the sudden late arrival of the Depression in France.

These problems reached their head the following November when a small creditor, owed only a few thousand francs, lost patience and put in a winding-up petition in the Paris courts. Unable to prove its solvency, on 21 December 1934, the mighty Citroën company was adjudged bankrupt and forced into receivership. Within a matter of weeks, in January 1935, it was taken over, lock stock and barrel, by its biggest creditor, the

During the summer of 1935, three examples of Citroën's Rosalie taxi model fitted with the 1750cc four-cylinder diesel engine car underwent endurance tests at the Montlhéry circuit near Paris, observed by a party of Citroën and Ricardo engineers. Seen here snapped by Jack Pitchford are Archibald Ferguson of Ricardo and, behind him, René Wisner (hatless), head of Citroën's diesel department.

Michelin Tyre Company of Clermont-Ferrand. Despite the resounding success of the Traction Avant (which was hailed as as technical masterpiece when it appeared at the Paris Motor Show in October 1934) André Citroën's greatest gamble failed, so that he lost not just his factory and his fortune, but also his life.

On 25 March 1935 Wisner wrote to Ricardo with the news that the new management of Automobiles Citroën had decided to proceed with the series production of the two Citroën–Ricardo diesel engines (the 1,767cc four-cylinder and the 4,578cc six-cylinder units) but purely for commercial vehicle use. It later emerged that the company intended to exhibit a complete range of Ricardo Comet diesel-engined taxis, lorries and coaches at the Paris Motor Show later that year, and that one of these vehicles was to be a taxi version of the new Citroën Traction Avant model, employing a slightly modified version of the 1,750cc four-cylinder engine with dimensions revised to 78 × 100mm as employed in the 1,911cc overhead-valve petrol engine powering the front-wheel drive car in its larger 11CV form. In the event, however, this latter development did not take place.

Unfortunately, Wisner's good news was tempered by sad tidings of his former *patron*: 'You will be sorry to learn that Monsieur Citroën is gravely ill and has entered hospital for treatment,' Wisner revealed. After undergoing an unsuccessful operation to remove a malignant stomach tumour, André Citroën died at the Georges-Bizet Clinic in Paris on 3 July 1935, aged only fifty-six.

It is known that the first example of the Type 10Di series diesel-engined saloon (chassis number 480000) was submitted to the French road transport authority, the Service des Mines, for type approval on 27 November 1934, as was required by law, but due to the difficulties currently being experienced by the Citroën company, the process of commercialising the design was interrupted for almost two years. From reports published in the French motoring press in April 1937, it is evident that in the previous year engines taken from a completed batch of 100 pre-production 1,750cc diesel units had been fitted to between 50 and 75 examples of the Type 10A Rosalie taxi or *conduite commerciale* (commercial traveller's saloon) models that, from June 1936 onwards, had been loaned to selected customers for extended in-service trials.

However, perhaps to raise some much-needed extra revenue, early in 1937 Automobiles Citroën's new owners instructed that all these cars (plus others fitted with the remaining engines) should immediately be sold off in the normal way. So it happened, maybe more by accident than design, that the Citroën–Ricardo car became the world's first diesel-engined passenger-carrying vehicle to be marketed to paying customers, by arriving in the showrooms almost a year ahead of its rival the Mercedes 260D, which did not make its appearance in Germany in comparable numbers until later in 1937. According to official Daimlar-Benz figures, 13 examples of the 260D were built in 1935, then 55 in 1936 and 366 in 1937. The French press reports stated that: 'These new commercial vehicles have a Citroën diesel engine rigorously tested and thoroughly prepared for production over the past three years. The engine starts first time and behaves with the flexibility and reliability of any petrol engine, functioning smoothly without giving-off smoke or odour and differing from its conventional counterpart only by its overwhelming economy.'

The exact number of diesel-engined passenger cars, taxis and light commercial vehicles produced by Automobiles Citroën between 1935 and 1940, when output at the Quai de Javel factory was interrupted by the occupation of France, is still unknown. Although a total of approximately 3,000 examples of the various different Citroën–Ricardo engines are believed to have been manufactured between 1937 and 1939, after a two-year delay in the diesel manufacturing programme that followed the Michelin takeover, their use was almost certainly confined to commercial vehicles – the Type 500Di and Type 850Di vans and the Type 23Di lorry, all powered by the 1,767cc four-cylinder unit; the Type 45Di lorry equipped with the original 4,578cc, six-cylinder unit; and the Type 32Di lorry powered by a new engine, a four-cylinder 94 × 110mm 3,052cc unit.

The demise of André Citroën must have come as a bitter blow to Harry Ricardo, spelling as it did a long postponement in the realisation of his hopes and ambitions for the mass production of the small high-speed diesel engine. Undoubtedly, he admired and respected Citroën as a fellow pioneer and saw his work for this entrepreneurial genius as crystallising the ideal relationship between the expertise of the small, responsive, specialist research consultancy and the vastly powerful but relatively inflexible resources of a multinational mass-manufacturer. Their friendship and cooperation, he had hoped, would set a pattern for the future, by demonstrating how new and better products could be brought to the market place through the interchange of ideas made possible by the common language of engineering, which transcended all national and political boundaries.

There was one small consolation, however. In August 1937, Automobiles Citroën's British subsidiary, Citroën Cars Ltd, announced the forthcoming arrival of a new conventional rear-wheel drive saloon, the long-wheel-base, seven-seater Family Fifteen, intended principally as a taxi or a limousine for private motorists with large families who hesitated to buy Citroën's front-wheel drive Traction Avant model which had been introduced onto the British market two years previously. Like all British-market Citroëns of that era, this right-hand drive car was to be assembled at Citroën's Slough Works from components sourced both in England and in France.

Exhibited on the Citroën Cars Ltd stand at the October 1937 Motor Show, at a price of £373, the Family Fifteen was, in effect, a right-hand drive version of one of a new stop-gap range of conventional rear-wheel-drive vehicles that Citroën had recently introduced onto the French market, the 11CV UA and UD Familiale and Conduite Commerciale models. These used the chassis and bodywork of the old Rosalie models, but offered the choice of two four-cylinder engines, both sharing the same 78×100mm dimensions – the 1,911cc petrol overhead valve engine from the Traction Avant, mounted the wrong way round to drive the rear wheels, and the same 1,767cc Citroën–Ricardo diesel engine that had first made its appearance in 1935. As was the usual practice, these Slough-built versions were to be suitably Anglicised by the addition of wire wheels and leather upholstery in the traditional British style normally adopted at Slough. The Citroën Family Fifteen was thus the very first compression-ignition-engined passenger car ever to be announced in the United Kingdom. Reporting on the new Citroën Cars Ltd range in its issue of 10 August 1937, *The Motor* stated that, in launching a diesel, Citroën had made 'an announcement of exceptional interest', declaring that the engine itself promised long-range economy, smoothness and robustness.

Almost a whole year earlier, in October 1936, Ricardo had anticipated this development by attempting to buy from Citroën Cars Ltd at Slough a right-hand drive Citroën saloon fitted with his diesel engine for his own personal use, with the idea that it would also act as a demonstration vehicle in his attempts to persuade British manufacturers such as Morris and Austin to use the Comet system on their passenger cars. In response to his enquiries, he was informed that although the company proposed to market in the UK a version of the Family Fifteen model equipped with the diesel engine, no decision had as yet been made as to when it would be available. The following November, he received a letter from Citroën's Quai de Javel factory, indicating that although there was no immediate prospect of such a vehicle being assembled at Slough, a right-hand drive example of the Conduite Commerciale equipped with the diesel engine could be supplied from Paris for the special concessionary price of £300, which represented a 15 per cent discount on the French price of 30,200FF. Ricardo accepted the offer and placed an order for the vehicle through Citroën Cars Ltd on 16 November 1936.

In the event, however, the Citroën Family Fifteen in its diesel-engined form never reached the showrooms either in England or in France. Consequently, as revealed by his long correspondence with the sales department of Citroën Cars Ltd filed in the Shoreham archives, Harry Ricardo had considerable difficulty in obtaining his car, which was not delivered until 16 March 1937. Although he had originally been keen that his car should have the leather upholstery and wire wheels of the proposed Slough version, the car delivered was, of course a left-hand drive vehicle, trimmed in cloth and finished in the French style. Actually, it was probably built at Citroën's Brussels factory along with a small batch of 100 diesel-engined 11UD Rosalies known to have been supplied for the

In the months leading up to the outbreak of war in 1939 an acute shortage of petrol was experienced in Holland. To save fuel, the use of petrol-engined passenger cars was banned on Sundays. By this time, a few Citroën diesel engined cars built in Belgium had been sold there, and these were exempted from the ban. In this posed press photo, the driver of the diesel car has been halted for questioning by two Dutch policemen. It is believed that Harry Ricardo's own Citroën diesel car was virtually identical to this model, except that it had right-hand drive.

Dutch market in 1937 – probably the only examples ever built. Certainly, no diesel-engined Family Fifteen was ever built at Slough.

Nevertheless, despite an unsuccessful request to Slough for the fitting of a four-speed gearbox, Harry Ricardo appears to have been well satisfied with his purchase, which was undoubtedly the first privately owned diesel-engined passenger vehicle ever to run on the British roads. Writing in 1937, his verdict on his handiwork was that 'the little [40 bhp] engine is rather swamped by a large car weighing 29–30 cwt (1,500 kilos), all the more so since it has only three speeds but, even so, it trundles along quite well'. It is interesting to note that Harry Ricardo's car bore the chassis number 480002, which suggests that it was only the third such vehicle to be built, following the construction of the prototype (number 480000) in 1934.

Other men who drove it also gave it the thumbs-up, though not, alas, the decision-makers of the British motor industry. In a letter dated 15 June 1937, the Chief Engineer of Morris Motor's engine department, Mr W.R. Boyle, wrote to Sir Harry saying that: 'I was greatly impressed by the performance of the Citroën diesel car and share your views on the possibility of a really light and cheap car with a diesel engine. You will understand, however, that my interest is personal rather than official, I know you appreciate that pioneering is not the strong point – and very rightly so – of companies such as Morris Motors, but I feel certain that a less conservative concern could shake the self-satisfaction of this money-grabbing trade with such a proposition, if properly carried out.' In fact, Morris had taken out a licence to produce the Comet in 1935, but did not pursue the option, so that before the war the Ricardo system was manufactured for installation on private car and light commercial vehicles only by a number of other well-known Continental automobile companies in addition to Citroën, including Fiat, Berliet and, of course, Chenard & Walcker.

Throughout the Second World War and for some time afterwards, Ricardo's car was heavily used for general transport duties by his firm. But by the early fifties it had fallen into neglect and, being beyond repair, it was scrapped. Fortunately, before the Family Fifteen went to the crusher, its engine was removed and stored at Shoreham, where it remained in a state of neglect for almost forty years until it was rediscovered in 1994, restored and fitted in a re-creation of the original vehicle. The only other known example of the type to run in the UK (the Motor Show car owned by Citroën Cars Ltd) was also used extensively during the war, only to be destroyed shortly afterwards.

Following the takeover of Automobiles Citroën by the Michelin company early in 1935, its licences were extended and the Ricardo firm continued to act as consultants to the Paris company until the German invasion of France in 1940, though most of the projects initiated previously by André Citroën were abandoned, including the plan to produce a diesel-engined version of the Traction Avant. Moreover, Citroën's new Michelin management agreed to waive its exclusive licence to manufacture the Comet head in France in favour of the commercial vehicle manufacturers Automobiles Berliet, who were granted a licence in May 1935. Berliet's first application, made in 1933, had been refused. The Ricardo–Berliet relationship thrived for many years, until the Lyons lorry firm became part of the Citroën group in 1967.

At the Quai de Javel, however, when production resumed there after the Second World War, in 1946, Automobiles Citroën's new owners chose not to pursue the experience gained by André Citroën's pioneering enthusiasm for the diesel engine, and the field was left open to Daimler-Benz, which re-entered the market in 1949 with the Mercedes 170D. Consequently, today it is the three-pointed star and not the double chevron that is most closely identified in the public mind with the origination of the diesel-engined passenger car. The Mercedes diesel engine employed an alternative type of cylinder head design and so the first postwar Continental car featuring the Comet combustion chamber principle was produced by Fiat in 1952.

Although the Ricardo firm was called in during the fifties to advise on a proposed diesel engine for the Citroën ID19 range of saloons and estate cars, thirty years elapsed before Automobiles Citroën re-entered the diesel passenger car market with the CX 2200 Diesel saloon in 1975. But following its merger with Peugeot the previous year, the majority of subsequent Citroën saloon and estate cars were offered in versions equipped with various derivations of the PSA XUD diesel engine, which was developed in collaboration with the Ricardo firm. Indeed, the relationship between the two firms continues to this day. Thus, the very latest Citroën diesel models are direct descendants of their illustrious Citroën–Ricardo ancestor, the world's first diesel-engined passenger car, proposed by André Citroën in 1934.

CHAPTER 18

War Clouds Threaten

The year 1933 was truly an *annus mirabilis* in the life of Harry Ricardo and his family. Not only did it witness the traumatic events of the Hillman-Humber legal case and the rather happier – but no less significant – matters surrounding the visit by André Citroën to Shoreham, but it also saw great upheavals on the domestic front as the family moved house. When he had brought his wife and children from London to Lancing in 1919, his new house, Penstone, had stood in open countryside, but gradually over the intervening thirteen years the surrounding farmland had been sold to speculative builders and had become built-up. Penstone and its large garden were now hemmed in on all sides by a vast new residential estate, which seemed to Ricardo to be spreading ever higher up the slopes of the South Downs with every passing day. 'All the charm of the countryside was fast disappearing and my wife and I scoured the neighbourhood in search of a new home,' he recalled.

Eventually they found a place that promised the isolation and solitude they both craved, 'a small but very charming old manor house of Elizabethan origins', Tottington Manor, which nestled under the north face of the Downs in quite unspoilt countryside near the village of Small Dole, only six miles from Shoreham. Built of Horsham stone, Tottington Manor was rather more than just a country house; it was a small agricultural estate comprising about 250 acres of farmland, woodland and open Downland pasture plus two farm workers' cottages and the usual range of farm buildings. After much heart-searching, the Ricardos bought the entire property for the sum of £7,000 – about £200,000 in today's money. 'We had never contemplated becoming landowners on so large a scale, nor did we know anything about farming, but the whole place had an irresistible charm for us,' Ricardo confessed. 'What did appeal to us was the protection a larger property afforded against the invasion of bricks and mortar which in only a few years had engulfed Penstone.'

The agricultural land was let to a local farmer on a long lease, leaving 90 acres of woodland as a playground for the family, and also as a sanctuary for birds and butterflies. By now, with numerous nephews and nieces besides his own three daughters to be amused and entertained during the holidays (his third daughter Camilla had been born at Penstone in 1921), Harry Ricardo found that the gatherings of his extended family in Sussex resembled those at Rickettswood in his grandfather's day, except that now the youngest children were no longer confined to the nursery but could be heard as well as seen.

'At Tottington Manor we started once again on a new mode of life in the depths of the countryside,' said Ricardo in his autobiography. One of his first tasks was to open up a clearing in the depths of the woods, where he could sit and watch the wildlife, far removed from the sight, sound and smell of engines, 'a silent, secluded spot which became our favourite haunt for reverie, siesta and picnics during the next eight years'. In early spring the clearing was carpeted with wild flowers and teemed with butterflies, not only of the commoner species. but also many rare beauties which flocked to the flowering shrubs that he had planted there. He had been interested in butterflies since his boyhood days and had amassed a large collection, many of which he had bred himself from the caterpillar stage. After his marriage, when living at Walton-on-Thames, he was able to share this hobby with his wife whose enthusiasm for butterfly breeding equalled his own. At Tottington Manor they embarked on a project to reintroduce the particularly rare and beautiful swallowtail butterfly, which had become almost extinct in Great Britain, rearing over thirty or forty examples each year from eggs obtained from a friendly keeper of the Insect House at London Zoo. He estimated that, over successive years, they must have released well over 100 of these rarities into the clearing. 'We had hoped that they would make the area their home, but in this we were disappointed for they all disappeared and our attempt to populate the countryside with a new species failed completely,' he admitted.

Harry Ricardo in 1945/6, President of the Institution of Mechanical Engineers.

Another enthusiasm that the couple shared was gardening, with Beatrice being responsible for flower growing and Harry for cultivating the fruit and vegetables. Naturally, the Ricardos employed a gardener who relieved them of the heavy manual work of digging the vegetable plots and mowing the lawns, but even so, when weeding and watering, Harry found himself saddled with the task of constantly lifting and replacing the many removable glass cloches which were then considered indispensable for vegetable growing. As the casualty rate in broken glass was excessive, he conceived the idea of building a single giant cloche to cover his vegetables, a kind of portable greenhouse that could be safely and effortlessly moved according to the crop in season and in which he could stand upright to do the hoeing and watering. After much deliberation, he concluded that the best way to move such a large and heavy glass structure was by flotation. Accordingly, he designed an ingenious floating structure resting on six 40-gallon oil-drums that acted as detachable and submersible pontoons. These ran in two long and narrow concrete water-troughs extending for a total length of 120 ft, so that the giant cloche could cover four separate plots in turn. To move the structure three or four times a year, all he had to do was to pump the water out of the pontoons, so that when these drums filled with air the whole structure became water-borne and could be floated to any position along the length of the concrete troughs (which he constructed *in situ* himself) with the minimum of effort. When the cloche had been manoeuvred into the desired position, the pontoons could be filled with water, allowing the structure to sink into place before, finally, the oil-drums were removed and the whole contraption was bolted securely and immovably into place. The floating greenhouse was named 'The Queen Mary' since it made its maiden voyage in 1938, the very same year as the famous liner. 'I had much fun over both the design and construction of "The Queen Mary",' Sir Harry recalled.

According to Jack Pitchford, the whole episode was yet another example of Ricardo's essential self-reliance and thriftiness which bordered on outright frugality. Although he was not a mean-spirited man and often behaved with remarkable generosity towards his colleagues and employees, he deplored all signs of material wastefulness or extravagance, especially in engineering terms. As a designer he was always seeking out ways to make economies, by avoiding or reducing the use of expensive materials or methods and by generally saving unnecessary expenditure. 'He was always reluctant to make even modest outlays on much needed capital equipment for the Laboratories,' said Pitchford. 'He was in fact by nature a "make do and mend" man, carefully preserving old tools and components as well as complete engines, obsolete, if not extinct, in the firm belief that he would be able, at some future time, to make good use of their parts. I well remember how delighted he was when in one case or another this proved to be possible. For example, many tentative designs for experimental engines grew around some existing connecting rod designed and made for some earlier and unrelated unit.'

Sadly, the pastoral bliss that Ricardo and his family had found at Tottington Manor did not last; by 1938, when 'The Queen Mary' made her maiden voyage in his garden, the war clouds were gathering ominously once again and within two years they were obliged to up sticks and move on, never to return. In July 1940, after the invasion of France, like many other similar country houses, their home was requisitioned by the military authorities and they were exiled to Oxford where they remained throughout the Second World War. In fact, the house was so badly damaged by its military occupiers that they were never able to reinhabit it.

In contrast to the situation in 1914, when he was taken aback by the sudden outbreak of war, during the thirties Ricardo was much better placed to foresee the turn of events in Europe and the inevitability of a second conflict with Germany, following the rise to power of Adolf Hitler and the Nazi Party early in 1933. Due to his extensive contacts with the German engine-building industry and his frequent visits to that country, this time he had an inside view of what was happening there and was able to alert the British military and political authorities to these developments, largely through his membership of the Aeronautical Research Committee (ARC) in which capacity he was called upon to write reports on his contacts abroad.

In fact, there is evidence to suggest that, as soon as their rearmament programme was under way, the Nazis actively encouraged visits by British engineers to the German aircraft engine factories, with the aim of showing off their newly created military and industrial might. By 1936 the output of the German aircraft industry had overtaken that of Great Britain, France and the USA combined, to make it the strongest in the world. By demonstrating its seemingly unassailable technological superiority to knowledgeable and influential men like Ricardo, the Nazis aimed to deter its potential enemies from entering into an arms race that would interfere with Hitler's plans for a new world order. Ricardo was therefore engaged in a form of intelligence gathering that stopped short of being outright espionage of the clandestine kind, since the important information he brought back from his trips to Germany was freely offered by his fellow engineers at companies such as Daimler-Benz, Junkers and BMW. On returning to London, he would report his findings to his friend Henry Tizard, who was Chairman of both the ARC and its Engine Subcommittee, and his views would very soon reach the eyes or ears of the successive Secretaries of State for Air during that period, Lord Londonderry and Lord Swinton, and also those of the Air Member for Research and Development, Air Marshal Sir Hugh Dowding.

It is known that by September 1935 Dowding and the Air Staff had reached the conclusion that another war with Germany was unavoidable and had embarked on preparations, which included the urgent development of a new generation of high-performance engines for interceptor fighters. Sir Harry Ricardo left no diaries from which exact details of his travels can be extracted, but it is recorded that in the years leading up to the Second World War he visited Germany regularly: in November 1936; in October 1937 (when he delivered a lecture entitled 'Some Problems of Aircraft Engine Design' at a conference held by the Lilienthal Gesellschaft fur Luftfahrt Forschung in Munich); and in September 1938 when he visited Berlin to receive the honour of membership of the German Academy of Aeronautical Research from the hands of the Commander-in-Chief of the German air force, Herman Göring.

Die

Deutsche Akademie

der Luftfahrtforschung

gegründet durch Erlaß des Führers

und Reichskanzlers Adolf Hitler

am 24. Juli 1936 zu Bayreuth ernennt

Herrn Direktor Harry R. Ricardo

zu ihrem Korrespondierenden

Mitgliede.

Berlin, im September 1938

Der Präsident

[signature]

Generalfeldmarschall

Reichsminister der Luftahrt und

Oberbefehlshaber der Luftwaffe

The certificate of membership of the German Academy of Aeronautical Research presented to Ricardo by Herman Göring, Commander-in-Chief of the German Air Force, in Berlin 1938.

As we have already noted, Harry Ricardo had been appointed to serve as an independent member of the Aeronautical Research Committee and its associated Engine Subcommittee in 1919 and he continued to sit on both these bodies for a period of over twenty-five years, until they were reformed in 1945. The membership of the committee consisted of four representatives from the Air Ministry, two from the aircraft industry, four from the appropriate academic or government research institutions – such as Imperial College, the National Physical Laboratory and the Department of Scientific and Industrial Research – one from the Royal Aeronautical Society and, finally, five independent scientists. The principal responsibilities of this assorted band were to advise on the scientific and technical problems relating to aircraft construction, to initiate, undertake or supervise research or experimental work as proposed by the Air Ministry, and, from time to time, to make reports to the Air Council on matters of national significance or concern involving the aircraft industry. However, the committee was not directly a government organisation, and having no executive powers or budget it acted purely in an advisory capacity. Even so, such was the authority and prestige of its membership that it exerted a powerful and all-pervasive influence on the strategic direction followed by aeronautical research activities in Great Britain throughout the interwar years.

The detailed business of the ARC was conducted through small subcommittees that concerned themselves with specific matters such as air-frames, engines and navigational systems, calling on the expertise of specialist experts and passing their conclusions back to the main committee, whose final recommendations guided the research and development expenditure sanctioned by the relevant government departments. This *modus operandi* was particularly true of aircraft propulsion matters where the Engine Subcommittee of the ARC acted as a link between the Air Ministry, the Royal Air Force, the Royal Aircraft Establishment at Farnborough and the major aero-engine manufacturers such as Rolls-Royce, Bristol, Napier and Armstrong-Siddeley, whose senior engineers and designers (such as Sir Roy Fedden, Chief Engineer of the Engine Department of the Bristol Aeroplane Company) were also represented among its membership at various times. In the light of the impressive technical achievements encouraged and promoted by the Engine Subcommittee throughout that interwar period and much of the Second World War, it is gratifying to observe that its enduring core throughout three decades comprised three scientists who had collaborated continually as friends and colleagues ever since their relationship had begun at Bridge Works, Shoreham, in 1919. These men were Henry Tizard (whose career involved periods as Secretary of the Department of Scientific and Industrial Research, Rector of Imperial College, and, simultaneously, Chairman of both the ARC and its ESC, most crucially between 1933 and 1943), David Pye (who from 1925 to 1937 was Deputy Director of Scientific Research at the Air Ministry, before becoming full Director) and, of course, Harry Ricardo.

In effect, this remarkable trio were the focal point of an informal network of like-minded individuals whose ideas and information were vital to the development of both military and civil aviation before the Second World War and, most especially, were instrumental in the setting up of the British air defence system prior to the Battle of Britain. Ricardo, Tizard and Pye knew everyone in the world of aero-engine research at home and abroad and through detailed inside knowledge gained in their social and professional contacts they were able to reach their conclusions and formulate their recommendations without the need for written policy documents or minuted discussions;

they knew exactly what investigations were going on, and where, and what the likely results were. More importantly, they knew precisely what technical problems had to be overcome to assure continued British superiority in the air; and if new work had to be commissioned to achieve this objective, they knew the best men for the job. Coming from the same public school and Oxbridge milieu, sharing the same attitudes, values and ideals, and speaking the same language, their minds were on the same wavelength. Over frequent lunches at the Athenaeum or the United Universities Club, they identified the most promising research directions for the aero-engine industry and thus ensured that, in due course, the Royal Air Force was properly prepared and equipped to respond to the German threat. In the words of Andrew Nahum, senior curator of the National Aeronautical Collection at the Science Museum, this uniquely British way of doing business 'could be described without flippancy as clubland at war'.

Moreover, in his role as a hands-on experimentalist at the head of Britain's leading internal combustion engine research establishment, Ricardo was also in a unique position to help translate his recommendations into reality, by undertaking the problem-solving forward research required to establish promising new directions in the aircraft engine industry. Having identified the requirements of the aircraft of the future, as often as not he would be awarded a contract by the Air Ministry to undertake the necessary long-range development work in association with the leading engine manufacturing firms under the supervision of Major G.P. Bulman, who held the key post of Director of Engine Development at the Ministry from 1923 until 1944.

Nothing could illustrate better the benefits resulting from the application of Ricardo's unsurpassed practical skills and experience than the achievements that resulted from his long association with Albert Hubert Roy Fedden, later Sir Roy Fedden, the dynamic yet domineering engineer-entrepreneur who led the Bristol aero-engine company throughout the interwar years. Although almost exact contemporaries (both were born in 1885) the two men were entirely different in their attitudes and personalities, one aggressively ambitious and egocentric and widely labelled difficult to work with, the other unassuming and retiring. However, the uneasy relationship they established was to have an enormous impact on both civil and military aviation throughout the twenties and thirties.

The fortunes of the engine department of the Bristol firm were founded on air-cooled radial engines, the first of which was the Jupiter, a nine-cylinder, one-row, poppet-valve unit designed by Roy Fedden in 1918 but which underwent progressive development for over a decade. The first British aero-engine to pass the Air Ministry's rigorous 100-hour test in 1921, the Jupiter was also the first of Bristol's engines to be adopted for service by the RAF. It was bought by many foreign civil and military customers, for whom it was manufactured under licence by seventeen constructors, notably in France, Italy and Germany. An outstandingly durable and reliable design and the holder of many early altitude records, in its Mk VII form it ultimately earned the distinction of powering the first aircraft to fly over Mount Everest. The Jupiter XIF (which was rated at 555hp, 50 per cent greater than the earliest versions) was also the engine chosen to power the new fleet of six Handley Page HP42 aircraft ordered by Imperial Airways in 1929 for its route to India, of which the famous Hannibal was the first example to take to the skies, the following year. By this time, the Jupiter had become the most important and successful aircraft engine in the world, completely dominating both military and civilian aviation as the principal engine of nearly half the world's airlines and more than half the world's airforces, no fewer than 7,100 examples having been built to power 262 different types of aircraft.

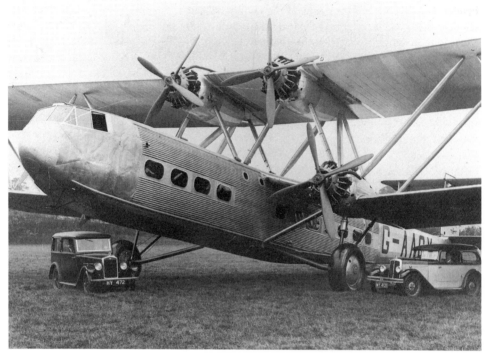

The prototype Handley-Page HP42 seen in November 1930 before entering service with Imperial Airways' fleet of six HP42s. Like the rest of the fleet, the *Hannibal* was powered by four 555hp Bristol Jupiter aircooled radial engines.

However, the development of the Jupiter was not entirely without its difficulties. In Sir Harry Ricardo's own words, as set down in *Memories and Machines*: 'About 1922–23, Fedden was in serious trouble with the crankpin bearing of his new seven cylinder [sic] single-crank radial engine and we were asked by him and the Air Ministry to investigate this as part of our research programme. For this purpose we designed and made a big-end testing machine in which we could, as far as possible, simulate the conditions obtaining in the engine.' The Bristol engine employed a forged one-piece crankshaft onto which the fixed master connecting rod and its eight articulated slave con-rods were attached at the crankshaft journal by means of a single split big-end bearing secured in the traditional way by bolts passing through its cap. Due to excessive friction, this bearing was subject to failure at speeds above 1,200rpm, but neither Fedden or Ricardo were sure if this was caused by friction due to distortion of the split big-end, or merely to the excessively high dynamic loadings that the part was subjected to by the thrust of the nine con-rods. 'To check this, Fedden made up a new master connecting rod with an unsplit big-end, which behaved a little better but not well enough to justify the use of a built-up three-piece crankshaft,' Ricardo recalled. 'Many years before, Sir Charles Parsons had told me how in his early turbines he had employed, with success, a freely-floating bush in his journal bearings and on the strength of his advice I had done the same in my home-made motor-cycle engine at Cambridge.' This was the same technique that he used again in his E35 variable compression engine at Shoreham. 'Both Fedden and the Air Ministry boggled at the idea of employing a built-up crankshaft with all that that would imply in the way of an extensive re-design of the engine,' said Ricardo in his book. 'They therefore urged that we should explore the possibility of using a split floating bush in a split big-end eye . . . but these experiments revealed a friction loss higher than with no floating bush at all.'

For his own use at Shoreham, Ricardo and his team had developed a form of built-up crankshaft in which the main-bearing shafts and con-rod journals were slid into the slotted webs and clamped in place by pinch-bolts. 'After much discussion with the technical staff of the Air Ministry, Fedden was given a contract to revise the design of his radial engine incorporating a built-up crankshaft to our design,' Ricardo recalled. 'When completed, the new version performed very well indeed. Its maximum rotational speed was no longer limited by its big-end bearings but by its valve-gear.' In the next version of the Jupiter engine (the Mk V) Fedden used an ingenious thermally compensated valve mechanism which allowed still higher speeds, sufficient to justify the use of a propeller reduction gear.

'As time went on the introduction of effective oil sealing rings permitted the use of a much greater flow of cooling oil through the crankpin bearing and therefore yet higher speeds of rotation, so that never again did this critical bearing set a limit to the performance of radial engines,' Ricardo concluded. 'The success of our built-up crankshaft led to its adoption both in this country and abroad by almost all makers of high powered radial engines,' he observed, although his innate modesty and sense of gentlemanly propriety prevented him from pointing out that Fedden never once acknowledged the contribution made at Bridge Works to the perfection of the Bristol Jupiter engine.

By 1926, the Bristol company had become the world's leading exponent of the high-powered, radial, air-cooled engine, and its management had reached the conclusion that an inherent demand existed for a single-row radial engine producing over 1,000 bhp. As a result, a programme of long-range development work was undertaken by the Bristol firm at its Filton factory throughout the next ten years with the aim of maximising the advantages of the air-cooled, radial aero-engine. In fact, it had no other option, for at that time it was prevented from building conventional water-cooled, in-line engines by a previous agreement with Rolls-Royce, its principal rival.

As a result of this development work, which involved many thousands of hours of static and in-flight testing, in 1932 Fedden introduced the nine-cylinder Mercury and Pegasus single-row poppet-valve engines, both direct descendants of the Jupiter which they duly superseded. In its supercharged form the Pegasus Mk III of 1935 (as fitted to the Fairey Swordfish) produced close on 700 bhp, almost twice the output achieved by the first version of the Jupiter ten years earlier. These engines proved so successful that by the end of that decade over 52 per cent of the strength of the RAF measured in horsepower terms was powered by Bristol air-cooled, radial engines.

Even so, the Filton firm had recognised quite early on that, with the fuel then available, there was a limit to how far the concept could be pushed because of the limitations imposed by the use of poppet-valves. Firstly, in the days before the problem was solved by using a sodium core in the valve stems to conduct away the heat of the exhaust gases, poppet-type exhaust valves tended to overheat and thus contributed towards any tendency to detonation. And secondly, it was extremely difficult to master

The famous Fairey Swordfish torpedo bomber, equipped with a 690hp Bristol Pegasus air-cooled radial engine. Despite its slow speed and antiquated appearance, its success in sinking enemy shipping during the Second World Was was spectacular.

the complex arrangement of push-rods and rockers required to actuate the four overhead poppet-valves fitted to each cylinder of a Bristol engine. Experiments aimed at increasing output by doubling the size of the engine simply by adding a second row of cylinders proved unsuccessful due to the problems encountered in arranging these operating mechanisms in an eighteen-cylinder two-row radial engine and Fedden was forced to consider abandoning the radial configuration and switching to straight-line or V12 air-cooled layouts instead.

In 1927, however, word of these problems reached the ARC and Fedden was encouraged by his former colleagues on the Engine Subcommittee, Ricardo and Pye, to consider the possibility of adopting cooler running sleeve-valves in preference to the traditional poppet-valves he had used hitherto. With some initial scepticism, therefore, Fedden agreed to widen the scope of his research programme at Filton to continue the work carried out earlier on sleeve-valve aero-engines at Farnborough and Shoreham. Accordingly, Ricardo's old friend T.B. Barrington (another former member of the Engine Subcommittee, currently employed by the Sheffield Simplex Company) was commissioned to carry out a detailed study of the most advantageous layouts possible for sleeve-valve engines. After examining twenty-eight possible configurations Barrington concluded that the best arrangements were single-row radial engines with an odd number of cylinders, two-row radials with fourteen or eighteen cylinders or, alternatively, in-line engines with twenty-four cylinders arranged as a superimposed double flat-twelve, a configuration later adopted by both Napier and Rolls-Royce when these manufacturers also adopted the sleeve-valve system at the insistence of the Air Ministry.

As we have already seen, Ricardo considered that his early work for the Air Ministry in 1920 had established the theoretical advantages of the sleeve-valve engine beyond question. Much later, in his 1937 Lilienthal lecture he told his German audience that in the course of this research he had 'fallen deeply in love with the sleeve valve, for its own sake. In those days we had to deal with very inferior fuels and I was very much impressed by the fact that, as compared with our overhead poppet-valve variable compression engine, we could employ one whole ratio higher compression on the same fuel and thus gain a very big advantage.' He was also impressed with its numerous other virtues, namely its higher volumetric efficiency, its ability to operate on very weak mixtures without risk of detonation or burnt exhaust valves, its ability to dissipate heat, its high reliability and consistency of performance, its smooth and quiet-running operation, its mechanical simplicity and fewness of parts, its minimal maintenance requirements and, lastly, its lack of overhead valves, which presented the designer with the opportunity to achieve an almost ideal form of combustion chamber with a central spark-plug and no hot surfaces caused by proximity to exhaust gases. In this system, it will be recalled, the fuel charge and exhaust gases entered and egressed through ports cut into a thin-walled tube sliding between the piston and the cylinder walls, and alternately opening or closing a series of ports, rather than through valves set into the cylinder head.

Clearly, Fedden's initial doubts were soon overcome by Ricardo's enthusiastic recommendations, and towards the end of 1926, the Bristol company committed itself to an extensive programme of research dedicated to investigating the large-bore sleeve-valve engine, conducted concurrently with the development of its poppet-valve range. For the first four years these efforts were concentrated on single- and two-cylinder research engines, but by 1932 a full nine-cylinder radial engine, the Bristol Perseus, was being built. After extensive testing by the Air Ministry and Imperial Airways, examples duly entered service in 1935 on the airline's London to Paris route, the first sleeve-valve aero-engine to be adopted for commercial and military use.

As Sir Harry Ricardo said, 'I succeeded in persuading Sir Roy Fedden to build a complete aero-engine. This with much misgiving he did, but it was not completed until about 1934.' This work, of course, the Ricardo firm had never been in a position to undertake itself. Sir Harry wrote:

Known as the Perseus it was a 9 cylinder radial engine. After a few initial troubles it proved a great success and was adopted as standard for the Empire flying boats. Later he [Fedden] developed a 14 cylinder version, now well known as the Hercules. On the outbreak of the present war, the entire capacity of the great Bristol aero-engine factory was turned over to the manufacture of sleeve valve aero engines. That so many years should have elapsed between the completion of the [Air Ministry funded] research and its practical application was bitterly disappointing to me; all the more so since the advantages of the sleeve valve aero engine were most apparent in the days when we were using relatively low octane fuels.

The final expression of Roy Fedden's creation was the 2,000hp Centaurus, an eighteen-cylinder supercharged double-row unit which first ran in July 1938 and which was subsequently installed in the Hawker Tempest, Fury and Sea Fury fighters. Eventually the Centaurus was developed to produce over 2,500hp and in this form it powered many postwar military and civilian transport aircraft including Bristol's own ill-fated prototype airliner, the Brabazon I, built in 1949 to carry 100 passengers non-stop from London to New York but abandoned due to technical problems. This monster machine was equipped with no fewer than eight 2,500hp Centaurus Mk XX engines, fitted as four coupled pairs, two to each wing. The author well remembers how as a boy he saw this aircraft pass low over Bognor pier, heading along the Sussex coast in the direction of Shoreham. Perhaps it was making a fly-past over Bridge Works, to pay tribute to the inventiveness of Sir Harry Ricardo, the true progenitor of the sleeve-valve engine!

Although Ricardo never failed to congratulate the Bristol firm on the magnificent industrial achievement brought about by Roy Fedden's dynamic leadership, it seems that Fedden himself overlooked Ricardo's contribution to the sleeve-valve project and claimed for himself the credit for having been first to espouse the single-sleeve-valve

One of Imperial Airways' fleet of twenty-eight Short S23 Empire flying boats over New York in 1935. Powered by four 740hp Bristol Pegasus X single-sleeve-valve engines, this aircraft could carry twenty-four passengers plus 1½ tons of mail for up to 800 miles non-stop, thus establishing the first global air-mail network.

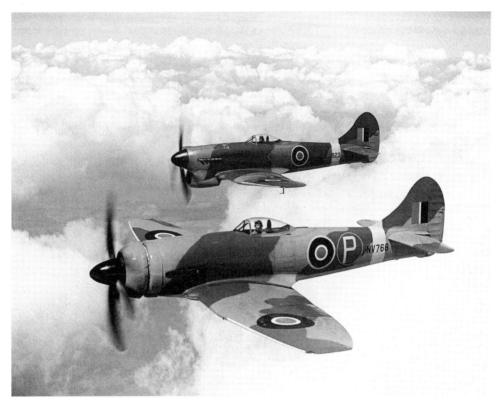

Two Hawker Tempest ground-attack fighters, powered by Halford's Napier Sabre engine. This outstanding aircraft caused havoc among the retreating German Army in Normandy in 1944. The lower of the pair is a prototype fitted with an experimental annular radiator.

system and for being its leading exponent. Neither he nor his biographer ever truly acknowledged his debt to Ricardo's work, yet as we have seen, Ricardo was undoubtedly the sleeve-valve's chief champion and protagonist. Undoubtedly, Ricardo was among the earliest engineers to recognise its virtues and he was certainly the first to devise the cranked ball and socket actuating mechanism that made the principle a viable proposition in an aircraft engine.

Thus in one respect only was Fedden's claim to be the father of the aircraft sleeve-valve engine fully justified: it was the Bristol firm (in association with the Firth-Vickers steel company) that was first to solve the metallurgical and manufacturing problems involved in sleeve-valve mass production, by pioneering a technique that allowed complete interchangeability of the sleeves and cylinder barrels. Until late in 1938, when a vast expansion programme for the RAF was already under way and one quarter of its aircraft strength was committed to sleeve-valve power, the sleeves and cylinders of each and every engine still had to be individually lapped by hand to achieve the absolute accuracy and concentricity necessary for a perfect match. But after 1939, when a way was found – almost by accident – to make each sleeve truly round by finishing it with a blunt grinding wheel incapable of cutting, thousands could be made by centrifugal casting in the certainty that every one would be a perfect sliding fit in its cylinder barrel without the need for rectifying and, moreover, that it would last for more than 1,000 flying hours without any sign of distortion that could lead to seizure.

No fewer than 143,000 sleeve-valve, air-cooled radial engines were built by the Bristol firm and various shadow factories during the war, for service in RAF bomber and transport aircraft such as the Bristol Blenheim and Beaufighter, the Vickers Wellington, the Short Sunderland and Stirling, and the Handley Page Halifax. In fact, over 1½ million sleeves were thus manufactured by Bristol during the Second World War to be employed in its own and other engines, such as the Napier Sabre, designed by Frank Halford, which powered Hawker Tempest and Typhoon ground-attack fighter-bombers. Indeed, altogether the total number of sleeve-valve aero-engines that saw service in the war was not far short of the 150,000 Rolls-Royce Merlin in-line, liquid-cooled engines produced. Later, Sir Harry Ricardo calculated that by 1945 over 200 million horsepower had been contributed to the war effort by these Bristol and Napier sleeve-valve engines. The five years of research work that made this achievement possible cost no less than £2 million, then a staggering sum and almost double the investment of £1.3 million made by the Air Ministry in the development of Whittle's gas-turbine engine, an entirely new form of prime mover.

Despite Harry Ricardo's heavy aeronautical workload in the years leading up to the outbreak of the Second World War, responsibilities that aged him visibly, it seems that he still had time for other work on the automotive side of his business. In 1943, in the 10 February issue of *The Motor*, there appeared an article written by the magazine's Technical Editor Laurence Pomeroy (son of Laurence Pomeroy Snr, the former Vauxhall designer who had been an old friend of Ricardo's) which began as follows: 'Possibly the most advanced racing car engine in Europe is the 1940 Alfa Romeo model. Stung by their defeats at the hands of their German rivals Mercedes-Benz and Auto-Union, the Italian company had embarked on the construction of an entirely new power unit for the 1940 racing season. It is a matter in which Englishmen can take credit that Alfa Romeo came to this country to obtain the design and asked that celebrated engineer Mr H.R. Ricardo to do the work for them.'

The article went on to report that Ricardo's answer to Alfa-Romeo's requirements was a 3-litre sixteen-cylinder engine employing numerous highly advanced features never previously seen on an Italian racing engine, such as a two-stage Roots-type supercharger. The engine boasted sixteen cylinders of square 62×62mm dimensions arranged in two banks of eight with a very wide angle of 135 degrees between them. This was the first time that an ultra-wide-angle V16 short-stroke engine had ever been employed in Grand Prix racing, Pomeroy avowed. Many of his readers were unconvinced, however. As there was no previous record that such a car had ever appeared in public, much less on a racetrack, most readers concluded that in publishing his surprising revelations, Pomeroy had made an elementary mistake by confusing Ricardo's name with that of a certain Spanish designer, Wifredo Ricart, who was known to have been employed by Alfa-Romeo at that time. Surely, it must must have been Ricart rather than Ricardo who was the architect of this extremely interesting engine, if it ever existed at all, said the doubters. The whole idea that the proud Italian marque could have called in an outsider with little previous experience of racing car engine design to solve its problems seemed too preposterous to be true, especially considering that Italian national prestige was also at stake.

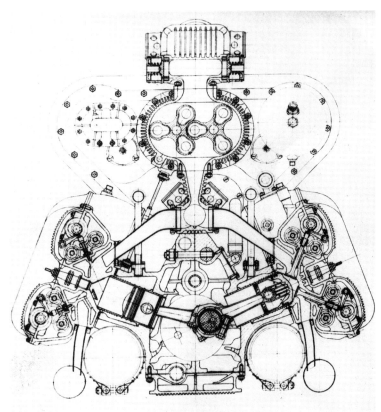

The highly advanced Type 162 Alfa-Romeo 3- litre V16-cylinder engine, designed jointly by Ricardo and Ricart, capable of producing over 600bhp at 9000rpm. Its wide-angled V (135°) configuration was later adopted for the postwar BRM Grand Prix racing car.

The proposed Alfa-Romeo Type 162 Grand Prix car of 1938. One prototype example only was produced, and all further development ceased when Italy entered the war in June 1940; it was never raced.

After the war, the question of the V16 engine's authorship became even more of a mystery to researchers because of the total lack of information from Alfa-Romeo on the subject of the prototype racing cars that were being prepared for competition in the months before the outbreak of the Second World War. It was not until 1965 when the first curator of the company's museum, Luigi Fusi, produced his authoritative model-by-model history of the marque that the existence of this racing car, the prototype Type 162, was confirmed. Moreover, the technical drawings published as illustrations in his book showed that the engine in question was exactly as Pomeroy had described it, although Ricardo was not acknowledged as its designer. Fusi's account revealed that the car had been developed in 1939 as a successor to the Type 316 and that although the necessary components for six examples had been produced, only one car had been completed for testing purposes. Its first and only trial took place early in June 1940, further testing being discontinued as a result of Italy's entry into the conflict later that month. Thus the Type 162 had never seen action on the track at any time, nor had any trace of it survived the upheavals of the war.

Therefore, in the absence of any further contradictory details from Milan, the true facts of this story would only emerge long after Sir Harry Ricardo's death from a study of the correspondence between the Ricardo and Alfa-Romeo firms that survived in the Shoreham archives. From these letters it is possible to trace the bare bones of the collaboration, and to prove that Harry Ricardo (as he then was) did indeed play a large part in the design of what was certainly a most significant vehicle in the history of Grand Prix racing (even though it was never entered in a race), since its concept undoubtedly inspired the layout of the British V16 BRM of 1945/6.

The Ricardo firm had been retained as consultants by Alfa-Romeo following Harry Ricardo's visit to Milan in 1937 and in the course of a routine visit to Milan the following year, on 13 June 1938, he was able to renew his acquaintanceship with the man responsible for Alfa's experimental racing projects, Wifredo Ricart, whom he had met on his first visit to Alfa-Romeo's offices. Born in Barcelona in 1897, and therefore twelve years younger than Ricardo, Ricart had arrived in Milan in the summer of 1936 as a refugee from the Spanish Civil War and had landed a job as head of Alfa's design and research and development departments, but on a consultancy rather than a permanent basis. A highly gifted engineer and designer who was equally at home with both aero- and automobile engines, Ricart had previously run his own firm in Barcelona, Motores Ricart & Perez, which specialised in building high-performance machines in the Hispano-Suiza mould. Tall and aristocratic in appearance, with dark hair that contrasted sharply with his very white skin and green eyes, he came from an upper-class military background and was described by the American automobile historian Griffith Borgeson as 'soft spoken, polished and charming, a gentleman of breeding and diplomacy, who was fluent in five languages'. A talented musician blessed also with a gift for drawing and painting, Ricart impressed Ricardo as being the sort of man he could do business with. Indeed, a lasting friendship soon developed, continuing long after the Spaniard had returned to Barcelona after the war, when he became involved in the affairs of the Pegaso car and lorry firm.

It could not have been easy for a foreigner to assume a role of such importance and influence within the Alfa-Romeo organisation at a time when, under Mussolini's regime, nationalism in Italy was at fever pitch and Ricart soon fell foul of Enzo Ferrari whose Scuderia Ferrari was responsible for running the Alfa-Romeo racing team. Ferrari formed an intense antipathy towards Ricart, objecting to his elegant dress and polished manners and also his sophisticated, cerebral approach to racing car design.

The talented Spanish engineer Wifredo Ricart (1897–1974), head of the Alfa Romeo design and research department in 1938.

Attempting to take the rise out of his rival at one of their encounters, with thinly disguised hostility Ferrari asked him why he habitually wore shoes with such thick rubber soles. To this calculated insult Ricart replied: 'The brain of a great technician is a delicate instrument that has to be carefully protected, and in order that it should not be damaged by rough ground or subjected to other irritations, it must be constantly cradled from shock.'

From the Shoreham letters it is evident that there was no such friction between Ricart and Ricardo. Two of a kind, these artist-engineers struck up an instant rapport and their discussions went far beyond the commercial topics in hand, so much so that Ricart invited Ricardo to make suggestions 'for the combustion chamber form for a maximum output racing engine', a request that he confirmed in writing one week later, on 20 June 1938, stating that the individual cylinder capacity was to be 187cc, that the engine was to be capable of 9,000rpm and that the use of water injection to produce extra power under racing conditions was to be considered. Ricardo replied on 27 June saying that he had given the matter a lot of thought, but that he had not yet had the time to set his ideas down on paper or to discuss them with his colleagues. 'The problem is a supremely interesting one, to me the most interesting of all,' he avowed. Mounting his familiar hobby horse, yet mindful of Roy Fedden's experiences, he added, 'I am strongly inclined to think that single sleeve valves will be preferable to poppet valves where the attainment of maximum power is the first consideration, but I would not advocate this at the moment since you have as yet but little experience with this form of valve, and it will clearly take some years of development work to learn the necessary technique.'

He wrote to Milan again on 18 July to say that he had set out several schemes on the drawing board for the racing car's combustion chambers and that after careful consideration he had reached certain definite conclusions on the design of the engine as a whole. Apparently these drawings followed on 22 July but have long since disappeared from the Ricardo archives, so that they cannot bear witness to the full extent of Harry Ricardo's contribution to this prestigious project. Nevertheless, the letter discusses the principal features that Ricardo recommended, such as detachable aluminium-bronze cylinder heads having four valves per cylinder, a light-alloy block with a vertically split crankcase, detachable wet cylinder liners and valve-gear comprising two pairs of hairpin springs to each valve. Most notably, the drive to the clutch was to be transmitted by a centrally mounted output shaft lying above the crankshaft, which was to be arranged in two independent groups of four throws each and linked to the output shaft by a short vertical take-off shaft located at its centre, at the very heart of the engine. 'This could be extended fore-and-aft to provide for a four-wheel drive should this be desirable,' Ricardo suggested! The con-rod bearings were to be of the caged roller type, which Alfa-Romeo had already perfected on its previous racing car design, the Type 316. Ricardo had already employed many of these unusual features on his 1922 Vauxhall engine, of course.

'So far as the upper part of the engine is concerned, I can see no reason why we should not be able to obtain an output of 500 bhp at 9,000–10,000rpm,' he added, 'providing that we can dispose sufficiently rapidly of the heat to the cylinder walls and pistons etc. Whether it will be found possible to design the lower half to deal with such revolution speeds is another matter but here we feel that you have much more experience than we have.' Ricart replied on 17 August saying that he just returned from Spain and that he had begun the detailed design work for the 3-litre, sixteen-cylinder car, and had decided to incorporate Ricardo's 'valuable suggestion' of a central drive and hairpin springs for the valves.

Within a month war had broken out in Europe, although at first Great Britain and Italy remained on peaceful terms. So on 25 November, having heard nothing more from Alfa-Romeo Italy on the subject, Ricardo wrote again saying, 'It is a very long time since I have seen or heard from you but my wife and I have still many happy memories of the delightful day we spent with you and Madame Ricart in Milan last March. I am wondering very much how the racing engine is getting on and whether you are still working on it.'

Ricart's reply of 6 December 1939 brought the news that work on the new sixteen-cylinder car had been retarded by other urgent business but that its engine was presently running its first hours on the test-bench. 'We also are busy, but racing has been relegated to a secondary importance,' he announced. The implication was plain; with its German rivals otherwise occupied, and with any Grand Prix contest with Mercedes and Auto Union unlikely for the foreseeable future, funding of the Alfa-Romeo project (almost certainly provided by Mussolini's government in a bid to impress Adolf Hitler and uphold Italian prestige on the Grand Prix circuits of Europe) had been withdrawn. Once again, circumstances had conspired to deny Harry Ricardo the opportunity to be identified, along with his partner Wifredo Ricart, as a mechanical designer of the highest calibre and a master of the design of high-performance engines.

It seems that he never mentioned the matter in public again except when in 1947 he received a letter from a well-known racing car collector Tony Brooke, the owner of the only surviving example of his 1922 Vauxhall design, who wrote to enquire about certain technical features of that car. 'The old engine did a very good performance for its date, so much so that we stuck substantially to the same general design for the 16-cylinder 3-litre engines we designed for the Alfa Romeo Company just before the war, but with a single central plug,' said Sir Harry in his reply. 'These engines when first tested in 1939 developed a maximum of 540 bhp at 9,000rpm. We have since heard that they have whacked them up to over 600 bhp, which is quite good going for 3 litres.'

Again, as in the Bristol affair, Harry Ricardo was denied the credit that was rightly his. Time and time again it was his misfortune to find that his name was never to be associated in the public mind with the exotic machinery of high-performance aviation and Grand Prix motoring. Even today, he is still regarded as being far more of a scientist, theoretician and experimentalist than a gifted and expert mechanical designer of internal combustion engines. But, again, he never complained of that fact. As a consultant he was accustomed to obscurity and quite content to work out of the limelight, avoiding publicity altogether. All forms of boastfulness and self-advertisement were anathema to him, and he sought only to win the respect of other professional engineers in the quiet confines of the Royal Aeronautical Society, the Institution of Mechanical Engineers and the Athenaeum.

In any case, with a business to run in troubled times he was simply too busy to dwell on matters of personal pride or prestige. For example, on 19 September 1939, a week or so after war with Germany was declared, Jack Pitchford wrote to Ricardo's long-standing French clients Automobiles Chenard & Walcker on his behalf. In the context of the contemporary political situation, the letter makes poignant reading: 'In view of recent events in Europe we would like to take the opportunity of assuring you that, so far as it is possible to predict, there need be no change in the scope and nature of our services to you', Pitchford wrote. 'Our organisation will remain unaltered in personnel and activity and we shall look forward to continuing our co-operation with your Company as happily and, we hope, as usefully as in the past. Personal visits may, of course, prove rather more difficult to arrange than hitherto, but when such visits are felt to be necessary they should always be possible.'

CHAPTER 19

The Oxford Years

A t first, the outbreak of the Second World War in September 1939 had little effect on the activities in progress at Bridge Works. For the first few months of the 'phoney war' it was business as usual, except for an inevitable reduction in the work being undertaken for European clients. Until the fall of France in June the following year, the only visible sign of hostilities was the sandbag walls built up in the yard on Oliver Thornycroft's instructions to protect doors and windows from blast damage in the event of a surprise Luftwaffe air raid. Thornycroft himself was seconded to service at the Admiralty later in the year, leaving Jack Pitchford to take his place as General Manager.

But on 21 June 1940, the day before the French signed an armistice with the invading German Army at a ceremony in the forest of Compiègne, the situation changed abruptly when a notice signed by Pitchford appeared on the Bridge Works' noticeboard summoning all personnel to assemble in the yard at 5.15 p.m. The directors and staff who gathered were surprised to be addressed by Harry Ricardo himself, for this was the first time in the memory of most people present that their shy and diffident employer had spoken to them *en masse*. But the news that Ricardo had to tell them must have come as even more of a shock than his unexpected appearance. In view of the events across the Channel, Ricardo announced, the military authorities had decided that the entire company was to be evacuated from Shoreham immediately, lock, stock and barrel, for the duration of the war.

As Ricardo explained, it was feared that the Germans would choose this part of the Sussex coast as a beachhead for their threatened invasion of England. To defend the area, therefore, it was proposed that the dykes surrounding the Adur and Arun estuaries would be opened, flooding the low coastal plain and leaving Bridge Works 6 ft under water at high tide. Ricardo also hinted at the fact that the authorities considered the activities then in progress at the works were so crucial to the national war effort that all precautions had to be taken to prevent the various research engines in the test-shops from falling into German hands in a surprise commando raid. Either way, the firm's activities had to be relocated in a safer place inland without delay and with the minimum disruption, for by now the Air Ministry (or rather the new Ministry of Aircraft Production) regarded the aero-engine research work currently under way at Shoreham as being of paramount importance. In fact, the threatened flooding did not take place, but all the same in 1941 a 20-mile wide stretch of the Sussex coast from Brighton to Littlehampton became a prohibited area and no travel within it was allowed without possession of a special permit.

The Ricardo firm was presently engaged on a programme of research involving an advanced aero-engine concept that Harry Ricardo had been advocating at meetings of the Aeronautical Research Committee for many years, and which had been selected by the Air Ministry to succeed the Rolls-Royce Merlin and Griffon four-stroke engines as the next generation of prime movers for the fighter and interceptor aircraft of the Royal Air Force. This single-sleeve-valve, fuel-injected, two-stroke engine technology was currently under full-scale development, and an evaluation programme involving a number of prototype single-cylinder research engines, code-named the E65 series, had been initiated by the Air Ministry in 1938 and given top priority over all the other projects under investigation by Bridge Works at that time.

The problem of finding suitable alternative accommodation in which to continue this research was a difficult one, but with the help of the government's Emergency Powers Committee, premises were eventually found some ninety miles away at Oxford. The move did not go smoothly, however, and on 8 July 1940, Ricardo was forced to write a private and confidential letter to his friend Sir Henry Tizard complaining about the situation in the strongest terms. 'I am utterly fed up with the Air Ministry and all to do with it,' he confessed.

For three weeks they have been just pure obstructive about our move, either actively or passively. Now the military have said that they can wait no longer, have occupied the Works, stationed a large force there and are threatening to flood the place. . . . We have not been able to get any kind of written authority [for the move] from any department of the A.M. although all agreed that we must go as soon as possible. . . . Is there no way of breaking down this hopeless tangle of red tape? . . . Damn the whole lot of them! I am feeling so thoroughly disgusted that I don't care a hang if they do swamp the whole place and all their blasted equipment is submerged for good and all.

For the next five years, the Ricardo company occupied workshops and offices in three locations at Oxford, all lying off the Banbury Road, just north of St Giles. The administration and technical departments were housed at 4 Norham Gardens in a sprawling red-brick Edwardian building that had formerly been an Oxford theological college, Wycliffe Hall. Almost opposite in Parks Road lay the University School of Engineering, part of the upper floors of which was requisitioned to house Ricardo's design and drawing office staff, while on the ground floor were installed the test-beds for five research engines, including the two E65 units together with various other pieces of experimental machinery. The third and largest location consisted of two-thirds of the floor space of a large garage and repair shop, which stood about a mile away from Norham Gardens, at the junction of South Parade and Banbury Road. This, of course, was Hartwells Garage owned by Percy Kidner who had become a director of the company in 1933.

Finding accommodation in Oxford for the staff was a severe problem; a hostel was established for single men while houses and flats were bought or rented for the use of married employees. Having been obliged to leave Tottington Manor, Harry Ricardo and his family found a temporary billet at 26A Norham Gardens. As elsewhere throughout England at that time, a cheerful spirit of improvisation prevailed among the reluctant evacuees. For the benefit of those personnel who were separated from their families in Sussex, the firm's diesel-engined, seven-seater Citroën Family Fifteen Saloon (one of only two such vehicles in the UK) made regular monthly trips to Shoreham and back, diesel fuel, unlike petrol, being readily available for such purposes until 1942 when fuel rations for all social and recreational purposes were withdrawn. The French engineer who had been responsible for the development of the Citroën–Ricardo diesel engine, René Wisner, was also a resident of Norham Gardens throughout the war. Having escaped from France in 1940, he had joined his friend Jack Pitchford in the university town and had been given a job as Ricardo's Company Librarian. But as his library (housed in the tiny upper room which also served as his *pied-à-terre*) contained only half a dozen books, and as he was so rarely on duty to issue them to readers, few would-be borrowers were taken in by this ploy.

Although the engineers who moved to Oxford were exempted from military service by virtue of their vital government work, they nevertheless donned uniforms to play their part in the nation's defence as soldiers in the Ricardo platoon of the local Home Guard, or as members of the Royal Observer Corps, a nationwide organisation of volunteers formed to supplement the Royal Air Force's air-raid warning system. In those critical days of 1940, when Britain stood alone with only the English Channel separating the British Isles from Nazi-occupied Europe, an enemy invasion seemed both imminent and inevitable. The whole population expected Hitler's Blitzkrieg to begin at any moment, heralded by a deluge of bombs, an attack that would rapidly be followed by hordes of German paratroops dropping out of the sky. Roadblocks were set up at major crossroads, and signposts were removed or turned in the wrong direction to confuse the enemy, and instructions went out to the clergy that church bells should only be rung as an invasion alarm. German fifth columnists and saboteurs were thought to be hiding in every haystack and the public was told to be on a constant lookout for spies and to report anything that looked suspicious. 'Careless talk costs lives' proclaimed a humorous poster campaign produced by the Punch cartoonist, Fougasse.

It was against this background of uncertainty, anxiety and high secrecy that Harry Ricardo spent the war years in a state of almost constant transit between Oxford and London, attending meetings at the Air Ministry, the War Office, the Royal Aeronautical Society, his own firm's offices in Westminster and, of course, the Athenaeum Club where he regularly lunched with his oldest friends and associates such as Henry Tizard, Frank Halford and Mervyn O'Gorman. His official responsibilities and workload, which had been growing steadily ever since the national rearmament programme had belatedly got under way in 1935, reached saturation point after the Dunkirk retreat in 1940, when the military procurement system went into top gear, working flat out around the clock to replace the enormous material losses sustained by the RAF and the British Expeditionary Force in France. Although nearly all activities for commercial clients other than Shell and Davy Paxman had ceased with the move to Oxford, there seemed to be yet more and more work for him and his colleagues to do, as the War Office, the Air Ministry and the Admiralty all called upon the Ricardo firm's unique independent consulting expertise to evaluate ideas and overcome ad hoc problems encountered in their urgent re-equipment plans. The internal combustion engine was indispensable to the prosecution of the war by land, sea and air, and its development had the highest priority; new aircraft, tanks, military lorries, warships, transport craft and submarines all required new and better engines, and it was to Ricardo that the military authorities and the manufacturers which supplied them turned for forward research and for specialist trouble-shooting technical know-how.

In view of his experience with the Mk V Tank in the First World War, it is hardly surprising that during the Oxford years Ricardo found himself occupied once more with the development and testing of engines for tanks and armoured vehicles. At the outbreak of the Second World War in September 1939, the number of tanks of all types in service with the

British Army had numbered approximately 1,000, but after the Dunkirk retreat when the bulk of its heavy weapons and mechanised equipment was left behind in France, the army was left with only 250 light tanks, based in the UK, with which to carry on the fight. The whole field army had to be reorganised, re-equipped and expanded from zero, and for this purpose in June 1940 the Ministry of Supply set up the Tank Board to supervise the design and production of armoured fighting vehicles, and appointed Ricardo as a consultant with special responsibility for developing a new range of tank engines.

Between 1919 and 1939 there had been little progress in the development of weapons for mechanised warfare, and although the Ricardo firm had been given a contract in the late twenties to produce a series of sleeve-valve diesel engines for a proposed new British medium tank, nothing had come of this project. The contract in question had been awarded by a certain General Peck, then the Director of the Department of Mechanical Warfare, who had been much impressed by the potential of the compression-ignition engine to extend the radius of action of tanks and armoured fighting vehicles as well as to reduce the risk of fire. However, after his retirement in 1931 his place was taken by an officer whose enthusiasm did not run to diesel engines, much to Ricardo's dismay. Nevertheless, the diesel option was not entirely abandoned by the War Office and one, at least, of the British tanks of the Second World War, the Valentine, was equipped with a 130hp AEC–Ricardo six-cylinder engine that had been developed for commercial vehicle use by the Southall bus and lorry firm before being abandoned in favour of a smaller unit.

As soon as the Hartwell's Garage test-shop got under way, a War Department section was established to investigate various diesel engines intended for military use and by April 1941, the Ricardo firm had designed an entirely new 600hp diesel engine for tank use. Little is known about this engine, except that once again its development was vetoed by those in authority at the Ministry of Supply.

As an alternative, Ricardo turned to examining other diesel possibilities, including an engine known as the Meteorite which was a V8 conversion of the V12 Rolls-Royce Meteor petrol engine, itself an unsupercharged automotive version of the Rolls-Royce Merlin aircraft engine. Following the entry of the American forces into the Second World War in December 1941, however, it was decided that petrol engines should be the standard equipment for tank propulsion and the Meteorite project was suspended. After the war it was revived, however, and it eventually went into service in the fifties as the power plant of the Thornycroft Mighty Antar tank-transporting vehicle.

Of all Ricardo's many secret Second World War tank activities, however, none was stranger or more hush-hush than the project that came his way in 1939 and which amounted to a bizarre replay of history. On the eve of the outbreak of the war, Winston Churchill had returned to the Admiralty, the position he had occupied twenty-five years previously in the early months of the First World War. Here he quickly took up the subject that had interested him so greatly in the days of his Landship Committee, the design and development of tanks and other items of mechanised land warfare. Within weeks he had commissioned the construction of a gigantic experimental excavator to facilitate the work of digging trenches, in case trench warfare should once again be a feature of the coming conflict with Germany. Mounted on caterpillar tracks and powered by two 450hp V12 Paxman–Ricardo diesel engines, this giant vehicle (known as Nellie) was designed to dig its way into the soil like a monster mole.

But Nellie was only the first of Churchill's inspirations. To encourage and promote the development of new tanks he also instigated a re-creation of the Landship Committee

The experimental TOG2 heavy assault tank produced early in the Second World War powered by a 600hp Paxman-Ricardo diesel engine. The initials TOG stood for The Old Gang, the veterans of First World War tank development, including Harry Ricardo, who were assembled to create it.

itself, by calling on the services of the very same men who had been responsible for the production of the original prototype tank in the First World War. In June 1939, the Chairman of the former First World War Tank Supply Committee, Lieutenant-Colonel A.G. Stern (by now Sir Albert Stern) was invited by the Minister of Supply to form a new committee under the auspices of both the Director of Naval Construction at the Admiralty and the Director of Mechanisation at the War Office. Its brief was to study the development and production of tanks in England, to inspect all experimental work currently under way and to investigate the possibility of producing an entirely new heavy assault tank capable of attacking deep into German territory after breaching the concrete defences of the Siegfried Line.

The principal members of this Special Vehicle Development Committee of the Ministry of Supply, which met for the first time in September 1939, comprised a familiar group of veterans – Sir Eustace Tennyson d'Eyncourt, General Sir Ernest Swinton, Major Walter Wilson and, of course, Harry Ricardo. Not surprisingly, the group soon began calling themselves 'The Old Gang' and the initials TOG were adopted as the official designation for the super-tank project, which was classified as Most Secret. The design and construction of the first prototype, TOG1, commenced in October 1939 with the work being carried out by William Foster & Co of Lincoln, the firm that had played the leading role in the development and manufacture of the first tanks in the First World War.

The specification for this monster 70-ton 'land battleship' required that it should be able to traverse shelled and waterlogged ground, cross wide trenches, surmount all other anti-tank obstacles, be fully protected against 47mm armour-piercing and 105mm high-explosive shells fired from 100 yd away and be equipped with a gun capable of piercing

7 ft of reinforced concrete, together with other armour-piercing weapons and machine-guns. Steered by a novel electro-mechanical transmission system powered by two generators coupled to a single 450hp Paxman-Ricardo diesel engine (the most powerful engine suitable for tank propulsion then available), its top speed was only 8½ mph, although it was envisaged that production versions would be equipped with hydrostatic transmission and the new Ricardo 600hp diesel tank engine referred to earlier.

The prototype TOG1 was fitted with a French 75mm field gun, reputedly acquired with the assistance of Colonel de Gaulle, and it shared the same familiar track system and lozenge-shaped profile of the First World War tanks. Design work commenced in February 1940 and the vehicle was ready for its first tests, attended by Ricardo, by October that year. But by that time, such monster tanks were entirely redundant, their original purpose having been obviated by the defeat of France. Even so, their development was allowed to continue sporadically until 1942 for research purposes, a Mk II version having been constructed in 1941. Neither tank was ever used in combat.

In addition to his work as a member of the War Office Tank Board (which superseded Stern's Special Vehicle Development Committee), throughout the Second World War Ricardo shouldered a yet greater burden of responsibility imposed by the Air Ministry, for in addition to his duties on the Engine Subcommittee of the Aeronautical Research Committee he acted as a consultant to all the major firms currently producing aero-engines for the RAF – Rolls-Royce, Bristol, Napier, Siddeley and de Havilland.

In November 1940, some three or four months after his firm had been installed at Oxford, Ricardo was given an additional task. Lord Beaverbrook, the head of the new Ministry of Aircraft Production recently established by Winston Churchill asked him to accompany the Deputy Director of Scientific Research at the MAP, Dr Harold Roxbee-Cox, on a visit to Leicestershire. At the Ladywood Works at Lutterworth he had talks with a certain RAF officer, Wing Commander Frank Whittle, about what could be done to help in the work of developing Whittle's invention, the gas turbine, which actually had been patented some ten years previously in 1930. Neither Whittle nor his jet engine were strangers to Ricardo, as the man and his machine had been a constant topic of discussion at the ARC ever since Whittle had submitted a paper shortly after taking out his patent. Later, in 1936, Whittle and his private production company, Power Jets Ltd, had obtained financial support from the Air Ministry in a bid to turn the idea into reality, but this was the first time that Ricardo had been asked by the powers that be to assist the inventor in the development of jet flight. Indeed, together with Tizard and Pye, Ricardo had been among the first men on the ARC to recognise the potential of Whittle's work and to encourage it, but even so he was essentially a piston-engine man with no specialist knowledge of this revolutionary new technology.

Indeed, although he declared himself to be 'a sincere advocate for jet propulsion' there is evidence to suggest that, as an engineer, he was less than enraptured by the turbo-jet, not because it posed a threat to the future of the piston internal combustion engine to which he had dedicated the greater part of his life, but because, as a machine, it lacked technical interest for him. Due to its rotational action the performance parameters of the turbo-jet could be accurately predicted with a slide rule, but the behaviour of the reciprocating piston engine, on the other hand, was a true mystery, accessible only to cognoscenti like himself. Its elaborate mechanism and complex interrelated dynamic forces made its study more of an art than a science, requiring instinct and intuition. And not only that; as a man brought up in the nineteenth century, long before the days of mass tourism, and whose notions of international travel were conditioned by the comfort and spaciousness afforded by a first-class ticket on the great trans-Atlantic liners or the equally luxurious and exclusive Empire flying boats, he simply could not foresee the use that the world would find for Whittle's invention. The turbo-jet would have important military applications, of course; it might even have a future as a prime mover for fast, high-flying mail-carrying aircraft. But who in their right mind would want to spend hours crossing the oceans at a height of 40,000 ft, cooped up in a pressurised aluminium box, he asked? That within fifty years the new jet age would lead to the creation of a vast air-transport industry carrying millions of passengers daily on inessential recreational journeys was quite beyond his comprehension. When speaking on the subject of high-altitude piston engines at a conference in Rome in 1935 he had concluded: 'Whether flight at such high altitudes will ever appeal to the travelling public is another question altogether. I rather fear that boredom and the extremely restricted quarters will be a serious obstacle.'

Frank Whittle was a most remarkable man. An exceptional pilot, a first-class aircraft engineer and a brilliant mathematician who had obtained a first in the mechanical science tripos at Cambridge after only two years of study, he pursued his goals with a relentless determination, overcoming all the difficulties in his path with an extraordinary single-mindedness. However, having trained in the RAF rather than in manufacturing industry, he had never had the chance to acquire the thorough knowledge of materials and production techniques that was one of Harry Ricardo's greatest strong points, and this disadvantage was seen to be hindering the project upon which Lord Beaverbrook, with his typical enthusiasm and impatience, had laid such high hopes. Moreover, Whittle and his small experimental team were severely under-capitalised and lacked the full range of skills and equipment required to turn his invention from a concept on the drawing board into a tangible prototype that could eventually be mass-produced by the aircraft-engine industry for service with the Royal Air Force. As a serving RAF officer first and foremost, fame and fortune meant little to him. His sole aim was to re-establish the supremacy of the service that he loved, and that he had joined as a cadet apprentice in 1923, at the age of sixteen.

Following his visit to Lutterworth, Ricardo suggested that there were two areas in which his firm could make a useful contribution, given its current greatly reduced capabilities at Oxford. Naturally, the first had to do with improving the design and manufacture of the combustion chambers employed in Whittle's prototype, and the Ricardo firm made about ninety burners incorporating a special fuel atomiser for Power Jets Ltd before this work was taken over by a manufacturing firm for series production. The second suggestion concerned the difficulties being encountered in regulating the fuel supply to the engine according to the aircraft's altitude, a problem for which no solution had as yet been found. By early 1941, the Ricardo firm had devised a novel altitude control device, the barostat, which automatically adjusted the pressure in the fuel line as the aircraft climbed, thus relieving the pilot from the need to continually adjust the throttle control to compensate for changes in atmospheric pressure.

Fully aware of the commercial value of his invention, Frank Whittle was extremely jealous and protective of it, and always on his guard against those who sought to wrest control of its manufacture in order to exploit its potential for their own ends. This protectiveness led him to be regarded by many of his collaborators as a difficult man to deal with, but Ricardo had nothing but praise for the RAF man's creativity and originality of thought. Whittle never failed to acknowledge the help that he had received from Harry Ricardo and Henry Tizard. Writing in his autobiography, he said, 'In our work on fuel system development we had the very valuable assistance of the Ricardo engineering company. We were indebted to them for such important components as a speed limit governor, a barostat relief valve . . . and so on. If others had shown the same unselfish disregard of proprietary interests as we received from Ricardo, months or even years would have been saved.' Of Tizard (who had arranged funding from the Air Ministry in 1937, thus saving the Power Jets' venture from collapse) he said in his autobiography *Jet*, 'Our best friend was Sir Henry Tizard, Chairman of the Aeronautical Research Committee.'

Installed in the experimental E28/39 aircraft, Whittle's engine made its first flight in May 1941, ushering in a new age of aeronautics. As time went by the development of gas-turbine aircraft became a new industry in the UK, and Roxbee-Cox (who, as Lord King's Norton, eventually became a director of the Ricardo company) conceived the idea of forming a Gas Turbine Collaboration Committee made up of technical people from all the major engine-building, component manufacturing and engineering consultancy firms involved, including Rolls-Royce, Rover, Power Jets and, of course, Ricardo. At one of the first meetings of this group, Harry Ricardo declared that he would waive all claims to royalties resulting from any patentable device arising from his gas-turbine work, at least for the duration of the war, and that he expected other member firms to do the same. In the main his request was observed, even though (as is well known) the relationships between the various individual firms involved were not always cordial, as they covertly competed for a share of the action in this new technology. Collaboration with the Americans was another matter, however, and one incident served only to confirm Ricardo's long-standing distrust of US business methods in those days. It happened that during the latter part of 1941, Whittle was sent to America by the British government to disclose full details of his gas-turbine work. Before a year had passed, the first US jet aircraft, built by the Bell aircraft firm, had made its maiden flight in October 1942. It was propelled by a copy of Whittle's engine produced by the General Electric Company and the Ricardo barostat with which it was equipped was also copied and patented by GEC in the USA without permission; indeed, for this US patent application GEC used an original sketch drawn by Ricardo's Chief Designer, R.J. Cousins. Fortunately, things are very different today.

In 1944, Whittle's company was taken into public ownership by the Ministry of Aircraft Production and renamed Power Jets (R&D) Ltd. With Roxbee-Cox acting as its first Chairman and Managing Director, its research and development work was merged with that of the National Gas Turbine Establishment at Pyestock, near Farnborough, which also took over Power Jets' Leicestershire base, now relocated to Whetstone. Both Harry Ricardo and Jack Pitchford served on its board for varying periods in the early postwar years and when visiting the Midlands to attend meetings, Ricardo always made a point of calling in to see the headmaster of his old school at Rugby to keep up with its affairs, in which he continued to take an active interest, having at one time been a governor there.

Towards the end of the war, the government became increasingly concerned about the effects of the so-called 'Baedeker' hit-and-run raids being carried out against British cities by fast twin-engined Messerschmitt Me410 fighter-bombers, which after dropping their bombs had just enough advantage in speed to evade the Mosquito night fighters, equipped with airborne radar, that were scrambled to detect and attack them. When consulted on this problem by the Air Ministry, Ricardo advised the authorities that, as a result of his own laboratory work, he could assure them that a very small measure of oxygen enrichment briefly administered to the Merlin engines of the pursuing Mosquitos would transform the situation, enabling them to overtake the unladen Messerschmitts and destroy them. Certain doubters among the technical staff at the Ministry refused to approve this measure, however. But then an examination of a Me410 that had been successfully shot down revealed that the aircraft was equipped with a series of gas bottles linked by pipes to the fuel inlet system of its engines. In fact, this apparatus had been installed solely to improve the initial cold-starting of the Me410's Daimler-Benz engines, but with the assistance of the then Minister for Aircraft Production, Sir Stafford Cripps, with whom he was on very friendly terms, Ricardo was able to use the shot-down aircraft as evidence that the Germans had themselves been using the very modification that he proposed. The doubters and outright opponents of oxygen enrichment for the Merlin engine were persuaded to withdraw their objections and the Mosquito night fighters were fitted with a simple system permitting a dose of nitrous oxide to be injected into the engines whenever a brief period of extra-high speed was demanded. The result of this stratagem was exactly as Ricardo had predicted and the Baedeker raids were quickly brought to an end with a sudden and dramatic increase in Me410 losses over England. Later, Jack Pitchford recorded that he remembered Harry's pleasure at receiving a very generously worded letter of thanks from the government.

For Ricardo there was much work to be done for the Admiralty too, for example as a member of the committee set up in September 1943 under the chairmanship of Sir Roy Fedden (he had been knighted in 1941) to examine the question of new, more powerful engines for the high-speed motor torpedo boats and gun boats of the Royal Navy. The committee's recommendation was that the development of a high-speed diesel rated at 2,500–3,000hp should be funded and although it was a gas turbine rather than a diesel engine that was eventually adopted by the Admiralty for this purpose, the eventual outcome of the project was the birth of the radical Napier Deltic diesel engine. Designed by H. Sammons, a member of the committee, this engine entered series production in 1952 and was subsequently adopted by British Railways to power its first diesel-electric traction locomotives.

Although the years of the Second World War were perhaps the most active and productive time of Harry Ricardo's long working life, they were far from being the happiest or most fulfilling. His deputy and confidant Jack Pitchford recalled that he disliked the Oxford period intensely, the more so when it became clear that Shoreham was neither to be invaded or bombed, and that the severe damage being inflicted on his property was due not to enemy action but to the carelessness of the occupying British and Canadian Army units. He deplored the fact that the great demands being made on his time by the interminable meetings he was obliged to attend left no opportunity for the practical design or experimental work that he thrived on. Ricardo had no time at all for 'political engineering' or bureaucratic red tape and got little pleasure or satisfaction out of the normal, routine activities of the many government boards and committees on which he served out of a sense of duty and patriotism. His dislike of all forms of fudging and compromise and his despair at the short-sightedness and parsimony of the Treasury caused him deep frustration, though conversely he was always ready to support and encourage individuals, like Frank Whittle, who were 'on the ball' and prepared to take effective, if unpopular, action. And most of all, in common with the majority of his age group who had survived 'the war to end all wars', he deeply regretted that his country was once again involved in a conflict with Germany, and that so little had been done to avoid this war by greater military preparedness.

On a personal level he sorely missed his home life in the peace and quiet of the Sussex countryside, especially since wartime regulations prevented him from enjoying his favourite pastime of coastal sailing. His only consolation was to be able to hear on his return to Oxford from London the exciting, raucous, shrieking sound made by his experimental two-stroke petrol injection engines undergoing trials at the University Engineering Laboratories, engines so powerful (and terrifyingly noisy) that they could not be run at full revs in this location for fear of them breaking loose from their improvised test-beds. These two E65 engines were single-cylinder prototype versions of a radical new single-sleeve-valve, fuel-injected, two-stroke engine currently being developed for the Ministry of Aircraft Production in association with Rolls-Royce at Derby.

There can be no doubt that Harry Ricardo regarded the highly advanced E65 project as of one of the most promising new directions in the history of the aero-engine, and it was most certainly an important milestone in his own career. According to Andrew Nahum, Curator of the National Aeronautical Collection at the Science Museum, the E65 was perhaps the most revolutionary piston aero-engine proposal ever developed by a major manufacturer. Its design represented the state of the art and incorporated several radical features that had never before been combined in a petrol engine, and have not been since. These were: two-stroke cycle action; open-end type sleeve-valves with uniflow scavenging of the exhaust gases (which overcame the familiar failing of the common-or-garden two-stroke engine, as used in lawnmowers); exhaust-driven turbocharging; direct fuel injection; and even stratified charge combustion. All of these ideas had been advocated and investigated by Ricardo since his youth, though never before in this particular combination.

The development of the E65 concept followed a very interesting course, both technically and politically. Technically, its line of development had begun with the RR/D diesel aero-engine concept which, as we saw earlier, had come about as the direct result of the interest expressed by Sir Henry Royce in adopting the compression-ignition principle for aircraft propulsion. With the financial support of the Air Ministry, in 1927 Royce had encouraged Ricardo to experiment in this direction by converting two Kestrel engines to diesel operation, at the same time employing single-sleeve-valves instead of poppet-valves, work that was actually carried out at Bridge Works in parallel with activities at the Royal Aircraft Establishment, Farnborough.

The performance of the RR/D had been disappointing in that it had failed to equal the output of the petrol equivalent so, as a follow-up investigation, in 1930 Ricardo designed and built a single-cylinder, two-stroke, compression-ignition research engine, the E40, and duly reported on his findings to the ARC in February 1932, suggesting that a full-size sixteen-cylinder, two-stroke engine (having four sets of four cylinders each, laid out in two horizontal banks) might well be worth exploring. The possibility of a V12-cylinder diesel engine incorporating the same features was also discussed with Sir Henry Royce at that time, on one of his frequent visits to Shoreham.

In 1933, the E40 was followed at both Shoreham and Derby by the E44, a high-speed version that proved particularly promising. Thus it was that, with the continued sponsorship and approval of the ARC, by 1933 the greater proportion of the advanced or forward research work on aero-engines being conducted in the UK by leading manufacturers such as Rolls-Royce, Napier and Bristol was being directed at exploring the potential of the two-stroke, sleeve-valve compression-ignition concept, with the aim of exploiting its superior fuel efficiency in order to achieve a greater range or duration of flight.

In 1937, however, when most of the fundamental mechanical problems affecting the concept had been overcome, there came a sudden change of direction in research policy, returning to the traditional fuel-injected spark-ignition ideas of former years, but retaining the two-stroke, sleeve-valve features of the E44 diesel. So it was that the famous E65 research engine was born, not so much freshly designed as closely adapted from the E44.

This abrupt change in requirements had come about as a direct result of changing objectives and priorities at the Air Ministry. As we have already noted, by September 1935 the Air Staff had come to the conclusion that a war with Germany was inevitable and had instigated a massive rearmament programme to equip the RAF for the struggle that lay ahead. In the period from 1935 to 1939 the Air Estimate (in effect, the total RAF budget for operations, equipment procurement and research) rose from £17.5 million (1934–5) to £56.5 million (1937–8) and reached £74.5 million in 1938–9. As well as sanctioning this huge investment in the building of large numbers of new aircraft and engines and the shadow factories needed to produce them, the RAF expansion programme also permitted a vast expenditure on scientific studies, perhaps the most crucial of which was devoted to finding a way to increase the warning time available in the event of a surprise mass night attack by enemy bombers on British cities. Hitherto, the defensive strategy of the RAF's Fighter Command had been to maintain patrols of aircraft continually in the air, loitering at height in pre-designated 'fighting zones' in the hope of detecting intruders visually and intercepting them before they could reach their targets. These patrols would be relieved periodically as their fuel supply became exhausted, so that only a proportion of the defending force could be in the air at any one time.

However, the air exercises held in the summer of 1934 had demonstrated beyond all doubt that this strategy was fatally flawed; unless a way could be found to detect incoming enemy bombers approaching at speeds of over 250 mph long before they crossed the British coastline, pure mathematics alone dictated that there was very little chance of British fighter aircraft ever making a successful interception, irrespective of the night-vision capabilities of their pilots. It was this conclusion above all that led to the widely held and thoroughly defeatist opinion that 'the bombers will always get through', which coloured with the yellow paintbrush of appeasement all negotiations with the Germans up to the time of the Munich Crisis in 1938.

Consequently, under the direction of the Department of Scientific and Industrial Research headed by David Pye, efforts were redoubled to devise a new technology employing radiant energy that would be capable of detecting or even destroying the enemy's bombers at long range. Astonishingly under the circumstances, by May 1935 this research and development effort had actually produced a viable result; not the death ray that had long been hoped for by many optimists in Whitehall, but instead an infinitely more useful and constructive invention. This, of course, was the radio direction-finding and ranging system – or Radar – developed by Professor (later Sir Robert) Watson-Watt of the Radio Research Department of the National Physical Laboratory at Slough. Radar made it possible to detect both the presence and direction of aircraft at long distance by means of reflected short-wave radio signals. In fact, within the year experiments at Orfordness had established that incoming aircraft could be detected at a range of 80 to 100 miles out over the North Sea, and the Air Council had approved the building of a chain of radar stations along the east and south coasts of the United Kingdom to forewarn of any impending attack.

In his capacity as Chairman of the Committee for the Scientific Survey of Air Defence, formed in January 1935 to oversee and coordinate these matters, Sir Henry Tizard was among the first to learn of this top-secret development. Almost immediately he began to discuss its implications with the Air Ministry and the senior officers of the RAF such as Air Marshal Sir Hugh Dowding who were, in the words of the distinguished defence scientist Professor R.V. Jones, Director of Scientific Intelligence at the Air Ministry, 'a cadre of officers of exceptional outlook, prepared to work with the scientists with the utmost urgency'. As a former pilot himself, Tizard realised that, given the advance warning offered by radar, it would no longer be necessary to maintain airborne patrols of fighter aircraft during times of crisis. Now the squadrons could wait in readiness at their airfields, conserving their strengths until the time came for them to be scrambled aloft *en masse* and directed to a predicted point of interception by radio operators located at centres of command and control on the ground, who were able to plot exactly the course being taken by the intruding bombers.

From his consultations with the RAF and the resulting experiments and exercises (most notably the Biggin Hill interception trials of February 1936 in which Fighter Command offered its unstinting cooperation), Tizard proposed a completely new strategy for the air defence of Great Britain, a plan in which every component part including aircraft and aero-engines was to play a part. This integrated air defence system, formulated by scientific analysis through the aegis of the Tizard Committee, provided the fighter control technique that was eventually used so successfully in the Battle of Britain during September 1940.

Moreover, the Tizard Committee's plan also called for the development of a completely different type of fighter aircraft to those currently in service or planned for the future. Endurance and fuel economy were no longer of paramount importance. What was needed to meet the German threat was a high-speed fighter-interceptor propelled by an ultra-high-power sprint or 'hot-rod' engine, using high-octane petrol and capable of climbing fast to reach high altitude in the minimum time, in order to gain the optimum position for a successful attack. It was also to have 'the maximum possible excess of speed over its opponents', in Tizard's own words.

This change of direction in aero-engine research was signalled by Tizard himself at a meeting of the Engine Subcommittee of the ARC held on 3 December 1935. Within a matter of weeks, on 10 January 1936, Ricardo submitted a paper entitled 'High Power Two Cycle Engines for Special Purpose Machines' in which he proposed 'an aero-engine of very high performance for short flights only without the usual regard for fuel and oil consumption, but with high specific output and small frontal area'. The engine that Ricardo proposed for these new circumstances was, of course, an adaptation of his E44 concept, modified from diesel to direct-injection petrol operation, and code-named the E65. In the form of a number of single-cylinder and V-twin research engines, this concept was destined to be subjected to an intensive programme of development over the next ten years, in a number of locations including the Royal Aircraft Establishment at Farnborough.

At first, when the go-ahead for the two-stroke project was finally given by the Air Ministry late in 1937, it was proposed that the design would be developed for manufacture by Bristol and Napier as well as Rolls-Royce. However, Bristol soon found that it had its hands full perfecting its sleeve-valve radial air-cooled engines and lacked the capacity, while Napier experienced problems with its own sleeve-valve engine, the 2,400hp, 24-cylinder horizontally opposed, water-cooled Napier Sabre (designed by Frank Halford), and was also obliged to withdraw, eventually leaving Rolls-Royce to go it alone, in conjunction with Ricardo's efforts at Oxford.

Rolls-Royce Managing Director Ernest Hives (later Lord Hives) envisaged that the E65 concept would form the basis of an entirely new generation of high-performance sleeve-valve aero-engines, all to be named after famous battles. The first of these, the Crecy, would replace the conventional Merlin and Griffon V12 engines as standard power plants for the fighter-interceptor aircraft of the RAF. Ricardo had forecast that in multi-cylinder form the E65/Crecy engine would have the potential to develop more than 4,000hp with virtually the same frontal area of the current Rolls-Royce Merlin Mk XX engine which powered the RAF's Spitfires and was rated at 1,395hp. By 1940, of course, the Merlin was an extremely well-proven engine, its development having commenced in 1933. A period of five or six years was then regarded as being the minimum development time required to take an engine from the first prototype stage to the point at which it could be accepted as being fit for service and mass production.

The 2400hp Napier-Halford Sabre liquid cooled supercharged aircraft engine of 1940. This employed twenty-four horizontally opposed cylinders arranged in a double-bank H configuration driving two crankshafts geared together. It also featured single-sleeve-valve operation – the system that Halford had first worked on with Ricardo at Bridge Works twenty years previously.

Rolls-Royce's immediate plans for the E65/Crecy involved building several single-cylinder and V-twin experimental engines and, in due course, six full-scale twelve-cylinder prototype engines. The latter were to take the form of two basic types: a version for single-engined fighters and another for multi-engined transport aircraft, which eventually evolved into a proposal for a compound or gas-generating engine incorporating a power recovery turbine to harness and exploit the prodigious exhaust thrust produced by the Crecy's huge through-put of air – the factor that was responsible for its characteristic exhaust note. It is said that, when the engine was first run under full power at Derby, air-raid sirens sounded at Nottingham as the ARP wardens had mistaken the noise for that of an approaching German V-1 'Doodlebug' flying bomb.

But despite its creator's high hopes, ultimately the story of the development of the Crecy was not a happy one. At the outbreak of the Second World War in September 1939 this top-secret project was considered to be the great white hope of British military aviation even though very few men were in the know about it. But by the end of the war it had been abandoned, dogged by endless difficulties and delays and, eventually, overtaken by events, not least of which, of course, were the arrival of the turbo-jet and the success achieved at Derby in developing Rolls-Royce's Merlin engine. The performance of this machine, acknowledged to be the finest aero-engine of its generation, was increased from 890hp to 1,395hp between 1935 and 1940, and ultimately it reached 1,760hp.

It appears that although in late 1939 Rolls-Royce had taken steps to form a dedicated two-stroke department and had appointed Harry Wood to be its Chief Engineer, and that under his direction the single-cylinder and V-twin experimental engines had been constructed the following year, little else had been achieved on the project at Derby by 1941, a state of affairs that caused Ricardo considerable anxiety. In March that year he wrote to Tizard, complaining that Rolls-Royce were not getting on with things. 'I don't want you to think or suggest that we have any grievance against R-R,' he added. 'They have been very frank and helpful to us, and I should hate to appear in any way ungrateful. I do think, however, that they have wasted a good deal of time and energy due to misdirected effort.'

From the start, he had been sceptical about Rolls-Royce's ability to undertake a project of this kind. In May 1939 he had written to Tizard saying that he was afraid they were not doing anything about his engine and that he did not really think that they were the right people to tackle it. 'They are quite the best people it has been my lot to work with and I have a boundless admiration for their ability and thoroughness,' he added, 'but they are, I think, too cautious, slow and meticulous for the development of such an engine. They are insistent that nothing short of perfection shall leave their Works or bear their name, and years roll by while they paint the lily.'

Throughout 1942 the disturbing situation continued, mainly due to metallurgical problems with the sleeve-valves, just as had been experienced by Fedden at Bristol. In September 1942, Ricardo's impatience prompted him to write to Tizard again, apropos discussions on the two-stroke at a recent meeting of the Engine Subcommittee of the ARC. 'One cause of the delay in getting on with the two-stroke is undoubtedly Rolls' habit of wanting to do everything differently, just for the sake of being different, but the main cause is the lack of any lead from the Ministry or the ARC as to whether it is really wanted or not. Isn't it time we made a definite recommendation? We blame Rolls-Royce, but surely the real blame rests with our Committee. If R-R were told that the thing was really wanted, and wanted badly, Hives would really get busy and get it going, but he is still waiting for that lead.'

In December 1941, the two friends had actually exchanged letters about their misgivings concerning the effectiveness of the ARC. 'I agree with you entirely that it has become very ineffective and that our recommendations are so often either ignored or action upon them postponed indefinitely,' wrote Ricardo.

I, too, have been wondering what is the cause of this state of affairs and what remedy to suggest, and had come to the conclusion that the Committee itself is at least partly to blame in that it is far too timid; that it thinks in terms of geological time and Woolworth expenditure; and that it lacks any sense of realism. As a result, by far the greater part of its time and energy is devoted to destructive criticism, to inventing reasons why so and so should not be done and generally to postponing decisions. My own opinion is that, to make the Committee effective, we should extend its membership to include those who are possessed of imagination and are face to face with realities, i.e. the actual engine designers. There are not so many of these that either we should be forced to make an invidious choice or the membership of the Committee would be too inflated. We need only invite Elliott of Rolls-Royce, Fedden of Bristol, Halford of Napier and De Havilland, Tresilian of Armstrong-Siddeley and, possibly, Whittle. These alone cover all those responsible for our aero-engine design . . . and they are all men of wide knowledge, experience and practical judgement.

Although by late 1943 the six complete Crecy engines had all been assembled and were on the test-beds at Derby, Ricardo had already come to the disappointing realisation that, under the pressures of war, the project was being starved of resources and was effectively being allocated a low priority in the long-term plans of both the Ministry of Aircraft Production and the Rolls-Royce company. He had proposed that the two-stroke should be regarded as an intermediate stage in the evolution of the aero-engine, acting as a bridge to link the production technology of the four-stroke piston engine with that of the coming turbo-jet, but Hives at Rolls-Royce had other ideas and, with his usual pragmatism, he shrewdly chose to leapfrog the gap and abandon the two-stroke altogether.

At a progress meeting held at Derby between Ricardo and Harry Wood of Rolls-Royce on 24 September 1944, by which time a mere 1,100 hours of running time on the full-scale twelve-cylinder engines had been recorded, it was concluded that the two-stroke had a 40 per cent advantage in power and a 10 per cent advantage in fuel consumption over conventional alternatives. Nevertheless, three months later in December 1944, on Hive's instructions all further work on the Crecy project at Derby was discontinued. With an eye to the future, in December 1942 he had concluded an agreement with the Ministry of Aircraft Production which gave Rolls-Royce both the sole commercial rights and the full technical responsibility for developing Whittle's turbo-jet technology for aeronautical purposes (the Rover car company retained an interest for automobile and other uses) and in due course Whittle's engine was manufactured at Derby, in a revised and improved form, to be marketed as the Nene.

The following year, in June 1945, Ricardo received a letter from Harry Wood at Derby which read as follows:

Described as the most revolutionary piston aero-engine ever developed by a major manufacturer, the Rolls-Royce Crecy included a combination of several radical features first proposed by Harry Ricardo in 1936. These included two-stroke action, direct fuel injection, exhaust driven turbocharging and, of course, single-sleeve valves. Developed from Ricardo's single-cylinder E65 experimental research engine of 1937, the first complete multi-cylinder examples were bench-tested in 1944. Unfortunately, due to the arrival of the turbo-jet, not one Crecy ever flew in an aircraft, to Sir Harry's great disappointment.

Dear Ricardo. I have not, for obvious reasons, written to you since R-R decided to take the Crecy off their programme in order to release personnel for other projects. After considerable thought, however, and reviewing the past five years work, I decided that you, at any rate, were entitled to have my own personal opinions about the engine in relation to other piston engines and to gas turbines with airscrews, and why there has been so much delay.

The first thing that strikes one is the fact that we have had only 1,100 hours running on the 12 cylinder engine in the 4½ years since the first acceptance test, i.e. 5 hrs per week, due entirely to low priority. . . . On other piston engines the firm has carried out 125,000 hours development running in the same time. This difference can be accounted for very largely by the war-time pressure put on service types which has paid very handsome dividends to the Nation.

On the other hand, 2 new engine types have been introduced in the past 3 years – the Eagle and its air-cooled counterpart the Pennine – neither of which had any chance of helping in the War, but both having been allocated to aircraft, and from the Rolls-Royce point of view, that constitutes a serious condition. Thus the firm has to work to a date and if an engine runs into trouble the whole resources of the firm from Hives and Elliott downwards are concentrated on the problem.

Wood's letter went on to say that at Derby there was no aircraft allotted to the Crecy and that 'This fact is accepted here as the reason for the lack of effort and interest in the Crecy and I feel that the Ministry of Aircraft Production has some responsibility for this situation.' No other engine currently under development at Rolls-Royce could show anything like such a good power/weight ratio as the Crecy, he avowed, adding that he was prepared to prove that it could finish a service acceptance test giving an engine weight of 0.9 lb per bhp. 'No-one here quarrels with my statements about the higher performance, lower specific fuel consumption and reduced cooling drag of the two-stroke engine . . . I am confident that another six months development would show a greatly improved performance and reliability, and that it would pay the MAP to allocate one of their test aircraft to a comparative trial of the Crecy and the Merlin. . . . I have enclosed a table which disproves very conclusively that, judged from development running time, the very novel project has taken a long time to develop,' he concluded. This table compared the progress of the development of the Merlin and Crecy engines and showed that between 1937 and 1945 the Merlin had undergone approximately 100,000 hours of actual running time on the test-bench, during which its maximum power rating was raised from 790hp to 1,125hp, whereas in the two years between 1942 and 1945, the Crecy had undergone just 1,000 hours of testing, raising its output from 1,000hp to 1,450hp.

In the event, however, no more work was done on the Crecy by Rolls-Royce, but after the war, at his own expense, Harry Ricardo reinstalled one of the single-cylinder E65 units from Oxford on a test-bed at Shoreham, merely to establish the limits of its performance. With the Air Ministry's permission it was run up to the maximum output possible with no regard to the risk of damage. This test established beyond all doubt that in its fully developed form the Crecy would ultimately have been able to deliver about 5,000 bhp – a phenomenal figure – for a gross weight of about 2,000 lb, and with little greater frontal area than the 2,400hp Rolls-Royce Griffon which it would have replaced.

The conclusion must be that events made the Crecy obsolete before its development was completed. Indeed, its true performance potential in flight was never ascertained for, sadly, it never flew at all, simply because no suitable airframe was ever designed in which to install it, although at one point there was talk of testing it in a Mosquito. Even so, in the view of Andrew Nahum and many other experts it remains a virtuoso achievement in the annals of the internal combustion engine.

After the war, cinema-goers flocked to see the films produced to celebrate the victory of British technology in the air. The most notable of these, perhaps, was *The Dambusters* in which the inventor of the bouncing bomb (Neville Barnes-Wallis, actually a close friend of both Tizard and Ricardo) was portrayed as a lone 'boffin', a shy and socially isolated genius struggling against the rigidity and incomprehension of officialdom before finally selling his ideas to sceptical officials and RAF officers. The reality behind this scenario was somewhat different, however, for the record shows that this and similar scientific triumphs were achieved by a closely integrated network of like-minded individuals who shared a common perspective and who met frequently to compare notes, not so much in the corridors of power as in the smoking rooms of London's clubland.

The story of the brief and unfulfilled life of the E65/Crecy concept clearly serves to demonstrate the pivotal influence exerted by Ricardo, Tizard and Pye and their friends and colleagues in directing the research effort (and thus the overall engine procurement policy) followed by the Air Ministry when rearming the Royal Air Force during the interwar years. The continuous presence of these scientists at the core of the Engine Subcommittee of the ARC was absolutely central to the formulation of policy, but, regrettably, their combined understanding, imagination and energy were never sufficient to overcome the bureaucratic vacillation and indecisiveness exhibited by the Whitehall authorities in the implementation of their more adventurous proposals.

So it was that by the end of the Second World War Ricardo's position at the head of his profession was acknowledged universally. More by virtue of his experience than his age (he was now sixty) he had assumed the mantle of the wise old man or guru of the British aero-engine industry, having acted as a consultant to all four of its leading manufacturers over the previous thirty years. His career as an experimentalist and a designer had embraced virtually the entire lifespan of the piston aero-engine in the United Kingdom from 1914 to 1944 and he was recognised as being among its greatest exponents, alongside such creative talents as Fedden, Halford and Rowledge. With them, he had been responsible for producing some of the first and last examples of this supreme test of the engineer's skill, and his contribution to the war effort in general, and to the achievements of the RAF in particular, had been decisive.

All these attainments had by now been accorded official recognition in Great Britain as well as on the Continent and in the USA. As early as 1930 he had been awarded an honorary doctorate in law by Birmingham University, and almost continually throughout that decade, scientific diplomas and medals were heaped upon him by the professional bodies to which he belonged, including the Institution of Mechanical Engineers (he was their President in 1944/5), the Institution of Automobile Engineers, the Royal Aeronautical Society and the Institute of Petroleum Technologists. However, the ultimate accolade was to come in the New Year's Honours List in 1949 when the title Knight Bachelor was bestowed upon him by King George VI in recognition of his services to the internal combustion engine industry. Yet, according to Jack Pitchford, of all Sir Harry Ricardo's many honours and distinctions, the one of which he was most proud was his membership of the Royal Society, to which he had been elected comparatively early in his career, in 1929.

CHAPTER 20

Eventide at Graffham

D uring the six years of the Second World War, the science of the internal combustion engine advanced more rapidly than at any other period as each of the major warring nations devoted vast resources to enhancing the combat capability of its warplanes, submarines, torpedoes, gunboats, tanks and other mechanised weaponry. Above all other power plants, it was the aero-engine that benefited in this forcing-house of development, for all the principal combatants were aware that victory could not be won without first achieving air superiority. But even so, other types of spark-ignition and diesel engines, large and small alike, were also greatly improved by the huge research and development programmes funded by government or military budgets and implemented by laboratories and research agencies such as the Ricardo firm. It was a source of great personal satisfaction to Harry Ricardo that Great Britain ended the war 'in a markedly superior technical position as regards aero-engine performance than any of the other participants'.

It is perhaps not surprising that a principal activity of the Shoreham company in the immediate postwar years was to report on the technical progress made by the enemy during the conflict by investigating the propulsion systems of captured items of equipment, such as aircraft, tanks and submarines, and advising on how the lessons thus learned might be employed in the new weapons being devised to fight the threatened Cold War against Britain's former ally, the Soviet Union.

Indeed, at Tizard's request, in 1945 Ricardo contributed four wide-ranging papers to the inquiry on the future of weapons that the War Cabinet Committee undertook for presentation to the Chiefs of Staff, dealing with likely advances in engines for tanks, armoured fighting vehicles, torpedoes and aircraft. In the latter case, Ricardo presciently acknowledged that:

The rapid development of the gas turbine following Air Commodore Whittle's brilliant pioneering work is likely to bring about just such a revolutionary change in aircraft power plant as did the steam turbine in marine work. . . . I would hazard a guess that in fifteen years time all military aircraft with the exception of a few small classes will be propelled by gas turbines alone, or where long range is required, by compound engines. At the same date [1960] more than half the total number of aircraft [including civilian freight and passenger machines] will still be equipped with piston engines. If this forecast is correct, then I can see but little need to attempt the development of new piston engines of more than 3,000hp. The technical difficulties in the way of developing piston engines of large power are enormous and increase in almost geometric proportion with increase in power above the optimum 3,000hp point. These considerations do not apply to the turbine which within certain limits becomes both an easier technical problem and more efficient the larger it is built.

In coming to this conclusion, which displayed the absolute honesty and integrity in engineering and business matters for which he was renowned, Ricardo effectively ruled himself out of the future of aero-engine research and development. His work as a consultant to the Air Ministry, which had commenced some twenty-five years previously, came to an end, although he continued to act for the Ministry of Supply, which had taken over responsibilities for the design and procurement of military aircraft from the Ministry of Aircraft Production.

Apart from continuing work on the barostat device, his final contribution to the story of flight was an attempt to exploit the exceptional fuel economy and reliability afforded by the compound engine concept with which he had been experimenting since 1939. The resulting prototype, arrived at in collaboration with Frank Halford, was the Napier Nomad, a supercharged, 24-cylinder, horizontally opposed, sleeve-valve diesel unit in which the very high flow of exhaust gases generated by the reciprocating pistons of the engine was used to drive the propellers by means of a turbine, rather than by a direct power take-off from the crankshaft as is conventional. Intended as the power plant for long-range maritime patrol aircraft such as the Avro Shackleton, it first ran in 1949 and was demonstrated at the Farnborough Air Show in September 1951, mounted in the nose of an Avro Lincoln bomber. Unfortunately, this promising idea was overtaken by the rapid advances then being made in the development of the gas-turbine-driven turbo-propeller engine and work on the project was suspended the following year. Ultimately, the Nomad had showed itself capable of producing 3,046bhp or 70hp per litre.

The return to Shoreham from Oxford took place gradually over the first few months of 1945, as the RAF gave up its occupancy of Bridge Works and the adjacent Shoreham airport. By the following year, however, the firm had successfully reoccupied its premises, reinstalled its experimental equipment in the renovated engine test-shops and, for the first time in its history, had become connected to mains electricity. The following year, with a view to expansion, it purchased the neighbouring Pad Farm, about 90 acres of tenanted water-meadows and grazing land lying between the River Adur and the grounds of Lancing College.

In 1948, the first new building to be constructed at Bridge Works since 1919 was erected, specially designed and constructed to provide secure laboratory accommodation for a new Admiralty contract that it had been awarded. This involved highly secret research on a range of projects involving the use of hydrogen peroxide (an extremely dangerous chemical) as an oxidant in underwater power plants, for example in submarine diesel engines and torpedo propulsion units. As this shop was built to government specifications and, indeed, was Crown property, no difficulty was experienced in either obtaining planning permission to build it or in obtaining supplies of building materials, the general shortage of which normally imposed a severe constraint on construction in those early postwar years. During the fifties and sixties, however, Bridge Works was considerably modernised and extended, but it was not until the completion of the A27 Shoreham bypass and the opening of the new Adur Bridge, in June 1970, that the site began to take on its present shape and size.

Harry Ricardo and his family also returned to Sussex early in 1945, but they never reoccupied Tottington Manor. The property had been somewhat knocked about by its military occupants during the war, and so rather than embark on lengthy and expensive renovations, Ricardo decided to offer Tottington to Pitchford on a short lease. (It was sold two years later, and is now a hotel.) The Ricardos made their home at Woodside, the house

Woodside, Graffham, West Sussex, the house designed and built by Halsey Ricardo, which was Sir Harry's home from 1945 until his death in 1974.

built by his father Halsey Ricardo at Graffham, near Petworth, which had stood vacant since the death of his mother Kate in 1941. Here, in the familiar Downland surroundings that he had first seen with his parents as a small boy, he was destined to live out the remainder of his days, although when moving in he could hardly have suspected that his stay there would last so long – no less than thirty years. In each of his homes Ricardo had set up a well-equipped workshop and Graffham was no exception. But whereas those at Walton and elsewhere had been used for research, the one at Woodside was intended for pleasure and relaxation only. Here he made, and stimulated his children and grandchildren to make, model yachts carved out of blocks of yellow pine, model steam engines and boilers, and even complicated full-scale machines for sawing logs and mixing concrete.

Regrettably, despite his unceasing efforts to promote it, the single-sleeve-valve technology that he had done so much to develop during the twenties and thirties did not survive the war in either military or industrial form and the very limited commercial success of these engines was certainly a great disappointment to him, although he never lost faith in the principle. As always, he took a realistic and philosophical view of the situation, recognising that despite its outstanding efficiency and durability the sleeve-valve was undoubtedly an expensive alternative to the conventional poppet-valve and somewhat ahead of its time.

Thirty years after the demise of the 'Silent Knight' engine, the reputation of the sleeve-valve principle remained irrevocably tarnished by its association with the

American invention, and was so deeply unfashionable among motor vehicle constructors that there was no hope at all in attempting to revive it for automotive use. Therefore, with the ending of the war and the gradual winding down of government-funded piston aero-engine research work, Ricardo decided to return to his investigations into automobile diesel engines, and made it a top priority to renew his association with commercial engine-builders and car manufacturers both at home and overseas, and especially those in France, Italy, Holland, Belgium and Germany with whom he had worked so closely before hostilities had interrupted relationships. The work of re-establishing contacts with these Continental clients and licence-holders fell to his deputy Jack Pitchford, who took over the role of roving ambassador that Harry Hetherington had played so well in the early days.

Fortunately, on commencing his visits to Europe, Pitchford found that interest in Ricardo's Comet combustion chamber design for use in private cars and light commercial vehicles was now even greater than it had been before the war, and so with the continuing collaboration of the Shell company, a new programme of research and development was begun, most notably in conjunction with Alfa-Romeo and Fiat in Italy, with the result that Fiat became the first manufacturer to produce a diesel-powered passenger car in postwar years – the Type 1400 introduced at the 1953 Turin Motor Show. Indeed it was the royalty income generated by the Comet system that provided the regenerative force behind the revival of the Ricardo firm during the fifties and sixties.

Despite the example shown by Automobiles Citroën in the 1930s, France was somewhat slower to take up the diesel engine again after the war because of the high level of duty imposed on derv by the French government during the forties and fifties, which greatly reduced the competitiveness of the diesel *vis-à-vis* the petrol engine in passenger car applications. Thus it was not Citroën but a new French client, Automobiles Peugeot (through its Indenor engine-building subsidiary) that resumed the Shoreham firm's long-standing French connection. In 1954 it commissioned the design of a Comet type cylinder head for installation in its passenger cars and light commercial vehicles.

The resulting engine, the 1,608cc Indenor TMD4 introduced in 1957, proved highly successful and in successive forms it was used throughout the sixties and seventies in the Peugeot 403 and 404 ranges. In 1961, the TMD engines were

Jack Pitchford, Sir Harry's successor as Chairman of the Ricardo firm and one of his closest colleagues and friends. Their association covered almost half a century.

superseded by the XDP series, which were basically of the same design and construction, but with increased internal dimensions and output. Indeed the family of Comet-type Peugeot–Citroën engines endures to this day, a quite remarkable situation considering that the principle was first invented by Harry Ricardo as long ago as 1932!

On his travels, Pitchford formed the opinion that his employer was always much more at ease with European automobile companies and their staffs than with their Anglo-Saxon counterparts, and that in general he had a far greater respect for Continental engineers than for those from across the Atlantic, with two outstanding exceptions in Harry Horning, President of the Waukesha Company, and Art Rosen of the Caterpillar tractor concern. 'Among the great European engineers in his field of interest he counted as personal friends Agnelli and Zerbi of Fiat, Andre Citroën and Maurice Sainturat of Citroën, Marius Berliet of Automobiles Berliet, Picard of Renault, Eckhardt-Schmidt of Daimler-Benz and Meurer of MAN,' Pitchford wrote. 'In all these early post-war contacts with senior engineers in France, Germany, Italy and elsewhere I was immediately made aware of the extraordinary esteem and regard in which Harry, as a person, and the importance of this work, was held,' he recalled many years later. Clearly, within the automotive community at least, at that point in time Ricardo enjoyed a far higher reputation among foreigners than among his own countrymen, and it was by observing this reverence at first hand that Pitchford was first able to understand the true significance of the part that his employer had played in the history of the internal combustion engine. 'I came to realise the stature of the man and his works and what an outstanding figure I had the good fortune to be associated with throughout my own career,' he acknowledged.

Indeed, on his later visits to India and the Far East, Pitchford discovered that Ricardo's achievements were by now well recognised as far afield as Japan. Following his trips there in 1964 and 1968, a steady stream of new clients began arriving at the Shoreham laboratories from that direction, starting with Isuzu in 1965 and followed by Mitsubishi, Toyota, Nissan and Yamaha – all of them companies that placed the highest value on thorough research and development, as well as on top quality standards of vehicle engineering and manufacture.

The Scandinavian motor industry also beat a path to Ricardo's door at this time, with both Volvo and Saab establishing consultancy agreements. In 1963, the Ricardo firm was commissioned to design a new four-stroke, four-cylinder engine to replace the three-cylinder, two-stroke unit then being used on Saab's 95 and 96 models. This was the first complete engine to be developed at Bridge Works since the Le Zèbre of 1923. In the event this Scarab engine did not go into production, as the Swedish company decided instead to buy in an existing Ford V4 engine for their 96 model, thus avoiding the cost of setting up new manufacturing facilities.

In general, the British motor industry was rather slower off the mark than its Continental competitors in calling on Ricardo's consulting services after the war. Although the importance and significance of his contribution to engine design was well appreciated abroad, he was not as yet acknowledged as a prophet in his own country. As Jonathan Wood observed in his classic study of the demise of the British motor industry, *Wheels of Misfortune*, this situation was little more than a direct reflection of the personalities and backgrounds of its two main protagonists before the war, William Morris, 'by nature a garage proprietor', and Herbert Austin, 'a mechanic, nothing more nor less. . . . Both were farmers' sons and essentially self-taught men, who succeeded by drive, intuition and sheer hard work but possessing little more than superficial technical knowledge,' said Wood. In essence, Austin and Morris were imitators not innovators, quite content to go on building not what was wanted but what they thought ought to be wanted, i.e. what they had always made in the past. Moreover, both were well aware of their lack of education, and out of a sense of inferiority they refused to employ university educated men in any capacity, much less the kind of properly qualified graduate engineers who might show up their ignorance. In 1930, Sir Herbert Austin had proclaimed that: "The university mind is a hindrance rather than a help," a sentiment echoed by Morris, who once accepted an invitation from a college to debate the motion that 'Oxford men are useless in the motor industry'. When one of his employees revealed that he held a Cambridge engineering degree, a fact of which Morris had previously been unaware, the motor magnate began to find fault with his work. As Wood revealed in his book, before long Morris had convinced himself that the sooner they parted company, the better it would be for his organisation. Having disposed of this unfortunate graduate, Morris then turned his attention to investigating the background of two more of his employees who showed suspicious signs of possessing imagination, enterprise and high engineering skill. Although these men had hitherto been giving satisfaction, when he discovered that they too were graduates, they also found themselves out of a job and without being told the real reason for their dismissal.

Given the conservative and unprogressive attitudes held by these two motor magnates, it is not surprising that the visits made by Ricardo's engineers to the Cowley and Longbridge factories were few and far between in the thirties and forties and that, as we saw earlier, very little progress was made in persuading either the Austin or Morris firms to manufacture a Ricardo Comet-type diesel engine while their founders were still in charge of affairs. Although a licensing agreement was concluded with Sir Herbert Austin as far back as October 1935, nothing whatever came of this and no Comet design was ever put into production by the Austin company until it built the Meteorite tank engine during the Second World War. Thus it was not until a merger between the Austin and Morris organisations took place in 1952 – as the British Motor Corporation under the management of Sir Leonard Lord – that the question of responding to foreign competition by offering a diesel engine was fully addressed and the compression-ignition principle was employed in significant numbers on the British roads in vehicles other than buses, heavy lorries and tractors. The engine in question, of course, was BMC's 2.2-litre, four-cylinder Ricardo Comet-type diesel conversion introduced in 1954 for its taxi and light commercial vehicle range; this rapidly ousted the petrol engine on London's taxis. Another diesel conversion of an existing petrol engine developed by Ricardo for the BMC group was the 1.5-litre, four-cylinder engine, fitted to Austin and Morris mid-range saloon cars of that era.

Actually, the most numerous and successful Comet-type, small, high-speed diesel engine to be produced in England at that time was the Standard Motor Company's 2-litre 23C commercial vehicle engine, developed specifically by Ricardo to power the Massey-Ferguson tractor and produced in very large numbers until the Massey-Ferguson firm acquired the Perkins Engine Company of Peterborough. Limited numbers of this agricultural unit were also fitted on the Standard Vanguard saloon of 1949, making it the very first British diesel passenger car. Another large user of the Comet Mk V cylinder head was the Rover company, which employed it on its 2.5-litre diesel engine, as fitted to the Land Rover.

A line-up of British-built diesel-engined vehicles of the 1950s, all employing Ricardo's Comet combustion chamber. The first use of the Comet system by the British motor industry was in 1954 on BMC's 2.2-litre engine, as fitted to the Austin London taxi and other Austin and Morris light commercial vehicles.

By the mid-fifties, partly through its long financial sponsorship of diesel engine research at Shoreham, the Anglo-Dutch Shell Oil Company had largely achieved its original objective of increasing world consumption of heavy oil. It was therefore decided that, with effect from the end of 1953, the original licensing agreement between Ricardo and the Anglo-Saxon Oil Company dating back to 1925 should be wound up, and that in future all proceeds from Ricardo's Comet patents should go to the Ricardo firm intact. In fact, Shell's decision to relinquish its rights and responsibilities merely formalised a situation that had existed for many years, as it had long been in the habit of making over its half share of royalties to fund further research at Shoreham. Nevertheless, the winding up of the partnership caused Ricardo some initial concern, lest he should be entirely abandoned by his former sponsors, whose assistance had been fundamental to the establishment of his firm. In the event, however, his worries were unfounded, for he continued to benefit from the association for many years to come; not only was his company favoured by many further lucrative research projects, and retained as consultants to the Shell organisation but he as an individual also remained under the benevolent care and protection of the multinational giant, which regarded him as being one of its own. In future years as in the past, whenever he travelled abroad on business or pleasure, be it to Egypt, India, Hong Kong, Jamaica, South Africa or the USA, he could always count on being taken under the wing of the local branch of the multinational company which would look after his travel and hotel arrangements and provide him with a car and driver.

Until 1950, nearly all the patents registered on the inventions emanating from Bridge Works had been granted in Ricardo's own name, but after receiving his knighthood he felt it appropriate that all existing patents should be transferred to his company's name and that all new ones should also be vested in the firm. That same year, his trusted lieutenant Jack Pitchford was appointed Joint Managing Director alongside him. At the age of sixty-five, Sir Harry had decided that it was time to begin the process of handing over his responsibilities to his successors, though he had no intention of retiring from the scene altogether. Instead, he planned to pick up his pencil as a designer once again and to enjoy himself by getting involved with projects that had special technical problems which interested him particularly, and by examining alternative technologies such as steam power, which seemed to him to be due for a revival as an alternative to the internal combustion engine in meeting anti-pollution legislation.

Sir Harry was a man of catholic interests technically speaking and was by no means wedded indissolubly to the internal combustion engine. The advantages of steam power had attracted him since his boyhood days when he studied the mechanisms not merely of steam ships and locomotives but also of steam cars and lorries. Indeed, he had become a great authority on the subject, and would undoubtedly have made a fine job of designing a truly modern steam locomotive if ever the opportunity had come along. Among his friends and associates he numbered two of the greatest living exponents of this art – Sir William Stanier (formerly the Chief Engineer of the London, Midland and Scottish Railway and the designer of the LMS streamlined 'Coronation' class Pacifics which hauled the 'Coronation Scot' express between Glasgow and London in the 1930s, and latterly the Chairman of Power Jets R&D Ltd) and Oliver Bulleid, formerly the Chief Engineer of the Southern Railway Company. Bulleid (who was Ricardo's contemporary on the Council of the Institution of Mechanical Engineers – both were Presidents, Ricardo in 1944/5 and Bullied in 1945/6) had made his name as the designer of the Southern Railway's streamlined light Pacific 'Battle of Britain' and 'Merchant Navy' class engines. He had followed this achievement by producing at the Brighton works an even more unorthodox machine, which carried the class name 'Leader'. This unusual locomotive had its cylinders mounted on two separate bogies located at either end of its frame together with two separate driver's cabs, and had its boiler and fuel tender slung between them. Its cylinders featured single-sleeve-valves, but not, unfortunately, of the type advocated by Ricardo. When these were shown to be prone to lubrication problems, he called in the Ricardo firm to advise on a solution, which, of course, involved a complete redesign. But before this could be accomplished, the railways were nationalised and the 'Leader' concept was scrapped in 1948. Bulleid then moved to Ireland where he eventually became Chief Engineer of the Irish State Railways and proceeded to design an even more radical sleeve-valve steam engine incorporating a turf-burning boiler, and for this (ultimately abortive) project he called again upon Sir Harry's consultancy for advice and expertise.

Oliver Bulleid was a keen supporter of another interesting railway project in which Ricardo had become involved. This was the so-called Fell Locomotive, the brainchild of Lieutenant-Colonel L.F.R. Fell, an engineer who, like Major Evans, had first entered Ricardo's life during the First World War. Subsequently Colonel Fell had joined the aero-engine side of Rolls-Royce at Derby where, during the Second World War, he became identified with the company's Flight Test Establishment at Hucknall. Fell had always been interested in railway traction problems as a sideline and in 1948 he approached Ricardo about a revolutionary type of diesel-mechanical main line locomotive featuring a novel propulsion system that he had conceived. The locomotive which resulted from these discussions was no. 10100, built at the then London. Midland and Scottish Railway Company's works at Derby, and financed by a company called Fell Developments Limited, a consortium chiefly comprising Davy Paxman and Shell, with the Ricardo firm acting as design and development consultants to the project.

Hitherto, as is well known, all railway locomotives powered by high-speed diesel engines had operated by having their prime movers linked to generators supplying electric current to the traction motors connected to their wheels, to overcome the inherent problem of gearing the speed of the engine to the speed of the wheels. A conventional automotive type of gearbox, of course, is quite unable to withstand the loads involved in starting a 500-ton train from rest and working it up to a full speed of over 50 mph, often up an incline. Fell had devised an ingenious, all-mechanical transmission system that not only solved this problem but also reduced the overall weight of the locomotive together with the power losses experienced in the conventional diesel-electric system. The locomotive, which was of the 4–8–4 type, was powered by four main Paxman–Ricardo V12 diesel engines developing 500hp each plus two auxiliary AEC–Ricardo marine-type diesel engines driving Roots-type superchargers. The four main engines were each linked by hydraulic couplings to a central gearbox incorporating three epicyclic differentials, and each could be engaged in a sequence in such a way that a constant horsepower could be maintained as their speed rose.

The 2,000hp Fell Locomotive, the world's first direct-drive diesel main line engine, was demonstrated to the press at London's Marylebone station in May 1951 (a ceremony at which Sir Harry was present) and shortly after that it entered service on a trial basis, hauling a regular passenger train on the route between Derby and Manchester. By this time, the railways had been nationalised and the old LMS company was no more. Acting on the 'not invented here' principle, the new British Railways regime found the Fell Locomotive something of an embarrassment, and sought ways to rid itself of the unconventional machine. Its chance came when the locomotive was pulling a St Pancras to Nottingham express through Kettering station and a seizure occurred on one of its driving axle boxes. It came to an unscheduled halt across a set of points at a junction, blocking all the main lines to London for nearly a day. Naturally, the Fell system was blamed for this disaster, but the culprit was actually an individual at the railway's maintenance depot, who had failed to put any lubricating grease in the axle box in question. Although the Fell Locomotive's promising career came to an abrupt and ignominious end, the Ricardo firm escaped any repercussions from this unfortunate incident and continued to advise British Railways on diesel engine matters for many years.

Three years later, Sir Harry was given the chance to design a steam engine of his own (though not, alas, a railway locomotive) and he seized the opportunity with great enthusiasm. In 1954 he was invited by the National Research Development Corporation (NRDC) – whose board included many acquaintances such as Professor P.M. Blackett of Imperial College, Sir Rowland Smith of Ford, Sir Ben Lockspeiser and Sir Henry Tizard – to build a range of prototype steam engines and power units that would ultimately be used to supply electrical or mechanical power to small factories and agricultural communities in developing countries such as India and Pakistan. The idea was that a

British Railways No.10100, the world's first diesel-mechanical locomotive, powered by four 500hp Paxman-Ricardo diesel engines coupled to a novel transmission designed by Ricardo's friend Colonel L.F.R Fell of Rolls-Royce. Although it entered service on the St Pancras–Nottingham–Derby line on an experimental basis in 1951, it was never adopted for series production.

steam engine, with a suitable boiler, would be independent of expensive imported oil or petrol supplies. By burning locally available fuels such as brushwood, straw or low-grade coal, it could 'live off the land' to pump water or drive machinery. Several engines of varying sizes and outputs were designed and built under this NRDC contract using automotive methods of construction. The design of the all-important boiler, for which Sir Harry was personally responsible, was particularly simple but ingenious. Apparently, he revelled in the work of testing his creation, which doubtless reminded him of his schoolboy experiments at Rugby. Sadly, by the time these engines were ready for mass production it had been discovered that affordable petrol supplies were widely available throughout the Indian subcontinent and that the small steam engine as such was unlikely to find a market. That was to be the end of Sir Harry's practical involvement with steam engines, but he continued to take an active interest in the subject, believing that steam power might still have a role to play in the development of a truly energy-efficient and environmentally friendly automobile that could meet all foreseen emission control laws. As a result, in the 1970s his firm became closely involved in a series of feasibility studies for steam-engined cars funded by, among others, General Motors, Chrysler, and the Scientific Energy Systems Corporation of the USA.

For Ricardo and his family the return to Shoreham in 1945 had meant a resumption of the boating activities from which they derived so much enjoyment. Shortly before the war, Ricardo's yacht the *Pearl* had become unseaworthy and had sunk at its moorings, leaving him with no alternative but to sell her to be converted into a houseboat. To replace her, in 1938 he had purchased an elegant motor cruiser, the *Nefertari*, in which he planned to cruise the rivers and canals of France. Yet scarcely had he got to know his new craft than war broke out, putting paid to all his hopes of leisurely holiday voyages down through the Midi to the Mediterranean. In 1940, the boat was loaned to the Admiralty and was sailed to France by a naval crew as one of the famous 'little ships' of Dunkirk used to evacuate British troops after the German invasion. Quite likely she was sunk during this adventure, as nothing was ever heard of her again. By 1946, the sailor in Ricardo had been shore-bound for far too long and he could wait no longer to find his sea legs once again. At first he considered the possibility of having a new boat built to his own specifications, but instead, after attending an Admiralty small craft disposal sale, he became the proud owner of a 60-ft pinnace powered by three 100hp, V8 Dorman–Ricardo diesel engines, which he named the *Caprella*. Built in 1944 for service in the Far East, this impressive launch had spent the last years of the war as an RAF torpedo recovery boat based at Portland harbour. After converting and fitting out the *Caprella* to his own requirements, replacing the central engine with a smaller, more economical 24hp Dorman diesel for cruising purposes, he was able to continue with his favourite pastimes of fishing and boating. It seems that for Ricardo half the pleasure of owning his new boat was the work of adapting it to suit its new purpose and he took great pride in designing and constructing many of the mechanical modifications himself.

The *Caprella*, the ex-Admiralty pinnace that served as Sir Harry's sea-going motor-cruiser from 1946 to 1955.

Although she was always laid up for the winter at Shoreham, during summer months the *Caprella* was based at Itchenor in Chichester harbour, and from there over the next ten years it was his greatest pleasure to be able to take his family and friends on weekend excursions to the Isle of Wight or just to potter about in Chichester and Langstone harbours – exactly the kind of 'messing about in boats' that is described so well in the books of his Rugby schoolfriend Arthur Ransome. Regularly every summer, however, he would invite a larger party to join him on a longer holiday cruise, voyaging westward along the coast to the ports and estuaries of Devon and Cornwall, as he had done under sail in the *Pearl* before the war. In coronation year, 1953, he took several groups of employees from Bridge Works on the *Caprella* to view the fleet assembled off Spithead for review by Queen Elizabeth II, and to see the firework display that followed.

That year marked a turning point in Ricardo's nautical aspirations, and before very long he had reluctantly decided that he would have to part with the *Caprella*, the upkeep of which was by now becoming an unjustifiable extravagance. She was sold in 1955. 'I am terribly sorry to part with *Caprella* for we had a great deal of fun out of her,' he admitted at the time. 'She was much the nicest boat I have ever had, but my wife and I are getting too old.' That year he reached the age of seventy. In future he would holiday in warmer climes abroad.

Another reason for his decision to put his boat on the market was that he knew there could be no summer holiday cruise as usual that year, as during June 1955 he was due to visit the USA to receive the honour of the Horning Memorial Award and to read the Horning Lecture at the golden anniversary meeting of the American Society of Automotive Engineers (SAE) to be held at Atlantic City in New Jersey. Entitled 'Some Early Reminiscences', his address was devoted to his memories of the arrival of the internal combustion engine before the First World War, which he later set down at greater length in his autobiography written thirteen years later.

Although he was fully conscious of the great honour that was about to be bestowed upon him by the Americans, it was with considerable trepidation that he sailed for New York on 1 June on board the *New Amsterdam* of the Holland America Line. Although he was still in the best of health in all other respects, by this stage in his life he had begun to suffer increasingly from deafness and failing eyesight, which made normal conversation and social communication difficult for him and served only to aggravate his natural shyness. It seems, however, that his fears were unfounded and that he greatly enjoyed his visit to the USA (his last), especially as while in New York he was able to get together with his cousin Terence Rendel who had made his career with the Shell Oil Company in North America and was currently based in the city. During his stay in the USA, where he was hailed by the press as 'The High Priest of the Internal Combustion Engine', he was also able to tour the East Coast and renew many old acquaintances. Even so, on his return to Shoreham, he felt compelled to write to his host Mr C.G. (Art) Rosen of the Caterpillar tractor and diesel engine-building firm (a personal friend as well as a valued client) to thank him for his kindness and hospitality and also for his sympathetic understanding of his own embarrassment and shyness during the proceedings. To the President of the SAE Mr J.A.C. Warner he wrote: 'I enjoyed myself enormously and it was a delight to see again so many old friends. For one as self-conscious as I, I naturally found the ceremony rather terrifying, but I only hope I did not disgrace myself too badly and that my address was not too egotistical.' There was a touching letter also for Mrs E. Horning, the widow of his old friend Harry Horning who had both founded and funded the Horning Award. 'I came away from Atlantic City with the uneasy feeling that I had behaved very badly and inadequately to you,' he confessed, 'but I was so overcome and bewildered by the ceremony and at the dinner after it that I am afraid that I quite failed to convey my feelings of gratitude and affection and must have seemed very boorish. I should like to have told you how flattered I felt by the award and how much it means to me . . . but I am afraid that in my embarrassment I must have appeared very churlish. Inability to express one's emotions is, I think, an English national failing and I have suffered from it all my life, but I hope you know us well enough to forgive it.'

By the time that Ricardo & Company, Engineers (1927) Ltd entered its fifth decade in 1960 (its name was not changed to its present form, Ricardo Consulting Engineers Ltd, until 1978), it had been agreed by all on the Board that the time had come to broaden and deepen the technical scope of the firm's activities to meet the new challenges that lay ahead. Revenue from Comet royalties, which had funded expansion during the boom years of the fifties, had already begun to decline as patents expired and it was now necessary to establish other sources of income. In the light of the ever-increasing environmental and anti-pollution legislation being brought into force around the world, particularly in the USA, the firm had already identified research into exhaust emission control and noise reduction technology as representing the most promising new direction for its international internal combustion engine consultancy activities, but to be fully effective in this area a major investment in new test-shops, laboratories and other facilities and equipment would be required. Accordingly, at a General Meeting held in March 1962 a resolution was passed to convert the firm from a private into a public company, with its shares quoted on the London Stock Exchange, so that capital could be raised from banks and other financial institutions on the security of these shares. Initially, the prospect of losing total ownership and control caused Sir Harry some considerable anxiety, as he was concerned that his firm might become exposed to an unwelcome takeover bid, most particularly from some foreign motor manufacturer or rival research agency which would threaten its independence. 'I view with horror the bare possibility that we might wake up one morning to find we had been bought up by, say, General Motors or Ford,' he wrote to a relation. At that time about 58 per cent of the controlling Founder's Shares were owned by members of the Board and their families (of which more than half, i.e. 30 per cent, belonged to Sir Harry and his family personally) yet Stock Exchange regulations required that at least 70,000 of those 1 shilling Founders' Shares (then valued at 20 shillings each) should be put on the market at the outset. His worries were allayed, however, when it was agreed that the Board should maintain a majority holding as a matter of policy, and that whenever any of the original Founders' Shares were put on the market, they would be taken up by other directors and their families, or by members of staff.

Actually, Ricardo's fears of a hostile takeover were unfounded, for his company owned little in the way of fixed assets or production capacity that would have attracted the attention of speculators and asset-strippers. Its capital rested in the skills and expertise of its staff, the people in whose abilities Sir Harry had invested and who owed their loyalty to him personally; these assets could walk out of the door at any time should their conditions of employment change for the worse. However, Ricardo clearly anticipated with distaste the events of the late sixties and early seventies when great chunks of British manufacturing business, owned by traditionally minded and paternalistic captains of industry like himself, were broken up and laid to waste by a new generation of ruthless

The Board of Directors of the Ricardo firm in August 1962. From left to right; E.N. Soar, Viscount Combermere, Sir Ben Lockspeiser, Sir Harry Ricardo, J.H. Pitchford, C.E. Marsh, D. Downs, P.C. Kidner, B.W. Millington.

entrepreneurs, concerned only with short-term profits and a high return on capital. He deplored the social and economic depredations brought about by these City speculators, believing that true and lasting wealth could only be created by designing and making better products that would maintain, or even improve, his country's share of world trade.

The previous year, 1961, experiencing worsening difficulties with his sight and hearing, he had decided to relinquish his administrative responsibilities as Chairman of the Board, but to continue working as Technical Director. Jack Pitchford became Chairman and Managing Director in his place, and Diarmuid Downs was made Deputy Managing Director. There were no boardroom battles or other political struggles to oust the king and seize the crown; the succession was secure. As Downs remarked some years later, Sir Harry was content to give up the reins of power gracefully and make way for his nominated successors, and then to refrain entirely from interference in their work. 'In a way that is uncommon in men who have achieved so much themselves, he stepped aside and passed on his authority to others, in good time to ensure the continued progress and prosperity of the organisation he founded and inspired,' Downs wrote in 1974.

The previous decade had seen a number of important changes in the management and administration of the company, as the old guard departed and a new, second generation of managers were appointed to the board, all of them talented engineers who had been recruited as young men by Ricardo personally, and who had flourished under his tutelage and patronage. Diarmuid Downs was a case in point. After graduating with first-class honours in mechanical engineering from London University in 1942 he joined Ricardo at Oxford and for the following fifteen years pursued a fundamental study of abnormal combustion phenomena in the gasoline engine, the results of which followed on from Sir Harry's own pioneering work in this area and were duly reported in a series of papers presented to various learned societies, earning him numerous research prizes and medals. While widening his managerial responsibilities within the company Downs then went on to become, like Sir Harry before him, a Fellow of the Royal Society, a President of the Institution of Mechanical Engineers and a member of numerous boards and councils in the engineering profession. Ultimately he was awarded the CBE in 1979 and was knighted in 1985.

Diarmuid Downs had actually joined the board in 1957, following the appointment of Charles Marsh and Ted Soar (both in 1954) but one year ahead of Brian Millington. Millington had joined the firm in 1937, following a very distinguished academic career at Southampton University. Later, in 1968, these three men were joined by two new directors, Clifford Walder and Cecil French, both of whom had also entered Ricardo's employment as

Sir Diarmuid Downs FRS, Sir Harry's successor as Managing and Technical Director at Bridge Works. Earlier, he had followed up Ricardo's scientific work by undertaking fundamental research into abnormal phenomena in the combustion process of internal combustion engines.

graduate recruits and had made their entire careers at Bridge Works. But to reinforce his board, during this period Sir Harry brought in three distinguished personalities from outside the company, all of them old friends and colleagues with whom he had already had a long association. These were Sir Ben Lockspeiser FRS, in 1957, Dr Charles Williams, in 1963, and Sir Harold Roxbee-Cox (later Lord King's Norton) in 1965. Lockspeiser had had a long career in the Scientific Civil Service, eventually following Sir David Pye as Director General of Scientific Research at the Ministry of Aircraft Production during the Second World War and ending up as Secretary to the Committee of the Privy Council for Scientific and Industrial Research. Williams was an oil man who had collaborated with the Ricardo firm for many years, and who had recently retired from the position of General Manager of the Shell Research company. Earlier he had been Manager of Shell's Laboratory at Thornton, Cheshire, following a period as Director of the

Sir Harry Ricardo and Dr C.G. Williams of Shell discuss the original E35 variable compression engine at Bridge Works in 1968

old Institution of Automobile Engineer's research laboratory. Roxbee-Cox had also had a distinguished career in the Scientific Civil Service, mostly in the field of aircraft engineering. He had been Director of the National Gas Turbine Establishment at Farnborough and Chairman of Power Jets (R&D) Ltd, and had ended his career as Chief Scientist to the Ministry of Fuel and Power. He was knighted in 1953 and became a life peer in 1965, shortly after joining the Ricardo board. These changes in the composition of the board were concluded by the retirement in 1963 of Lord Combermere and Percy Kidner, thus severing the last links with Sir Harry's original network of outside help.

Although he had partially retired, during the early sixties, Sir Harry continued to visit Bridge Works nearly every day to use his office, where he liked, above all, to chat informally with the newcomers and younger members of his team, enquiring about their work and giving them his much-appreciated encouragement. In this way he was able to keep in touch with activities and developments both at the firm and within the engineering profession in general. His technical memory was quite remarkable and of enormous value in the appraisal of approaches to new projects; time and time again his colleagues would proudly suggest what they thought were original new ideas, only to hear him say that it had all been done before, quoting chapter and verse that proved disconcertingly accurate. Also, in Pitchford's words, 'As a practical researcher and experimenter he enjoyed the advantage of being a superb craftsman to whom what could or could not be done with different materials was almost instinctively obvious. Whether he was dealing with the highest or the most lowly, his charm and courtesy were unfailing, just as within him there was sometimes a stubborn determination to achieve his objective, even if it were only to prove a point, but never in such a manner as to give discomfiture to another.' In short, he was a great teacher, and communicator, and not merely of mechanical engineering matters either. 'The maintenance of high ethical standards in the conduct of his affairs was basic to Harry's way of life, and he expected – sometimes vainly – a similar outlook in others,' said Pitchford.

Early in 1965, just before his eightieth birthday, Sir Harry took the decision to retire completely, and accordingly was appointed President. The following year, Diarmuid Downs became Joint Managing Director with Pitchford, though in 1967 he took over as sole Managing Director, with Pitchford remaining as Chairman until his own retirement in 1976. By now, Downs was also Joint Technical Director as well, his partner being Brian Millington, with Cliff Walder acting as General Manager.

Stepping down after almost fifty years at the helm, Sir Harry had cause to take satisfaction in his life's achievements. His company was now firmly established as the foremost engineering consultancy operating in the internal combustion engine field, providing a design, development and research facility for a clientele that already included the majority of the significant engine builders and road transport and agricultural vehicle manufacturers throughout the industrialised world.

However, it would be misleading to suggest that his intention in retiring was to devote more time to his family, because as a husband, father, grandfather and family man he had never failed to do so in the past. By the time of his diamond wedding in 1971, he had nine grandsons and three granddaughters, who in their turn had produced three great-grandchildren with four more yet to come during his lifetime.

In his biographical memoir of Sir Harry, written for the Royal Society in 1976, the distinguished Cambridge engineer Sir William Hawthorne FRS, Master of Churchill College, related that: 'All his life children had meant a great deal to him and he had won all their hearts. He never talked down to them and always assumed that they shared his own great interest in making things. His first question to all his young relations was "What are you making now?" and he listened with interest to their hopes, plans and problems. For his grandchildren he invented a number of tall stories which he was eventually persuaded to write down and which were charmingly illustrated by a neighbour.' These innocent and thoroughly entertaining stories featured a character known as Little Black Sambo and would doubtless be regarded as the height of political incorrectness today. But then, Sir Harry's own literary and musical tastes had been formed in Edwardian times, as is indicated by his own love of the books of P.G. Wodehouse and the songs of Gilbert and Sullivan, which he was fond of singing to his assembled offspring. At Bridge Works he began the tradition of holding a children's Christmas party, which is still upheld today.

Sir Harry Ralph Ricardo's last great achievement was the publication in 1968 of his autobiography, entitled *Memories and Machines – The Pattern of My Life*, which is generally agreed to be the finest ever written by an engineer in the English language. Its quality of content and expression seems all the more remarkable when it is realised that it was dictated verbatim from memory using a tape recorder, as Ricardo was by this time unable to see well enough to write down his reminiscences in long hand, which had always been his habitual way of working hitherto. The tapes on which he set down these recollections still exist, bearing witness to his patrician voice and precise Edwardian diction. The book has only one failing, for with his usual modesty and reticence Sir Harry neglected to mention events after 1935, so that the reader is presented with an account of his work that is less than half complete.

Despite having been an inveterate pipe-smoker for most of his life, Sir Harry Ricardo reached the grand old age of eighty-nine in his usual good health and buoyant spirits, notwithstanding his deafness and blindness. In his latter years he often became depressed by the fear that he might become a burden on those around him, but his worries were unfounded for he always remained alert and interested in life, and his innate charm and courtesy to everyone he met was quite undiminished by his afflictions.

But then, in March 1974, while walking in his garden at Graffham he stumbled and fell, breaking his hip bone. He underwent an operation at St Richard's Hospital, Chichester, which was described by his doctors as being successful, though he never regained consciousness. Shortly afterwards he was transferred to the King Edward VII Hospital at Midhurst, Sussex, where he died peacefully on 18 May 1974, in his ninetieth year. In 1967 he had been made an Honorary Fellow of his alma mater, Trinity College, Cambridge. Directly on learning of his death, the Master of Trinity, the former Conservative cabinet minister R.A. Butler, ordered the college flag to be flown at half mast.

Ricardo was cremated at Chichester and his ashes were strewn at Graffham. His memorial service, held at St Margaret's church, Westminster, on 24 July 1974, was attended by his extended family together with many relations, friends, colleagues and admirers from the worlds of engineering, industry, government and defence. The service was notable for the beautiful music played, and for the address delivered by his closest friend and colleague Jack Pitchford, who said in valediction of their fifty-year-long association: 'I do not wish to dwell on the sadness and the loss, but rather on the great enrichment which Harry gave to all who knew him and, indeed, indirectly through his great abilities and power of vision, to the world we live in today. . . . The search for knowledge and its effective application in his chosen field, a wonderfully happy family life and the enjoyment of his boats seemed to constitute all he would wish to ask from life. That he died a happy, contented and fulfilled man, I have no doubt whatever.'

Sir Harry Ricardo FRS,
pictured towards the end of
his sixty-year career,
devoted to the advancement
of the internal combustion
engine on land, at sea and
in the air.

   Sir Harry Ralph Ricardo had just cause to die a happy and contented man, having seen the company that he founded grow to become the world's foremost independent internal combustion engine research establishment, retained as consultants by the majority of the world's leading motor car, truck and tractor manufacturing concerns. His legacy is that, today, Ricardo Consulting Engineers Ltd continues to go from strength to strength, as the last successful vestige of the British motor industry remaining in British ownership, a lasting testament to his lively, enquiring and well-informed mind, and to the high technical and ethical standards that he set throughout his long and distinguished career.

   Such is the pace of change in the automobile engineering industry these days that all too often the study of history is regarded as having no relevance to the present, much less the future. But as this book will surely have demonstrated, Sir Harry Ricardo knew otherwise. Together with his colleagues and associates, the very internal combustion engine pioneers who made history by bringing about the progress in transportation that has transformed the world over the past one hundred years, he valued the lessons of the past and, while always facing forward eagerly to meet the challenges ahead, he constantly strove to work within a tradition of historical continuity.

Appendix

Sir Harry Ricardo's Honours and Awards.

Honours
1929   Fellow of the Royal Society
1944–5   President of the Institution of Mechanical Engineers
1948   Knight Batchelor

Honorary Degrees and Academic Distinctions
1930   Hon. Doctor of Law, Birmingham University
1960   Hon. Doctor of Engineering, Turin University
1965   Hon. Doctor of Science, University of Sussex
1967   Hon. Fellow of Trinity College, Cambridge

Certificates, Diplomas and Medals
1917   Member of the Institution of Automobile Engineers
1917   N.E. Coast Institute of Engineers & Shipbuilders Gold Medal
1922   Member of the Society of Automotive Engineers, USA
1925   Royal Aeronautical Society – Silver Medal
1926   Fellow of the Royal Aeronautical Society
1926   Institution of Automobile Engineers – Crompton Medal
1927   Institution of Automobile Engineers – F.W. Lanchester Medal
1929   Fellow of the Royal Society
1929   Institution of Petroleum USA – Horning Fellowship
1930   Institution of Mechanical Engineers – Clayton Medal
1932   Member of the Athenaeum Club
1933   Member of the Institution of Mechanical Engineers
1934   Royal Netherlands Institute of Engineers – Honorary Associate
1935   The Institute of Fuel – Melchett Medal
1936   The Institution of Petroleum Technologists – Redwood Medal
1938   Deutsche Akademie der Luftfahrtforschung – Foreign Member
1940   The Institution of Mechanical Engineers – James Edwood Ewing Medal for
             Engineering Research
1940   Royal Society – Rumford Medal
1944/5   President of the Institution of Mechanical Engineers
1951   Institution of Mechanical Engineers – James Clayton Prize
1953   Institution of Mechanical Engineers – James Watt Medal
1955   Society of Automotive Engineers, USA – Horning Medal
1956   Society of Automotive Engineers, USA – Certificate of Thirty-Five Years' Membership
1964   Société d'Encouragement pour la Recherche et l'Invention, Paris – Commander of
             the Order of Merit Medal
1971   Society of Automotive Engineers, USA – Certificate of Fifty Years' Membership

Bibliography

Works by Sir Harry Ricardo

The Internal Combustion Engine, vol. I *Slow Speed Engines*, vol. II *High Speed Engines*, London, Blackie & Son, 1922, 1923.

Engines of High Output, London, Macdonald & Evans, 1926.

The High Speed Internal Combustion Engine, second edition, revised by H.S. Gylde, London, Blackie & Son, 1933; third edition, 1943; fourth edition, 1953.

Memories and Machines – The Pattern of My Life, London, Constable & Co., 1968.

Other works consulted

Byrne, Andrew, *Bedford Square – an architectural study*, London, The Athlone Press, 1990.

Campbell-Swinton, Alan A., *Autobiographical and Other Writings*, London, Longman, Green & Company, 1930.

Clark, C.S., *The Lanchester Legacy*, Coventry University Enterprises, 1995.

Clarke, Ronald W., *Tizard: A Biography*, London, Methuen, 1965.

Golley, John, *Whittle: The True Story*, Shrewsbury, Airlife, 1987.

Gunston, Bill, *Fedden: The Life of Roy Fedden*, Rolls-Royce Heritage Trust, 1999.

Hamilton, Mark, *Rare Spirit: The Life of William de Morgan,* London, Constable & Co., 1997.

Lane, Michael, *Baron Marks of Woolwich*, London, Quiller Press, 1986.

——, *The Rendel Connection*, London, Quiller Press, 1989.

Lumsden, Alec, *British Piston Engines and their Aircraft*, Shrewsbury, Airlife, 1994.

Nahum, A., Foster-Pegg, R. and Birch, D., *The Rolls Royce Crecy* , Rolls-Royce Heritage Trust, 1994.

Ransome, Arthur, *Autobiography*, London, Jonathan Cape, 1976.

Reynolds, John, *André Citroën: The Man and the Motor Cars*, Stroud, Sutton Publishing, 1996.

Schram, Philippe, *L'epopée de la société Le Zébre*, France, privately published, 1997.

Soar, E.N., 'The History of the Bridge Works', Ricardo & Co. Engineers (1927) Ltd, 1975.

Sraffa, Piero, *The Works and Correspondence of David Ricardo*, Cambridge University Press, 1955.

Stocks, Mary, *My Commonplace Book*, London, Peter Davies, 1970.

Swinton, Major-General Sir Ernest, *Eyewitness*, London, Hodder & Stoughton, 1932.

White, Graham, *Allied Aircraft Piston Engines of World War Two*, SAE Inc. USA, 1995.

Whittle, Air Commodore Sir Frank, *Jet: The Story of a Pioneer*, Muller, 1953.

Wood, Jonathan, *Wheels of Misfortune, The Rise and Fall of the British Motor Industry,* London, Sidgwick & Jackson, 1988.

Articles, Lectures, Pamphlets and Periodicals

Bertram, Mark Ricardo, 'Halsey Ricardo: A Dissertation', Cambridge University, 1966.

Bridgewater, T.H., 'A.A. Campbell-Swinton', *Royal Television Society Monograph* 1, 1982.

Fedden, Roy, 'The Development of the Mono-Sleeve-Valve for Aero Engines', *Proceedings of the Lilienthal Society for Aeronautical Research*, October 1938.

——, 'The First 25 Years of the Bristol Engine Department', *Journal of the Royal Aeronautical Society*, May 1961.

French, Dr Cecil, *Ricardo at Shoreham*, Sussex Industrial History Society, 1995.

Hawthorne, Sir William, *Harry Ralph Ricardo*, *Biographical Memoirs of Fellows of the Royal Society*, vol. 22, 1976.

Levrant, Stephen, 'The Life and Work of Halsey Ricardo', unpublished thesis, 1975.

Lovell, Brian, 'Ricart, Ricardo and the Alfa V16 Racing Engine', *Historic Racing*, December 1994.

Nahum, Andrew, 'Two-Stroke or Turbine? The Aeronautical Research Committee and the Development of the High Power Aero Engine in the Years Leading up to the Second World War', *Technology and Culture*, April 1997.

Reynolds, John, 'British Diesel that Pipped the Germans', *Daily Telegraph Weekend Review*, 5 March 1994.

——, 'De Eerste Diesel Citroëns', *Citroexpert*, The Netherlands, 1999.

Walder, C.J., *Reminiscences of the Oxford Years*, Ricardo Consulting Engineers Ltd, 1994.

Worthington-Williams, Michael, 'Dolphin Motorcars', *Veteran Car (The Gazette of the Veteran Car Club)*, spring/summer 1969.

——, 'Dolphin Motors of Shoreham', *Journal of the Sussex Archaeological Study Group*, Phillimore, Chichester, 1971.

Wright, Edward, *The Historic Engines of Ricardo*, Ricardo Consulting Engineers Ltd, 1996.

Photographic Credits

Index

Addison Road, Holland Park, London 31
Admiralty Landships Committee 111, 112
Aeronautical Inspection Directorate 91, 94
Aeronautical Research Committee (later
    Council) 95, 142, 143, 180, 182, 201, 203,
    205, 206, 209
Air Ministry 138, 146, 155, 158, 159, 182,
    183, 185, 187, 190, 196, 197, 198, 205,
    207, 215
Alcock & Brown (transatlantic flight), 108
Alfa-Romeo 190, 192, 194, 217
Anglo-Dutch Shell Oil Group 104, 138, 142,
    159, 220
Anglo-Saxon Petroleum Company 157, 160,
    163, 166, 168, 220
Argyle Motor Co. 158
Armstrong, William (Lord Armstrong of
    Cragside) 17, 18, 101
Arrol-Johnston Motor Co. 63, 64, 69
Ashley Place, Westminster 124
Associated Equipment Company (AEC) 161,
    164
Athenaeum Club 84, 183, 195, 198
Austin, Sir Herbert 139, 156, 218, 219

Bagnall-Wilde, Col R.K. 91, 93
Banks, Wg Cdr R. 151
Barnes-Wallis, Sir Neville 143, 212
barostat 202
Barrington, T.B. 88, 89, 134, 136, 137, 186
Beardmore Halford Pullinger engine 93
Beardmore, William, & Co. and Sir William
    Beardmore 92, 93, 94
Beaverbrook, Lord 201, 202
Bedford Square, Bloomsbury, London 1, 4,
    5, 15, 24, 25, 26, 42, 46, 63, 77
Bentley, Capt W.O. 63, 136, 137

Benz, Carl 51
Berliet, Marius & Automobiles Berliet 177,
    218
Betjeman, John 31
Birmingham University 213
Bizet, Jacques 139
Blackett, Professor P.M. 222
Blackie & Sons 84
Bloomsbury Set 15
Boerlage, G.D. 159
Boothman, Flt Lt J. 151
Borgeson, Griffith 192
Boyle, W.R. 176
Bridge Works, Shoreham 122, 123, 130, 136,
    142, 150, 159, 161, 166, 185, 188, 196,
    197, 215, 218, 221, 230
Brinton, Roland 23
Bristol Aircraft Co. (aircraft & engines) 183,
    188
Britannia Engineering Co. 75
Broeze, J.J. 159
Brogly, Maurice 169
Brooklands racing track 77, 83, 128, 130
Brotherhood, Peter & Co. 7, 89, 90, 99, 117,
    119, 145, 159, 164
Brull, Charles 166
Bryant, Cdr 89, 90, 91, 99, 145, 159
Bulleid, Oliver 221
Bulman, Maj G.P. 183
Burne-Jones, Sir Edward 14, 15, 33, 37
Burt & McCollum single-sleeve valves 134,
    158
Butler, R.A. 231
Butterfield, William 4, 13,

Cambridge University Automobile Club 56,
    58, 115

Campbell-Swinton, Alan Archibald 84, 99, 100, 103, 107, 109
Caprella (motor cruiser) 224, 225
Caterpillar company 218
Chenard & Walcker, Automobiles SA 43, 169, 177, 195
Chorlton, Sir Alan, MP 80, 99
Chrysler Motors Corpoeation 223
Churchill, Sir Winston 110, 111, 199, 201
Citroën, André and Automobiles Citroën 139, 166, 167, 169, 171–4, 177, 178, 217
Clerk, Sir Dugald 43–5, 64, 82, 83, 84, 97, 100, 118, 126
Combermere, Viscount 102, 103, 126, 230
Comet combustion chamber 161–4, 168, 170, 177, 219
Committee for the Scientific Study of Air Defence 143
Cooperative Fuel Research Committee of USA 146
Cousins, R.J. 203
Crane, Walter 15
Cripps, Sir Stafford KC 154, 204
Crossley Bros Co. Ltd/ Crossley Motors 99, 116, 164

Daimler Motors (British-built engines) 62, 113, 118, 121, 158
Daimler, Gottfried 51
Daimler-Benz (German-built engines and Mercedes cars) 174, 177, 204
Darwin, Sir Charles 96
Davy Paxman Co. 165, 222,
Debenham, Ernest 14, 31
de Brey, J.H.C. 159
de Havilland, Geoffrey 53, 91, 93, 133
de Kok, J.F. 159
de Morgan, William 14, 15, 28, 29
de la Rue, Stuart 102, 103
Department of Scientific and Industrial Research 143, 182, 206
Dicksee, C.B. 161
Diesel, Rudolph 157, 158
Dolphin engines and cars 64, 67, 68, 70, 71, 76, 78, 81
Dowding, Air Marshal Sir Hugh 181, 207
Downs, Sir Diarmuid 227, 228, 230

Elles, Maj Gen H.J. 121
Engine Patents Ltd 102, 103, 104, 119, 120, 122, 124
Evans, Major Aubrey 104, 123, 126, 136, 221
Eyston, Capt George 165

Farman, Henry 54
Farrar, Campbell 99, 103, 126
Farren, Sir William 97
Fawcett, Millicent Garrett 76
Fedden, Sir Roy 95, 182, 183, 185, 187, 188, 189, 193, 204, 213
Fell, Lt Col L.F.R and Fell locomotive 221
Ferguson, Archibald 117, 172
Ferrari, Enzo 192
Fiat 217
Flying Spray (record-breaking car) 165
Ford, Henry 1, 44, 86, 127, 156
Foster, William & Sons 112
French, Dr Cecil 228
Fusi, Luigi 192

Gas Turbine Collaboration Committee 203
Gatcombe Park 10
General Motors Corporation 154, 223
Girouard, Sir Percy 21
Gladstone, William 19, 76
Goodenough, Frederick 99, 102, 126,
Göring, Herman 181
Great George Street, Westminster 17, 26, 27, 78, 79, 84

Hale, Beatrice Bertha (wife) 76
Hale, Dr Charles Bowdish (father-in-law) 76
Halford, Major Frank 1, 93, 104, 127, 128, 129, 131, 132, 190, 198, 208, 213, 215
Hartley, Sir Harold 143
Hawthorne, Sir William 230
Hesselman, Dr 86, 162
Hetherington, Harry 56, 64, 74, 75, 82, 88, 91, 99, 103, 104, 126, 127, 168, 171, 217
Hives, Ernest (Lord Hives) 95, 136, 208, 209
Hobson, Polly (great aunt) 20
Holt, George 117
Hopkinson, Professor Bertram 57–62, 64, 79, 82, 83, 95, 96, 99, 126, 143

Horning Memorial Lecture 8, 128, 225
Horning, Harry 127, 152, 156, 218
Humber-Hillman affair 154, 156, 178

Imperial Airways 187
Imperial College, London 143, 182
Institute of Petroleum Technologists 213
Institution of Automobile Engineers 156, 213
Institution of Mechanical Engineers 82, 195, 213
Internal Combustion Engines Ltd 99

Japanese clients 218
Junkers, Professor Hugo 87

Kettering, Charles 145
Kewley, Mr (Chief Chemist of Shell Oil Co.) 106, 107, 108, 129, 143
Kidner, Percy 83, 99, 131, 154, 156, 197, 230
Kipling, Rudyard 37–8
Kitchenor, Lord 109, 112,
Knight, Charles and Silent Knight engine 113, 114, 158, 216

Lanchester, Frederick 82, 138
Lindemann, Frederick (Lord Cherwell) 96
Lloyd & Plaister 67, 72, 74, 80
Lloyd George, David 54, 111, 121
Lockspeiser, Sir Benjamin 222, 228
Londonderry, Lord 181
Lord, Sir Leonard 156, 219

Mackintosh, Charles Rennie 27
Marconi, Guglielmo 1, 100,
Marsh, Charles 228
Massey-Ferguson tractor company 219
Maxim, Sir Hiram 109
Melbury Road, Kensington, London 31
Memories and Machines (Sir Harry Ricardo's autobiography) 48, 184, 231
Michelin Tyre Company 173, 177
Midgeley, Thomas 145
Millington, Brian 228, 230
Ministry of Aircraft Production 205, 210
Mirrlees, Bickerton & Day Ltd 80, 99, 116, 117, 159, 164

Mitchell, R.J. 150
Moore-Brabazon, J.T.C. (later Lord Brabazon of Tara) 54
Morris Motors 176
Morris, William (Lord Nuffield) 1, 139, 218
Morris, William (Arts and Craft Movement)
Mudfish, The (boat) 148

Napier, Montague & Napier aero-engines 83, 116, 133, 134, 208, 215
National Physical Laboratory 146, 182, 206
National Research Development Council 222
Nefertari (motor cruiser) 224
Noble, Sir Andrew 21
Norham Gardens, Oxford 197

O'Gorman, Mervyn 54, 55, 84, 198
Otto, Dr Nicholas 44

Palmer, Sir Frederick 79
Pankhurst, Emmeline 76
Parsons, Sir Charles 84, 101, 184
Paxman–Ricardo engines 199
Pearl (yacht) 149, 150, 224, 225
Penstone, Lancing 123, 147, 155, 178
Perkins engine company 219
Perry, Sir Percival 156
Peugeot, Automobiles 177, 217
Pitchford, J.A. (Jack) 141, 169, 171, 172, 180, 195, 196, 198, 203, 217, 227, 230, 231
Plunkett, Dennis 93
Pomeroy, Laurence (snr and jnr) 82, 132, 138, 190
Power Jets Ltd 201
Pullinger, T.C. 93
Pye, Sir David Randall 96, 142, 182, 201, 206, 213, 228

Ransome, Arthur 41, 225
Regent Street Polytechnic, London 46, 63
Renault, Louis 172
Rendel, Sir Alexander (father-in-law) 2, 14, 18, 23, 48, 49, 52, 76, 78, 79, 86, 98, 104
Rendel, Catherine aka Kate (mother) 2, 14, 22, 28, 33, 76
Rendel, Edith 21, 22, 76

Rendel, Eliza or Leila, née Hobson (mother-in-law) 20, 98
Rendel, George 18, 19, 21
Rendel, Hamilton 18, 19
Rendel, Helen 21, 22,
Rendel, Henry Wedgwood (Harry) 21, 22, 78
Rendel, James Meadows 16, 17
Rendel, Stuart (Lord Rendel) 18, 19, 77, 100
Rendel, Terence (cousin) 225
Rendel, William 21, 78
Rendel, Palmer & Tritton 79, 88, 98, 104, 112, 115
Rendel & Robertson 67, 79
Ricardo, Angela Edith (daughter) 85
Ricardo, Anna (sister) 5
Ricardo, Arthur Ralph (uncle) 12, 13, 77
Ricardo, Camilla Bertha (daughter) 85, 147
Ricardo, Cicely Kate (daughter) 77, 85, 141
Ricardo, David MP 10
Ricardo, Esther (sister) 5
Ricardo, Halsey Ralph (father) 2, 4, 5, 13, 14, 15, 24-32, 33, 61, 67, 76, 77, 115, 124, 125
Ricardo, Harry (grandfather) 11, 13
Ricardo, Sir Harry Ralph 1, 2, 5, 7, 10, 15, 19, 23, 24, 25, 32, 34, 39, 42, 45, 51, 55, 56, 68, 75, 76, 77, 78, 82, 87, 90, 93, 105, 107, 113, 114, 116, 118–22, 124, 138, 141, 145, 152, 156, 157, 161, 166, 169, 171, 175, 176, 181, 185, 188, 190, 192–4, 196, 198, 200, 202, 203, 204, 209, 213, 214, 221, 223, 227, 228, 230, 231, 232
Ricardo, Major Harry (uncle) 12, 13
Ricardo, Percy Ralph (uncle) 12, 41
Ricardo, Ralph (cousin) 41, 46, 63, 64, 68
Ricardo, Ralph (great grandfather) 11
Ricardo & Company, Engineers (1927) Ltd 126, 226
Ricardo Consulting Engineers Ltd 66, 84, 141, 226, 232
Ricardo–Halford–Armstrong engine 94, 129
Ricart, Wifredo 190, 192–4
Robertson, Frederick 79
Roe, A.V. 54
Rolls-Royce (company, cars and engines) 88, 107, 108, 111, 116, 134, 137, 139, 150, 165, 185, 190, 199

Rolls-Royce Crecy/E65 project 197, 205, 208, 209, 210, 212
Rosen, Art and Caterpillar company 218
Rottingdean School 33, 35–7
Rover car company 219
Rowledge, A.J. 134, 136, 138, 150
Roxbee-Cox, Sir Harold (later Lord Kings Norton) 201, 203, 228, 230
Royal Aeronautical Society 182, 195
Royal Air Force 202
Royal Aircraft Establishment, Farnborough 84, 158, 182, 205, 215
Royal Flying Corps 92
Royal Naval Air Service, 20 Squadron 111, 112
Royal Society 32, 213
Royce, Sir Henry 1, 47, 83, 95, 123, 134, 135, 138
Rugby School 11, 33, 36, 39-47, 203
Rickettswood, Charlwood, Surrey 14, 20, 30, 43, 48, 50, 76, 77, 79, 98, 178

Sainturat, Maurice 166, 218
Salomon, Jules 139, 167
San José (boat) 148
Sassoon, Michael 64, 88
Schneider Trophy seaplane races 149, 150
Shaw, Lt Francis RNAS 112, 113, 115
Slade School of Art 76
Smith, Sir Alexander Rowland 222
Soar, Edward N. 228
Society of Automotive Engineers, USA 8, 127, 128, 225
Southwell, Sir Richard 97
Speed of the Wind (record-breaking car) 165
Standard-Triumph motor company 219
Stanier, Sir William 221
Stephenson, Robert 17
Stern, Col Sir Albert 111, 112, 115, 118, 120, 200
Stocks, Mary, Baroness Stocks (cousin) 14, 23
Sueter, Rear Adm Sir Murray, MP 110
Suffolk Street, Westminster 103, 124
Swedish cleints 218
Swinton, Lord 181
Swinton, Maj Gen Sir Ernest 109, 110, 112, 114, 121, 200

Tank, Mk V 104, 117, 118, 121, 198
Tank, TOG 200
Tank Supply Committee/Department 112, 113, 115, 116
Tawney, R.H. 41
Taylor, Sir Geoffrey 96
Telford, Thomas 16
Tennyson d'Eyncourt, Sir Eustace 102, 111, 116, 118, 200
Thomson, Professor Sir J.J. 97
Thornton, Fielding 64, 72
Thornycroft, Oliver 56, 88, 99, 104 115, 118, 126, 127, 141, 145, 196
Thornycroft, Sir Hamo 15, 115
Thunderbolt (record-breaking car) 165
Tizard, Sir Henry 95, 97, 142, 147, 181, 182, 198, 201, 203, 207, 209, 213, 222
Tottington Manor 178, 179, 215
Trinity College, Cambridge 18, 56, 63, 142, 231
Tritton, Sir Seymour 79, 112
Tritton, Sir William 112
Triumph-Ricardo motorcycle 129, 131
Two Stroke Engine Company and Dolphin Works 64, 66, 67–70, 72, 75, 124

University College, London 143

Vauxhall Motors Ltd 99, 131, 190, 194

Walder, Clifford 228, 230
Waley-Cohen, Sir Robert 104, 105, 107, 142, 157, 163
Walton-on-Thames, workshops and Walton engine 77, 80, 81, 89, 93, 99, 105, 124, 128, 179
War Office Tank Board 199, 201
Warner, J.A.C. 225
Watson-Watt, Professor Robert (later Sir) 206
Waukesha Motor Company, USA 127, 136, 146, 165, 218
Wedgwood, Sir Ralph 21
Wedgwood, Revd Robert 11
Whittle, Air Commodore Sir Frank 190, 201, 202, 204, 214
Williams, Dr Charles 228
Wilson, Maj Walter Gordon 111-113, 117, 200
Willans & Robinson 47
Wisner, René 169, 171, 172, 173, 198
Wood, Harry 209, 210, 211
Woodside, Graffham, West Sussex 28, 32, 45, 81, 215

Zébre, Le, Automobiles S.A. 139, 218